By

P. F. Adams, P. Eng.
Professor of Civil Engineering,
University of Alberta.

H. A. Krentz, P. Eng.
Vice-President,
CISC, Willowdale, Ontario.

G. L. Kulak, P. Eng.
Professor of Civil Engineering,
University of Alberta.

ISBN 0-88811-042-1

Printed in Canada by
Universal Offset Limited
Don Mills, Ontario

PREFACE

Perhaps the most important advance in recent years for the design of steel structures has been the introduction of the limit states method of design. As synthesized in Canadian Standards Association Standard S16.1-1974, the designer is required to examine certain requirements under specified loads (such as deflection) and certain other requirements under factored loads (strength and stability). In addition to the major advantage that the strength and stability of a member or a structure are best described on the basis of ultimate strength, the introduction of limit states design for steel structures brings a unity of approach to the design of both steel and reinforced concrete structures. In the future, the CSA Standard for timber structures will also use a limit states approach.

The major impetus for writing this book, therefore, has been to provide a reference document based on the limit states approach. At the same time, the authors have taken the opportunity to present the material in their own style and with their own emphasis. The book is intended primarily for a one or two term course in structural steel design at the third or fourth year university level. Teachers of structural steel design at technical institutes also may find the book suitable. Although the book is intended principally as an undergraduate teaching text, it should be useful for practicing engineers as an introduction to limit states design of steel structures. The discussion portions of the text refer to members used in both bridge and building construction although detailed comment on design standard requirements is restricted to the pertinent clauses of Canadian Standards Association Standard S16.1, "Steel Structures for Buildings — Limit States Design". References are provided at the end of each chapter so that the reader can study areas of interest in more depth.

The first two chapters of the book deal with the interrelationship of design and analysis, various aspects of steel construction, the structural steels and sections available and the characteristics of each, the International System of Units and the philosophy of the limit states design approach. This initial portion is followed by five chapters that consider the behaviour of the basic types of members found in bridge or building construction — tension members, columns, beams, and beam-columns. Chapters 8 and 9 describe the design processes for composite beams and plate girders, while Chapter 10 deals with connection design. An example design, for a steel framed building, is presented in Chapter 11. The intent of this chapter is to illustrate the design process for a complete structure. In each chapter, the emphasis is placed on the structural situations basic to that member. Situations that occur only rarely are not discussed. Example problems are used to illustrate the basic principles and references are made to the design aids contained in the Limit States Design Steel Manual published by the Canadian Institute of Steel Construction.

The authors would like to thank the Canadian Institute of Steel Construction for participating in the publication of this book. The authors thank also the many people who have contributed to the material in this book — the practising engineers who reviewed parts of the manuscript, the students who used various portions of the material in the classroom, and the authors' colleagues serving on the CSA Committee on Steel Structures for Buildings who provided helpful discussion.

July, 1977   *P. F. Adams*
H. A. Krentz
G. L. Kulak

TABLE OF CONTENTS

FOREWORD

For many years the CISC has supported the educational efforts of Canadian universities and other educational institutions by providing research grants, scholarships, films, slides, computer programs, Handbooks and other literature. As part of this continuing interest in education, the CISC is pleased to publish this textbook.

The Canadian Institute of Steel Construction does not assume responsibility for the contents of this book, nor for errors or oversights resulting from use of the information contained herein. All suggestions for improvement of this book will be forwarded to the authors for their consideration for future printings.

The Head Office of the CISC is located at 201 Consumers Road, Willowdale, Ontario, M2J 4G8. Regional Offices are situated in Vancouver, Calgary, Winnipeg, Toronto, Montreal and Halifax.

CHAPTER 1

INTRODUCTION

1.1 The Design Process

Structural design is a creative art and, at the same time, a reasonably exact science. A structural designer must endeavour to:

1. provide a safe, reliable structure which satisfactorily performs the function for which it was intended,
2. provide a structure which is economical to build and to maintain,
3. in most cases, provide a structure which is aesthetically pleasing.

The design process for any structure contains many steps, not all of which involve the structural designer, although he should be involved in most of them. These steps are:

1. a prospective owner must have a need for the structure and must arrange the financing necessary to build the structure,
2. for a building, an architect and an engineer must study the applicable building by-laws and building codes to ensure that fire protection, health and safety requirements are met,
3. for a bridge, an engineer must ensure that navigation clearances, and highway or railway geometric requirements are met,
4. the structural designer must investigate the site to determine how site conditions will affect the structure (e.g. buried water mains on a building site; potential ice jams at a bridge site),
5. the form, shape and size of the structure must be determined,
6. the probable loads (wind, earthquake, occupancy loads, ice pressures on a bridge, etc.) must be estimated by the designer,
7. the most suitable structural material, or materials, must be selected, with due consideration of required performance, cost, supply, transportation to the site and construction on the site,
8. the structural designer must compare various structural systems and arrangements of structural members,
9. a structural analysis must be performed to determine the forces which the anticipated loads will impose on the structural members,

10. the structural designer must arrange and proportion the elements of the structure so that the expected loads are carried safely, and the elements and the structure as a whole perform satisfactorily,

11. the structural designer must convey to the fabricator and erector, and also to the general contractor, his concept of the structure, principally by means of drawings and specifications,

12. the structural designer must inspect the work of the fabricator and erector, and the general contractor, to ensure that the structure is built in accordance with his plans and specifications.

These twelve steps briefly summarize major portions of the design process for a structure. This book will deal with several of these steps, but will cover in detail only step 10—the arranging and proportioning of the structural elements to safely carry the expected loads, and to ensure that the elements and the structure perform satisfactorily.

For simplicity, most explanations and examples will deal specifically with the design of elements of buildings. For bridges and other structures, design procedures are similar to those followed in the design of buildings, although the governing design standards may differ in some requirements. In particular, for heavily travelled bridges of relatively short span, or floor beams of any heavily travelled bridge, the possibility of failure by fatigue rather than by exceeding the static strength of a member, must be considered.

1.2 Codes, Specifications and Standards

Building codes are written for the purpose of protecting the public. Within a building code can be found recommended design wind loads, snow loads and earthquake loads for a given locality. Recommended design floor loads, for buildings of various types and sizes are provided. Fire protection requirements for buildings fulfilling various functions are stipulated.

Building codes contain rules governing the ways in which loads can be considered to be applied to buildings. Design rules for steel, concrete and other materials are included in building codes, either in the form of detailed requirements or by reference to standards which provide specific design rules.

A building code represents the consensus of opinion of experienced engineers, architects and others. It does not cover in detail every situation which a structural designer may encounter, and the designer often must exercise judgement in interpreting and applying the requirements of a building code.

The National Building Code of Canada[1.1] serves as a model code for cities and municipalities in Canada, and is incorporated, in whole or in part, in most Canadian building by-laws. Published initially in 1941, the 1977 edition of the Code is the Seventh Edition. Currently, a new Edition is published every two years, but the Code is under continual review, and the frequency of publication may be changed in future.

Place Ville Marie in Montreal required consideration of earthquake loads.

Until recently, each Canadian city had its own building by-law. Although most of these by-laws were based on the National Building Code of Canada, each contained some differences, which caused confusion and frustration for designers who designed buildings for more than one city. Now, many Canadian provinces have developed provincial building codes, based on the National Building Code of Canada, and other provinces are preparing such codes. These provincial codes provide uniform requirements for all cities and municipalities located in one province.

Project specifications, along with design drawings, comprise the designer's instructions to the builder. Specifications and drawings vary from company to company, but they include items such as the materials that must be used in the structure, sizes of structural members, methods of joining the members, and general instructions on how the construction work is to be conducted. Unambiguous specifications expedite the successful completion of a structure. In many companies, specifications are written by professional specification writers, but the structural designer should always be involved in preparing, or approving the technical contents of, a specification.

Standards make it possible for the construction industry to function efficiently. Without standards governing such things as quality of steel, dimensions of screw threads on bolts, and dimensions of steel beams, each structure would be "custom-made" and would be prohibitively expensive.

In Canada, the preparation of standards for all commodities is co-ordinated under the auspices of the Standards Council of Canada. Various standards-writing organizations, accredited by the Standards Council of Canada, are responsible for writing standards in specific subject areas. Standards for steel structures are written under the auspices of the Canadian Standards Association (CSA). Standards of the Canadian Government Specifications Board (CGSB) and the Steel Structures Painting Council (SSPC) are used for paint. American Society for Testing and Materials (ASTM) and American National Standards Institute (ANSI) standards are used for certain steel products. Design and construction standards of the American Welding Society (AWS), the American Association of State Highway and Transportation Officials (AASHTO), the American Railway Engineering Association (AREA) and similar organizations are also used to some extent.

However, CSA Standards govern the design and construction of most Canadian steel structures.

Several of the more important are:
1. for buildings—S16.1—"Steel Structures for Buildings—Limit States Design",

2. for bridges—S6—"Design of Highway Bridges",

3. for welded structures—W59—"Specification for Welded Steel Construction",

4. for steel—G40.20—"General Requirements for Rolled or Welded Structural Quality Steel" and G40.21—"Structural Quality Steels".

In this book, since most of the design explanations deal with buildings, most references will be to the current (1974) edition of CSA Standard S16.1. References to steel material Standards will usually be to G40.21, although some ASTM Standards also will be used.

CSA Standards are written by committees representing producers, designers, educators, fabricators, government bodies and other interested parties. Most steel standards are under continual review and new editions are issued every few years. With Canada in the process of converting to the metric system, standards are now (1977) being converted from the Imperial system of units (the inch-pound system) to the International System of Units (SI).

1.3 Loads on Structures

One of the most important steps in the total design process is determination of the design loads for the structure. Typical loads that a designer considers for a building are dead load, live load, wind load, earthquake load and temperature effects.[1.1] Special consideration is sometimes given to impact and vibrations that may occur due to cranes, elevators or other machinery. In bridge design, loads resulting from the centrifugal force and the longitudinal force of moving vehicles, ice pressure, earth pressure, buoyancy and stream flow pressure must be considered.

Dead load consists of the weight of the structure itself plus the weight of permanently installed equipment. It includes the weight of the structural members, floors, ceilings, ductworks, exterior walls, permanent partitions and unusual items such as water in swimming pools. Dead load can usually be estimated with reasonable accuracy, and should be checked after the structure has been designed. Published information[1.2] is available to assist the designer in estimating dead loads.

Live load includes the loads specified by building codes for various uses and occupancies of the building. These specified loads cover the occupants, furniture, movable equipment, fixtures, books, etc., and are the minimum gravity live loads for which the building can be designed, within the jurisdiction of that building code. In some circumstances, the designer may be justified in using higher design live loads. Live load also includes loads due to snow, ice or rain, and earth or hydrostatic pressure.

Design wind loads are stipulated in building codes. Canada's National Building Code (1977) is one of the most progressive in the world in its treatment of wind load. For most structures, wind load can be treated as a static load and is computed with the aid of reference velocity pressures, gust factors, exposure factors and shape factors. Tall, slender buildings must be designed using a dynamic approach[1.3] to the action of wind gusts or with the aid of experimental methods, such as wind tunnel tests. Some of the world's tallest buildings (Sears Building, Chicago; World Trade Center, New York; U.S. Steel Building, Pittsburgh; Commerce Court, Toronto; First Bank Tower, Toronto) have been designed with the aid of testing done at the Boundary Layer Wind Tunnel at the University of Western Ontario.

Wind tunnel tests were used in the design of the First Bank Tower
(foreground), Toronto.
(Photo courtesy Olympia and York Developments Ltd.)

Building codes also stipulate earthquake loads. Conventional earthquake (seismic) design procedures replace the dynamic earthquake loads with equivalent static loads. Alternatively, the National Building Code of Canada specifies that a dynamic analysis may be used. The earthquake loads which are stipulated in most codes are recognized to be much less than the maximum loads possible from a very severe earthquake. However, most codes attempt to stipulate earthquake loads large enough to:

1. prevent structural damage and minimize other damage in moderate earthquakes which occasionally occur,

2. avoid collapse or serious damage in severe earthquakes which seldom occur.[1.4]

Temperature effects include contraction or expansion due to temperature changes, shrinkage, or moisture changes; creep in component materials; and movement due to differential settlement.

The designer must consider combinations of the various loads that can be imposed on the structure. As the number of loads included in the combination increases, it is customary to introduce a "load combination factor" which takes into account the improbability of the maximum value of each load occurring simultaneously.

For bridges, the design standards[1.5, 1.6] provide detailed information which covers most design situations. For railway bridges, live load classes ("E" loading) are established which are intended to simulate the wheel loads of railway locomotives and the more uniform load of the cars they pull. For highway bridges, "H loadings" simulate the effect of a two-axle truck, while "H-S loadings" simulate a tractor truck with semi-trailer. On the basis of extensive research, a new concept in highway bridge loading, based on actual measured vehicle loads and axle spacings, is being introduced in a new Ontario Highway Bridge Design Code, scheduled to be in print early in 1978. Since bridges, depending on their location, carry different types and volumes of traffic, the actual magnitudes of the loads for which bridges are to be designed customarily are established by the future owner of the bridge.

1.4 Structural Systems

The art of structural design is manifested in the selection of the most suitable structural system for a given structure. The arrangement of beams, girders, joists, trusses and columns to support the vertical (gravity) design loads and the selection of a method to resist the horizontal (lateral) design loads determines the economy and functional suitability of a building. Much of the cost of a multi-storey building is in the floor system and numerous trial designs might be necessary to ensure that the most economical suitable system has been selected. Judicious use of design aids, such as handbooks,[1.7] graphs, tables and computer programs[1.8] make such studies practical in a design office. For relatively high buildings, the "premium for height" necessitates a thorough study of lateral load resisting systems. Again, computer programs[1.9] and other design aids are very useful.

7

In bridge design, the choice of continuous or simple-span structures, plate girders, box girders or trusses, steel orthotropic deck (bridge floor) or concrete deck will determine not only economy but aesthetic appeal.

Some broad classifications of structural systems for buildings can be listed. The applicability of any system to any particular type or size of structure varies from place to place and from time to time.

1. Bearing-wall construction—the ends of rolled beams or open-web steel joists (light trusses) are supported on bearing walls, usually of masonry construction. This is generally suitable for one or two storey industrial buildings, commercial buildings, schools or residential-type buildings. However, this type of construction has also been used for apartment buildings exceeding ten storeys in height.

2. Rigid-frame, single storey construction—structural frames consisting of two vertical columns and two sloped beams rigidly connected, into one unit, usually by welding, form a pitched-roof type of structure. Roof beams (purlins) and wall supports (girts) span between rigid frames. They are generally used for industrial structures, stores, arenas, and auditoriums, but are also used for churches because of their aesthetic appeal.

3. Beam and column construction—this comprises the majority of steel framed structures and is suitable for low structures of many spans, such as large industrial buildings, shopping plazas and schools, or for multi-storey buildings, such as office buildings, hospitals, or student residences. It consists essentially of regularly spaced columns joined by beams or girders. Open-web joists or secondary beams span between the girders or main beams and support directly the floors or roof.

Beam and column construction is separated in design standards[1.10] into "simple construction" and "continuous construction". Simple construction assumes that the ends of beams and girders are connected to transmit transverse shear only and are free to rotate under load in the plane of bending. Connections are usually made by welding plates or angles to a beam or column in the fabricator's shop, and bolting to the connecting beam or column in the field (i.e. on the building site). Lateral forces are generally resisted by direct acting bracing—often angles or flat bars—forming vertical or horizontal trusses, as required. The unbraced portion of the building frame, in effect, leans on the braced portion to keep from falling over. In multi-storey buildings, the vertical steel bracing trusses are sometimes replaced by reinforced concrete "cores".

Continuous construction assumes that beams and girders are continuous over, or rigidly framed to, supports and that beam-to-column connections at working load have sufficient rigidity to hold virtually unchanged the original angles between intersecting members. Connections are usually made, in both shop and field, by welding. Lateral forces are resisted by the flexural action of the "rigid-frames" of the structure, or sometimes by a combination of "rigid-frame action" and bracing.

Open web joists, beams and columns are used extensively.
(Photo courtesy Heavy Construction News)

4. Long-span construction—long spans between columns, such as for large arenas, auditoriums, theatres, airport hangers or hotel ballrooms require special consideration. Deep welded plate girders or box girders, long span open web joists or trusses may suffice. For very long spans, deep trusses or arches may be necessary. Space frame structures, using two-way trusses, lattice work domes or cable suspended roofs may be required to cover very large open spaces. Long span construction is also being used more frequently in office buildings. Here closely spaced open-web joists or trusses span from exterior wall to exterior wall, without interior columns, or span from exterior walls to an internal "core". In addition to providing large open areas for office planning, this system, with its open trusswork, facilitates the installation of electrical and mechanical building services.

5. High-rise construction—tall buildings become an economic necessity in large cities where land costs are very high. To build tall buildings

economically, the designer must pay particular attention to the resistance to lateral forces. The framed tube system simulates the action of a perforated hollow tube, by utilizing closely spaced exterior columns joined to, and interacting with, deep spandrel (exterior wall) beams. The 110-storey World Trade Center towers in New York use this system, as does the 72-storey First Bank Tower in Toronto. The 100-storey John Hancock Center in Chicago uses a trussed tube system. In this system large exterior columns are connected with diagonal members, making all exterior columns act together as a rigid tube. Carrying the tube concept still further, the world's tallest building at 1450 feet, the Sears Building in Chicago, uses the bundled tube concept. In this concept, a number of relatively small framed tubes or diagonally trussed tubes are bundled together for great efficiency in resisting lateral forces.

1.5 Analysis and Design

In the structural design process, "analysis" usually means the determination of the forces and bending moments which the individual structural members must resist. "Design" can mean the development of the structural layout, or arrangement of members, but it usually means the selection of sizes of members to resist the imposed forces and bending moments.

For statically determinate structures, the analysis is relatively simple, and the laws of statics can be used to determine the forces and moments on each member. These depend only on the geometry of the structure, and methods used to connect the members. The relative stiffnesses of intersecting members do not affect the analysis. When the analysis has been completed, and the forces and moments on each member are known, the member size can be selected, using an appropriate design method, and there is normally no need for a re-analysis and re-design of the structure.

For statically indeterminate structures, the procedure is more complex. Numerous analytical methods have been developed, such as slope-deflection, portal method, cantilever method, moment-distribution, energy methods, unit-load and unit-displacement. In these methods, assumptions are made regarding the distribution of applied load among members and relative stiffnesses of connecting members. After the analysis has been completed, and the members have been designed, it is usually necessary to re-analyze the structure to check the validity of the original assumptions. Re-design of the members may then be necessary. For complex structures, several cycles of analysis and design may be required.

In designing statically indeterminate structures, it is often advantageous to arrive at preliminary member sizes, using approximate methods. Handbooks[1.2] provide formulae and coefficients to simplify the preliminary design of continuous or rigidly-framed members. Some computer programs[1.9] use approximate analytical methods to arrive at preliminary sizes, which can then be checked, if necessary, using computer programs[1.11] that incorporate more exact analytical methods. In all cases, it is important for the designer to be aware of the assumptions used in any analytical method and to ensure that his structure falls within the scope of those assumptions. No amount of mathematical precision makes up for the use of an analytical method which is not applicable to the structure being designed.

Until recently, most steel buildings in Canada were designed using the allowable stress method and some structures were designed using plastic design methods. Both methods are covered in CSA Standard S16-1969 "Steel Structures for Buildings".

With the publication, late in 1974 of CSA Standard S16.1 "Steel Structures for Buildings—Limit States Design", a set of comprehensive design rules for the limit states design concept became available. It is expected that this relatively new design method will become the dominant procedure used in Canada for steel buildings and bridges.

1.6 Limit States Design

Limit states design is a design method in which the performance of a structure is checked against various limiting conditions at appropriate load levels. The limiting conditions to be checked in structural steel design are ultimate limit states and serviceability limit states. Ultimate limit states are those states concerning safety, such as exceeding of load-carrying capacity, overturning, sliding and fracture due to fatigue or other causes. Serviceability limit states are those states in which the behaviour of the structure is unsatisfactory, and include excessive deflection, excessive vibration and excessive permanent deformation.

In essence, the designer attempts to ensure that the maximum strength of a structure (or elements of a structure) is greater than the loads that will be imposed upon it, with a reasonable margin of safety. This is the "ultimate limit state" criterion. In addition, the designer attempts to ensure that the structure will fulfill its function satisfactorily when subjected to its service loads. This is the "serviceability limit state" criterion.

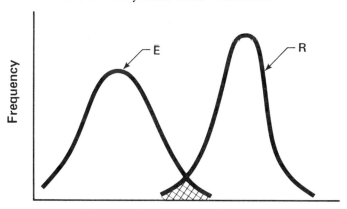

Magnitude of Effect of Loads (E)
or Resistance of Element (R)

Figure 1.1
Frequency Distribution Curves

The ultimate limit state criterion can be illustrated by Figure 1.1. This figure shows hypothetical frequency distribution curves for the effect of loads on a structural element and the strength, or resistance, of the structural element. Where the two curves overlap, shown by the shaded area, the effect of the loads is greater than the resistance of the element, and the element will fail. Designers must proportion their structures so that the overlap of the two curves is small, and hence the probability of failure occurring is low enough to be acceptable.

The basic equation for checking the ultimate limit state condition is the following:

$$\phi R \geqslant \gamma \left[\alpha_D D + \psi \left(\alpha_L L + \alpha_Q Q + \alpha_T T \right) \right]. \tag{1.1}$$

In this equation,

ϕ = performance factor

R = nominal resistance of a structural element

γ = importance factor

ψ = load combination factor

$\alpha_D, \alpha_L, \alpha_Q, \alpha_T$ = load factors

D, L, Q, T, = specified loads, for dead load (D), live load (L), wind or earthquake load (Q) and influences resulting from temperature changes, shrinkage or creep of component materials, or from differential settlement (T).

Considering first the left hand side of Equation 1.1, the performance factor, ϕ, is a factor applied to the nominal member strength, or resistance, to take into account the fact that the actual strength of a member may be less than anticipated due to variability of material properties, dimensions and workmanship. In some limit states design methods, the performance factor also takes into account the type of failure anticipated for the member and uncertainty in prediction of member resistance. In CSA Standard S16.1-1974, these influences are not included in the performance factor, ϕ, but have been included instead in the formulas which establish the theoretical member strengths (or member resistances). One exception to this general definition of ϕ occurs in the ϕ value assigned to bolts in bearing-type connections (see Chapter 10). In CSA Standard S16.1-1974, ϕ is specified to be 0.90 except for bolts in bearing-type connections, where it is 0.67.

The resistance, R, of a member, connection or structure is the nominal strength based on specified material properties, nominal dimensions and equations describing the theoretical behaviour of the member, connection or structure. Thus, in limit states terminology, the factored resistance of a structural element, ϕR, is the product of the resistance and the performance factor and, as expressed in Equation 1.1, must equal or exceed the effect of the factored loads (the right hand side of Equation 1.1).

The importance factor, γ, in the right hand side of Equation 1.1 is a factor that takes into account the consequences of collapse as related to the

12

use and occupancy of the structure. The importance factor is taken equal to 1.00 for most structures but could be greater than 1.00 for structures such as hospitals, radio stations, power generating stations and other structures that might be required to remain serviceable after a major earthquake or other disaster. It can be taken as less than 1.00 for farm storage buildings or other structures not intended for human occupancy (CSA S16.1 Clause 7.2.5).

The load combination factor, ψ, is a factor that takes into account the reduced probability of a number of loads from different sources acting simultaneously. For example, it is unlikely that full wind load and full snow load would act on a structure at the same time. Accordingly, ψ is specified in S16.1-1974 to be 1.00 when only one of L, Q and T (from Equation 1.1) is considered to act in conjunction with D. The load combination factor is reduced to 0.70 when two of L, Q and T are considered to be acting on the structure at the same time and is further reduced to 0.60 when all of L, Q and T are considered to act on the structure at the same time.

In Equation 1.1, D, L, Q and T are specified loads prescribed by the authority having jurisdiction. Typical specified loads are listed in the National Building Code of Canada.[1.1] The product of a specified load and the appropriate load factor is called a factored load. Factored loads must be used when checking ultimate limit states, while specified loads are used when checking serviceability limit states.

One exception to this general rule occurs when designing structures for resistance to fatigue. Fatigue failure is usually considered to be an ultimate limit state, but the structure is designed to resist the effects of fatigue under the specified loads. This apparent anomaly exists because fatigue failure occurs due to a very large number of applications of the maximum load normally expected to act on the structure (that is, the specified load). Other ultimate limit state failures, such as the failure of a column, could occur due to a single application of a greater load than would normally be expected to act on the structure—thus the factored load is used in design calculations.

The load factor, α, by which a specified load is multiplied to obtain a factored load, takes into account the possibility that loads larger than those anticipated may act on the structure, the uncertainty involved in predicting the loads, and approximations in the analysis of the effects of the loads on the structure. Different load factors, α_D, α_L, α_Q, and α_T are assigned to the different load effects, thus recognizing for instance, that the uncertainty of predicting dead load (as measured by α_D) is less than the uncertainty of predicting live load (as measured by α_L). In CSA Standard S16.1-1974, the load factors have been assigned the following values:

α_D = 1.25 (except when overturning, uplift or stress reversal are involved, in which case α_D = 0.85)

α_L = 1.50

α_Q = 1.50

α_T = 1.25

As an example of the use of specified loads and factored loads, Figure 1.2 illustrates the basic design checks required for a beam. The deflection, Δ_s, when the beam is subjected to bending moment M_s, computed using specified loads, must be within the limits specified in CSA Standard S16.1-1974. When the bending moment reaches M_f, computed using factored loads, the beam would fail or be on the verge of failure.

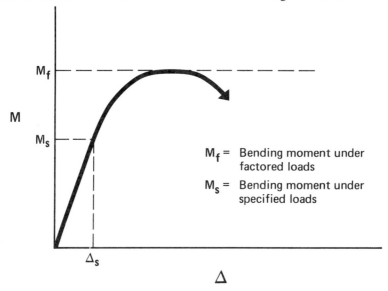

Figure 1.2
Moment-Deflection Curve

More information on limit states design is contained in References 1.12 and 1.13. Chapters 3 to 11 inclusive contain more detailed information on the design of members using limit states design procedures. The design function is facilitated, in practice, by the use of design aids such as handbooks, manuals[1.7] and computer programs.[1.14]

Example 1.1

Given

The loading conditions for a roof beam in a building are to be determined, using limit states design. The specified loads are:

    1. live load (snow) on roof = L = 30 pounds per square foot

    2. dead load on roof = D = 40 pounds per square foot

    3. $\gamma = 1.0$ $\alpha_D = 1.25$ $\alpha_L = 1.50$

Solution

For ultimate limit states, such as yielding or buckling of the beam due to applied bending moment, factored loads must be used. Using Equation 1.1, the factored loads are given by the expression

$$\gamma \left[\alpha_D D + \psi \, (\alpha_L L) \right].$$

14

Since only dead load and live load are acting in combination, $\psi = 1.00$ (CSA S16.1 Clause 7.2.4).

Then the sum of the factored loads acting on the beam is

$$1.00\left[(1.25 \times 40) + 1.00\,(1.50 \times 30)\right].$$

or 95 pounds per square foot.

In design of the beam for the ultimate limit states this factored load would be used to determine M_f, the bending moment under factored loads (see Figure 1.2).

For serviceability limit states, such as deflection, the specified loads are used. Normally, live load deflection is of most concern, and only the specified live load, 30 pounds per square foot, would be used in the design check.

The bending moment determined using this specified live load would correspond to M_s in Figure 1.2.

If a dead load deflection check was required, the specified dead load, 40 pounds per square foot, would be used to determine M_s; if the total deflection was to be checked the sum of the specified loads, 70 pounds per square foot, would be used.

1.7 The International System of Units

The eleventh General Conference of Weights and Measures, in 1960, adopted the name International System of Units for a coherent system which includes the metre as the base unit of length and the kilogram as the base unit of mass. The international abbreviation of the name of this system, in all languages, is SI.

Canada is a signatory to the General Conference on Weights and Measures, and in 1970, the Canadian government stated that the eventual conversion to the metric system is an objective of Canadian policy. Since that time, metric conversion activity in Canada has developed to the point where, in 1977, material and design standards, building codes and technical literature are being developed using the SI units. In recognition of the state of the transition in which the Canadian construction industry finds itself in 1977, this book has been written in the familiar Imperial units, with this section provided as an introduction to SI units.

Designers using SI units must transform loads given in mass (kilograms) to forces, using the relationship force = mass times acceleration. In the design of structures on earth, acceleration is the acceleration due to gravity, designated by "g" and established as 9.80665 metres per second per second at the third General Conference on Weights and Measures in 1901.

The unit of force to be used in design is the newton (N) (or multiples thereof) where a newton is defined as the force that, when applied to a body having a mass of one kilogram (kg), gives the body an acceleration of one

15

metre (m) per second squared (s^2). The unit of stress is the pascal (Pa), which is one newton per square metre (m^2). Since this is a very small unit, designers of steel structures will generally use megapascals (MPa), where one megapascal is one million pascals and equals one newton per square millimetre (N/mm^2).

Properties and dimensions of steel sections will be given in millimetre units and millimetres should be used for dimensioning steel structures. Some relationships and values of interest to steel designers are as follows:

1. Density of steel = 7850 kg/m^3

2. Modulus of elasticity = 200 000 MPa

3. Coefficient of expansion = 11.3 x 10^{-6}

4. Acceleration due to gravity = 9.80665 m/s^2
   $\simeq$ 9.81 m/s^2

5. One kip (1 000 pounds) = 4.448 222 kilonewtons (kN)
   $\simeq$ 4.45 kN

6. One kip per square inch (ksi) = 6.894 757 MPa
   $\simeq$ 6.9 MPa

7. One pound per foot = 1.488 16 kg/m
   $\simeq$ 1.49 kg/m.

Reference 1.15 recommends that multiples of base units that represent 10 raised to a power that is a multiple of 3 should be used. Thus, common structural steel design units would be:

Force — newton (N), kilonewton (kN)

Stress — pascal (Pa), kilopascal (kPa), megapascal (MPa)

Length — millimetre (mm), metre (m)

Mass — kilogram (kg), megagram (Mg).

The tonne is a special unit, equal to 1 000 kg (or 1 Mg) that will be used in the basic steel industry, but should not be used in structural design calculations.

For a more complete description of SI, Reference 1.15 should be consulted.

1.8 Construction Contracts

The procedure used to select the steel fabricating company (fabricator) which will actually build the steel structure conceived by the designer can have a significant effect upon the speed with which the structure is erected and, in some cases, the quality of the completed structure. For a large or complex project, it is common for the future owner (or his representative— the architect, engineer or project manager) to negotiate a contract with one of a few selected firms that he considers capable of completing the project to his satisfaction.

In this case the cost of the structure and construction time schedule are negotiated, and the contract is awarded to the company that offers the combination of price, technical capability, experience and schedule for completing the structure that is most satisfactory from the future owner's point of view. For commercial projects, such as office buildings, a saving in construction time can mean earlier renting of the premises and increased revenue for the owner. Thus speed of construction is an important aspect of the construction process.

For publicly-owned structures, such as bridges, and for many privately owned structures, contracts are awarded after the calling of public tenders. In this case, the fabricator submitting the lowest "bid" (or price) is usually awarded the contract, provided that the fabricator meets any pre-qualification requirements stipulated in the tender "call". For steel buildings and bridges, it is good practice to stipulate that the fabricator be certified by the Canadian Welding Bureau in accordance with the requirements of CSA Standard W47.1 "Certification of Companies for Fusion Welding of Steel Structures". This Standard provides three Divisions of certification, based primarily upon the qualifications of the personnel, employed by the fabricator, who are responsible for welding. It is usually advantageous for the owner (or his representative) to stipulate that the fabricator be certified in the Division that seems most appropriate for the structure under consideration. CSA Standard S16.1 for buildings and CSA Standard S6 for bridges each stipulate that fabricators assuming responsibility for welded construction must be certified for Division 1 or Division 2 of CSA Standard W47.1.

For many structures, it is desirable to consider other methods of pre-qualifying bidders, as well as certification by the Welding Bureau, to ensure that only competent fabricating firms submit bids.

Steel box girders being erected in winter.
(Photo courtesy Heavy Construction News)

For construction contracts it is good practice to use a Canadian Standard Form of Construction Contract developed by a joint committee of the Canadian Construction Association, The Royal Architectural Institute of Canada, The Association of Consulting Engineers of Canada, Construction Specifications Canada and the Engineering Institute of Canada. Three different types of contract are provided, depending upon the method of payment. These are:

1. Stipulated Price

2. Stipulated Unit Prices

3. Cost Plus.

The Cost Plus type of contract is relatively rare and is usually used for emergency repairs or renovations, or a structure that must be completed with maximum speed and minimum notice of intention to build. It will often cover design, fabrication and erection and, as the name implies, is based on the actual cost of the work performed, plus a fixed fee.

The Stipulated Price (or Lump Sum) contract is possibly the most common and provides for a fixed sum of money to cover the cost of fabricating and erecting the structure as described in the job specification and drawings. This type of contract is probably most advantageous when the structure can be designed completely before tenders are called. It is, however, not unusual for modifications to be made to the structure after the contract is signed, and therefore, it is desirable to include provisions in the tender call and the contract for additions or deletions to the lump sum contract.

The Stipulated Unit Prices contract is used when it is not possible to call for "Stipulated Price Tenders" because the design drawings are not complete. In this type of contract, the fabricator provides unit prices for various structural steel members and the final contract price is determined when the design has been completed and total weights can be computed. In this type of contract, it is necessary to have a standard method of computing contract weights, and the method normally used is described in the "CISC Code of Standard Practice for Structural Steel for Buildings". This Code, contained in the CISC Handbook of Steel Construction,[1,2] covers usual industry practice with respect to the furnishing of structural steel for buildings. It should normally be specified in tender calls to ensure uniformity of bidding practice.

1.9 The Construction Process

The construction process is the end result of the design process. For a steel structure, the construction process involves the fabrication, erection and inspection of the structural steel. Inspection is a part of the construction process and also the final step of the design process.

In its broadest sense, the word "fabrication" includes interpreting design drawings and specifications, preparing shop fabrication and field erection drawings, procuring the required material, cutting, forming, assembling and fastening the material into units, and shipping the material to the construction site. It is the designer's responsibility to convey to the fabricator sufficient information to permit him to properly interpret the design drawings and specifications. Guidance for the designer is provided in CSA Standard S16.1 "Steel Structures for Buildings—Limit States Design" and other publications.[1.16] Most fabricators stock the most popular sizes of beam and column sections and some steel plate. However, this stock material will normally be adequate to supply the material for only relatively small structures. For larger structures, some or all of the steel must be ordered from a steel mill.

Steel mills in Canada usually roll structural sections and plate in accordance with a published rolling schedule, based on demand for the various rolled steel products. Thus, several weeks may elapse between the time a fabricator orders steel from a mill and the arrival of that steel at his plant. This "lead time" is normally used by the fabricator for preparation of "shop" (fabrication) drawings. Nevertheless, to speed up the construction process, the designer should endeavour to supply the fabricator, as early as possible, with the design information required for ordering steel. For rush jobs, and small orders, if the required steel is not in the fabricator's own stock, he may order it from a steel warehouse. However, warehousing requires more handling and hence higher overhead costs, necessitating a higher retail price for the steel. Thus, if large quantities of steel must be ordered from warehouses, the cost of the structure will be increased.

Steel plate being flame-cut by a multiple head burner.

Shop drawings, sometimes called detail drawings, are prepared by the fabricator to show in detail the information required to make the component parts of the structure and assemble them into shipping pieces. Erection drawings are also prepared and comprise a set of plans with elevations and cross sections which locate all pieces and provide information required by the erection crews.

Fabrication operations usually include cutting main members to the correct length, cutting connection pieces from larger pieces and possibly cutting pieces from steel plate. Cutting is usually carried out by flame-cutting with oxygen-acetylene, or other gas mixture torches, which are normally controlled automatically. Thin material may be cut with heavy shears and for very smooth cuts or extreme precision, cold sawing with specially hardened blades may be performed. If bolts are to be used to connect pieces, the holes are punched or drilled. Heavy punches can punch various size holes, singly or several at a time, in all but very thick or very hard material. In general, the diameter of the hole punched must equal or exceed the thickness of the plate.

The punching operation may cause minute cracks or may make the material brittle in a very narrow rim around the hole. For this reason design standards usually assume that the hole is 1/16 inch larger than the hole actually punched in the material. Also, holes in locations subject to plastic hinge rotation, in plastically designed structures, must be drilled rather than punched. Drilling can be performed on material of any thickness, with single or multiple drills, but is slower and more expensive than punching. For this reason, fabricators usually try to place holes for connections in thin material, so it can be punched, and weld connection material in the shop to thick main members. The location of holes produced by either punching or drilling can be accurately controlled with modern methods.

Dimensional tolerances permitted by standards for straightness of structural sections and plate supplied by steel mills may sometimes permit deviations from straightness that are unacceptable in the finished structure. Such material is straightened by using rolls or presses, or sometimes by the local application of heat.

After the holes have been punched or drilled, and the pieces cut to the required size or shape, the components necessary to form an assembly are fitted together and connected, by bolts or, more often in the shop, by welding. The use of rivets for structural steelwork in Canada has virtually disappeared. Fabricators try to plan their fabrication operations to make maximum use of automatic or semi-automatic welding equipment, for improved weld quality and for maximum efficiency. Machine finishing (usually called "milling" or "facing") may be required for the ends of certain compression members required to have a very smooth bearing surface. Bridge bearing plates and thick base plates for large building columns may also require "milling". After assembly in the shop, the shipping piece is given a coat of paint (shop primer) if required, then various identification numbers are painted on the piece and it is stored until it can be shipped to the construction site.

The erection of structural steel is the phase of the construction process where the ingenuity and experience of the fabricator/erector can save considerable time and money. Few structural designers have extensive experience in on-site construction, and therefore, particularly for large or unusual structures, the designer should consult with an experienced fabricator/erector to ensure that the designer's proposed structure can be built. The erection of structural steel often requires extensive calculations, by the fabricator/erector, to ensure that adequate margins of safety are maintained when erecting the structure. It is customary to use lower margins of safety for erection loads than for the design loads on the completed structure. Thus a structure will often be subject to its most severe stress condition while it is being constructed.

Several types of erection cranes, for lifting the component parts of the structure, are used. A truck crane consists essentially of a crane mounted on a heavy truck chassis. It can travel over highways under its own power and is widely used to erect low buildings involving relatively light individual pieces. Some of the larger truck cranes are used, often in pairs or triplets, to lift heavy bridge girders for overpasses. Crawler cranes are similar to truck cranes, except that they have caterpillar tracks instead of wheels. Unlike truck cranes, they must be transported to the job site.

Erection ingenuity on CN Tower, Toronto.

Guy derricks are used principally for the erection of tall multi-storey buildings. A guy derrick consists essentially of a long vertical column (called a "mast") supported laterally by wire cable "guys". An inclined member, called a "boom" is attached to the base of the mast and can be raised or lowered, and can swing in a complete circle, thus enabling a guy derrick to cover a large hoisting, or erection, area. Guy derricks are unique inasmuch as they "lift themselves" up a building as the building rises. This self-lifting capability, combined with the maximum height of column that can be handled when the boom is extended to its maximum reach, makes it possible to erect columns for multi-storey buildings in pieces two or three storeys high.

A relative of the guy derrick is the stiffleg derrick in which the guy wires are replaced by two inclined structural members capable of resisting either tension or compression. Tower cranes, characterized by tall vertical towers and horizontal or inclined booms are gaining increased use. Various types of climbing or creeping cranes have been used recently in the erection of tall buildings. Derrick boats, locomotive cranes and traveller cranes are specialized types of cranes developed principally for the erection of large bridges. New ideas in erection equipment are continually being tried by ingenious erection engineers.

Inspection of the structure, and its component members, is the final step of the design process. The quality control programs of fabricators involve inspection of members before they are shipped to the construction site and the "quality assurance" philosophy is being emphasized more and more by fabricators, designers and owners. However, it is the responsibility of the structural designer to ensure that the structure has been fabricated and erected in accordance with his drawings and specifications. Non-destructive testing techniques have been developed for testing high-strength bolted joints and welded joints. It is completely impractical to test every connection joint in a structure. A comprehensive inspection programme will test the more critical joints of a structure (such as a welded splice in a highly stressed bridge girder tension flange) and representative joints elsewhere. The purpose is primarily to ensure that the welding or bolting technique being used provides the required quality in the connection. A knowledge of the significance of weld defects is particularly important for the designer. Many times, a weld "defect" detected by a sensitive inspection method will not be particularly detrimental to the behaviour of the structure, while the attempted repair of the defect may introduce a condition that is more detrimental. Thus, an acceptance level for defects must be established by the designer for the guidance of his inspectors.

1.10 The Role of the Structural Designer

The suitability and economy of any steel structure is determined by the structural designer. He is the key man in most of the steps in the design process, listed earlier. In a building, heating and air conditioning requirements, architectural requirements or other factors may dictate the use of a structural system that is not the most suitable from a purely structural viewpoint, but is best in the overall consideration of the total building. It is the structural designer's role to ensure that the best structural system is selected, within the scope of the constraints imposed upon him. Furthermore a structural designer may fill one of several roles in the design and construction process. He may be employed by an architectural or consulting engineering firm, and be responsible for the actual design of the structure. He may work for a fabricator and do "detail design" or prepare erection schemes. He may work for an owner—a government body or private company—and be responsible for supervision and inspection. All roles are important and require a good knowledge of structural design.

Today's structural designer can avail himself of handbooks, computer programs and other "design aids" that minimize the need for him to personally perform extensive computations. Instead, he can spend more time thinking of design concepts. Should the building have a lateral bracing system to provide stability under gravity loads and resistance to wind and earthquake loads or should the flexural capacity of a rigid-frame type of building be used? If bracing is used should it be in the form of a concrete core, steel—truss core, or a bracing system in the exterior walls of the structure? Can the floors act as diaphragms to transmit lateral loads from points of application to points of resistance (bracing system)? Can steel cladding on the walls be utilized to stiffen the structure and reduce the amount of other bracing required? Are expansion joints needed in long industrial buildings to minimize temperature effects? Is the building shape such that severe torsional effects are encountered under wind and earthquake loads? Is the layout of floor beams and girders the most efficient and economical that can be used?

Triangulated steel space trusses in Winnipeg's Pan-Am Swimming Pool.

Selection of the most suitable grade of steel is an important design decision. In the past it has been customary for structural designers to assume that "least weight means least cost" for a steel building. This is a good general principle, but it should not be carried to extremes. Using a very high strength steel to reduce weight often will not reduce cost because the increased unit price of the higher strength steel will make the lighter design more costly than a design using a less expensive, lower strength steel. The most economical design, for buildings in particular, is usually achieved by using a steel with a reasonably high strength and relatively low base cost. At the time of printing, in most parts of Canada, CSA G40.21 grade 44W steel will generally prove to be most economical for buildings. However, for many buildings, comparative designs using various structural layouts and different grades of steel are justified and can be prepared quickly and economically with the help of design aids.[1.8, 1.9]

For bridges, a higher-strength steel, such as CSA G40.21 grade 50A will often be the most suitable steel to use. In addition to economy, the bridge designer is interested in using a steel that is "tough" (to resist the propagation of fatigue cracks) and has good resistance to atmospheric corrosion.

In bridges and buildings, the type of corrosion protection selected by the designer will greatly affect the economy of the structure. Certain steels, such as CSA G40.21 grade 50A or 50R provide their own protection against atmospheric corrosion by forming a dense, tightly adhering coat of rust which inhibits further corrosion. These steels require no paint or other coating for most environments. Other steels, exposed to the weather, can usually be protected satisfactorily with several coats of paint, such as those listed in CSA Standard S16.1.[1.10] For severe corrosive environments, special treatment such as galvanizing with zinc may be justified.

In many buildings, where the steel will be protected from the weather and the ambient environment is basically non-corrosive, no corrosion protection need be applied to the steel.

The protection of buildings and building occupants against the hazards of fire is an important consideration also for designers and owners. Building codes stipulate fire protection requirements based on the proposed use of the structure (type of "occupancy") and the size of the structure. Life-safety is a primary consideration and restrictions on the composition of finishing materials (carpets, wall coverings, etc.) in a building, use of smoke detectors and automatic sprinkler systems are being given increased attention in building codes. Building codes also stipulate that beams and columns must have certain "fire ratings". The required ratings differ for different types of buildings. For some buildings or parts of buildings, unprotected steel is adequate; for others, some type of insulating material or fie protective system is added to the steel. Guidance on fire protection of steel construction is available in published literature.[1.17, 1.18]

Suitability for the intended function, safety, economy and aesthetics must all be considered by the structural designer. Structural steel is a versatile material that can be used for virtually any type of structure. For most structures the designer should attempt to use a grade of structural steel that is readily available, keep the structural layout and structural details as simple as possible, and use the maximum possible repetition of sizes and lengths, and connection details.

Port Mann Bridge near Vancouver — North America's first orthotropic plate deck bridge.

References

1.1 National Research Council of Canada, "National Building Code of Canada 1977", Ottawa, Ontario.

1.2 Canadian Institute of Steel Construction "Handbook of Steel Construction", Second Edition, 1976, Part 7, Toronto, Ontario.

1.3 National Research Council of Canada, "Commentaries on Part 4 of the National Building Code of Canada 1977", Ottawa, Ontario.

1.4 Muto, K. "Theme Report", Technical Committee 6, International Conference on Planning and Design of Tall Buildings, ASCE-IABSE Conference Preprints, 1972, Lehigh University, Lehigh, Pennsylvania.

1.5 Canadian Standards Association "Design of Highway Bridges", CSA S6, 1974, Rexdale, Ontario.

1.6 American Railway Engineering Association, "Steel Structures", Chapter 15, 1975, Chicago, Illinois.

1.7 Canadian Institute of Steel Construction, "Limit States Design Steel Manual", First Edition, 1977, Toronto, Ontario.

1.8 Canadian Institute of Steel Construction "Rapid Evaluation of Steel Structures (RESST)", 1977, Toronto, Ontario.

1.9 Canadian Institute of Steel Construction, "GALE-STRIF (Geometry Assemblage and Lateral Load Estimation—Steel Rigid Frame program)", 1973, Toronto, Ontario.

1.10 Canadian Standards Association "Steel Structures for Buildings—Limit States Design", CSA S16.1-1974, Rexdale, Ontario.

1.11 Canadian Institute of Steel Construction, "STRUDL II—CSA S16", 1970, Toronto, Ontario.

1.12 Allen, D. E., "Limit State Design—A Probabilistic Study", Canadian Journal of Civil Engineering, March, 1975, National Research Council of Canada, Ottawa, Ontario.

1.13 Kennedy, D.J.L., "Limit States Design—An Innovation in Design Standards for Steel Structures", Canadian Journal of Civil Engineering, September, 1974, National Research Council of Canada, Ottawa, Ontario.

1.14 Canadian Institute of Steel Construction, "Column Selection Program 3 (CSP3)", 1977, Toronto, Ontario.

1.15 Canadian Standards Association "Canadian Metric Practice Guide", CSA Z234.1-76, 1976, Rexdale, Ontario.

1.16 Canadian Institute of Steel Construction, "General Information on Structural Steel", 1975, Toronto, Ontario.

1.17 Stanzak W. W., "Structural Fire Protection—an Engineering Approach", Proceedings of 1972 Canadian Structural Engineering Conference, Canadian Steel Industries Construction Council, Toronto, Ontario.

1.18 Stanzak, W. W., "Fire Protection in Steel Construction", 1977, Canadian Steel Industries Construction Council, Toronto, Ontario.

CHAPTER 2

STRUCTURAL STEEL

2.1 Composition and Manufacture

Steel is the most useful metal known to man. With an infinite variety of uses, ranging from paper clips to space vehicles, steel has become the backbone of our modern civilization. As a structural material, steel is widely used for buildings, bridges, towers and other structures.

Although composed almost entirely of iron, steel also contains minute quantities of other elements which greatly affect its physical properties. Carbon is the most important of these elements. Increasing the carbon content of steel causes an increase in strength and hardness, but a decrease in ductility and toughness. Accordingly, standard specifications[2.1, 2.2] for structural steel limit the carbon content so that it comprises about 0.15 percent to 0.30 percent of the total chemical composition.

Manganese affects steel properties in a manner similar to carbon, except that increasing the manganese content increases the toughness of steel. In structural steel the ratio of carbon to manganese is carefully controlled to obtain the desired combination of strength, ductility and toughness. Structural steel normally contains from 0.50 percent to 1.65 percent manganese.

Phosphorus, sulphur, silicon, copper, vanadium, nickel, chromium, columbium, molybdenum and aluminum are some of the other elements that may be restricted in, or added to, structural steel. More information on the chemical composition of steel is available elsewhere.[2, 3]

The manufacture of steel at the steel mill begins at the blast furnace. Iron ore, limestone and coke (made from coal) are charged into the top of this huge vessel and molten pig iron issues forth at the bottom. The pig iron, in turn, is converted into steel in special steel making furnaces. In North America at the present time, almost all structural steel is produced in open hearth or basic oxygen furnaces. There is, however, a trend towards increased use of electric furnaces for the production of structural steel.

Oxygen is essential to all steelmaking processes. It is used to oxidize the excess of elements such as carbon, but must be carefully controlled to avoid trapping gas pockets in the steel ingots. Gas pockets can lead to defects in the final rolled steel product.

Deoxidizers, such as silicon or aluminum, are used to control the dissolved oxygen content. Steel which has the highest degree of deoxidation is termed killed steel; semi-killed steel has an intermediate degree of deoxidation while rimmed steel has the lowest degree of deoxidation. Structural steel is customarily produced either as killed or semi-killed product, depending on thickness and intended use.

The chemical composition of the steel dictates its potential mechanical properties, but its final mechanical properties are strongly influenced by rolling practice, finishing temperature, cooling rate and subsequent heat treatment (if any). In the rolling process, the material is passed through two rollers revolving at the same speed in opposite directions. Rolling shapes the steel, reduces it in cross section, elongates it and increases its strength. Normally, ingots from the steelmaking furnace are first rolled into slabs, billets or blooms and later rolled into final form (plates, bars or shapes) in a finishing mill. In the continuous casting process, steel is cast directly as slabs or blooms (bypassing the ingot stage) and subsequently into the final product form.

Some of the various steps in the steelmaking process are illustrated schematically in Figure 2.1. This figure shows the raw materials entering the blast furnace, followed by processing in either an open hearth or basic oxygen steelmaking furnace, and then the pouring of the molten steel into ingot form. The ingots are subsequently re-heated in a "soaking pit", and then are passed through the bloom mill, the breakdown mill and finally the finishing mill where the product achieves its final shape. Some steps in the steelmaking process, at any particular steel mill, could differ from those illustrated in Figure 2.1.

A chemical analysis, known as the heat analysis (formerly ladle analysis), is performed on samples taken from the molten metal. This analysis is reported on the mill test certificate covering the related "heat" of steel. A heat of steel is one production lot of steel from a steelmaking unit. Most heats of steel produced in North America comprise from fifty tons to three hundred tons of metal, depending on the size of the furnace, although larger heats are produced in some mills. The time required to produce a heat of steel ranges from one hour to eight hours, depending on the type of furnace used.

Tests to determine mechanical properties of the steel are conducted on material taken from the final rolled product. One or more tensile tests to determine yield point, tensile strength and elongation (a measure of ductility) are specified in standard specifications,[2.4] and are reported on the mill test certificate. These reported mechanical properties, which normally exceed the specified properties by a significant amount, simply certify (along with the other information reported) that the heat of steel covered by the test certificate meets the requirements of a specific steel material specification. It should not be assumed that each piece of steel from the heat of steel covered by the mill test certificate has precisely the properties listed thereon. For this reason, designers should always use the properties specified in the standard steel specification, for design purposes, and not the test values reported on the mill test certificate.

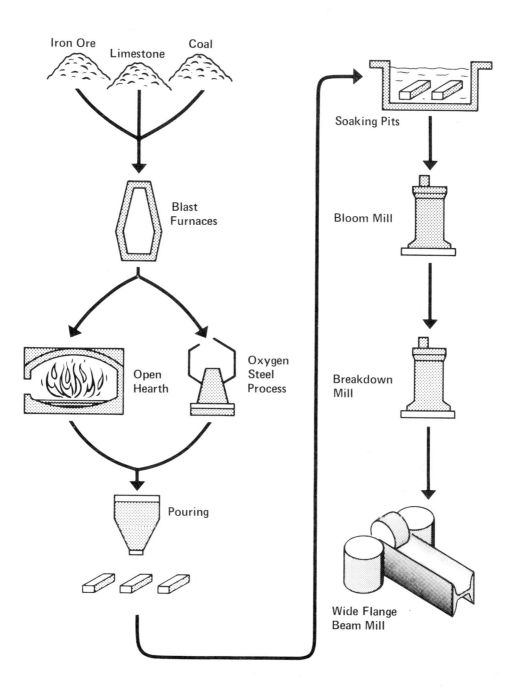

Figure 2.1
Steps in the Steelmaking Process

2.2 Strength and Ductility

Structural steel is important to designers primarily because of its very favourable strength and ductility properties.

The great strength of structural steel makes it possible to build structures that otherwise could not be built; for more usual structures, the strength of steel permits the use of long, clear spans with a minimum of columns, and relatively small members, providing minimum dead load. Steel's ductility relieves overstress in portions of structures by permitting a steel element to yield and cause a redistribution of stresses in the structure.

Strength and ductility of steel are customarily measured by means of a standard tension test. This test consists of pulling a standard-size prepared specimen[2.4] until fracture occurs. From the load-elongation relationships, the yield point (or similar property), tensile strength and percentage of elongation occurring within a prescribed gauge length, can be computed. A stress-strain curve can also be drawn, using the load-elongation data.

A typical stress-strain curve for a structural steel is shown in Figure 2.2, while an enlargement of the initial portion of the curve is shown in Figure 2.3. Referring to these curves, it can be seen that steel obeys Hooke's law under initial load, with the elongation (strain) being directly proportional to the applied load (stress). This straight line relationship holds true until the proportional limit is reached. The steel continues to behave elastically (no permanent deformation) until the elastic limit is reached. In a test, it is difficult to distinguish between the proportional limit and the elastic limit, and they are often considered to occur at the same point on the curve.

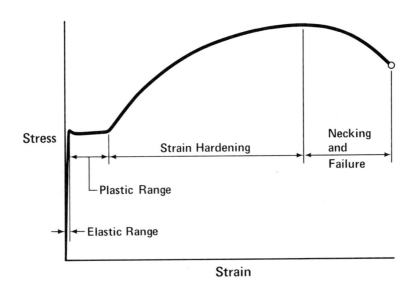

Figure 2.2
Typical Stress-Strain Curve

When passing from the elastic range to the plastic range, gradual yielding of the cross section begins. Low and medium strength structural steel test specimens exhibit a definite yield point. The yield point is defined[2.5] as the first stress in a material, less than the maximum attainable stress, at which an increase in strain occurs without an increase in stress. The yield point is illustrated in the stress-strain curve by a long, flat plateau. The strain which the specimen undergoes between the attainment of the yield point and the beginning of strain-hardening is typically ten to fifteen times as great as the strain incurred in the elastic range.

When the specimen begins to strain-harden, the load-carrying capacity of the specimen increases until the maximum load is attained. At this point the cross section of the specimen begins to reduce rapidly, the load that can be carried decreases, and the specimen fractures.

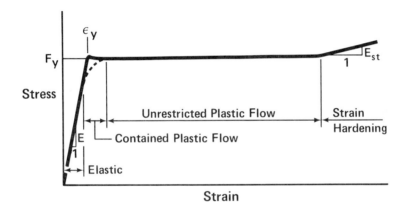

Figure 2.3
Initial Portion, Stress-Strain Curve

A typical stress-strain curve (Figure 2.2) indicates that the stress in the specimen is reduced between the time the maximum load is attained and the time the specimen fractures. This is a "mathematical phenomenon" which occurs because, conventionally, the stress is computed by dividing the applied load by the original cross sectional area of the specimen. If the reduced area was used in the computations, it would be seen that the actual stress in the specimen does not decrease as indicated by Figure 2.2.

Some steels (notably high-strength quenched and tempered steels) do not exhibit a well-defined yield-point but yield gradually. Since the yield point is considered by designers to mark the limit of structural usefulness of many structural steel members, an arbitrary value, called the yield strength, is selected for these steels which do not have a yield point. Yield strength is defined[2.5] as the stress at which a material exhibits a specified limiting deviation from the proportionality of stress to strain. The deviation is expressed in terms of strain. The term yield stress[2.5] is often used to denote either the yield point or the yield strength, as applicable.

31

The other strength characteristic measured in a standard tension test is the tensile strength. This is defined[2.5] as the maximum tensile stress that a material is capable of sustaining and corresponds to the highest point on the stress-strain curve.

"Ductility is the ability of a material to undergo large plastic deformation without fracture".[2.6] In a standard tension test, ductility is measured by the amount of elongation the specimen undergoes over a standard gauge length (8 inches or 2 inches). Elongation is usually expressed as a percentage, and standard steel material specifications[2.1] normally require from fifteen to twenty percent elongation in an 8 inch gauge length. A ductile steel is characterized by large total strain, before fracture, on a stress-strain curve.

The favourable ductility characteristics of steel enable many structural parts designed using simplified but not necessarily correct assumptions to perform satisfactorily. When ductility is reduced, through poor design details or fabrication practices, brittle fracture or low fatigue strength can result.

2.3 Cross Section Properties

A characteristic of importance to designers is the local buckling strength of steel. Relatively thin steel elements subjected to compressive loads will sometimes buckle before reaching the yield point. The local buckling strength of these elements depends upon the ratio of the width of the element to its thickness, and upon the types of support provided at the edges of the element. The compression flange of a beam for instance, supported at only one point (the beam web), will buckle (for the same applied load) at a lower width-thickness ratio than will the web of a beam, which is supported at two edges by the beam flanges. Design standards[2.7] limit the width-thickness ratios of elements subject to compression. Thus the designer need not concern himself with the local buckling problem if he uses steel members conforming to the width-thickness limits specified. Provisions are made allowing designers to deviate from the specified limits, when necessary, by performing a buckling analysis.

Another characteristic of interest to designers is residual stress. Residual stresses are the stresses that remain in an unloaded member after it has been formed into a finished product. Examples of such stresses include, but are not limited to, those induced by cold bending, cooling after rolling or by welding.

Residual stresses are of particular importance in column design (Chapter 4). When a hot rolled steel product cools, certain portions cool more quickly than other portions. In a W shape, for instance, the flange tips and the middle of the web cool more quickly than the rest of the cross section. As steel cools, it shrinks. The shrinkage of the still warm portion of a W shape exerts a compressive force on the cooler flange tips and middle of the web. When the whole cross section has cooled, therefore, the flange tips and middle of the web will contain "residual" compressive stress while the remainder of the cross section will contain "residual" tensile stress. The presence of these "locked-in" stresses will affect the load-carrying capacity of all structural steel members to some degree. The effect will be treated in subsequent chapters.

Residual stresses resulting from the steel rolling procedure usually range from about 10 to 15 ksi. Not all residual stresses reduce the load carrying capacity of members. For instance, box sections formed of four welded plates will generally have residual tensile stress at the corners—a desirable residual stress pattern for columns subject to axial load plus bending.

2.4 Other Properties

Toughness, the capacity to absorb large amounts of energy, can be an important design criterion, particularly for structures subject to impact loads (e.g. bridges) and for structures subject to earthquake loads. At room temperature, common structural steels are very tough and fail in a ductile manner. As the temperature drops, a point is reached at which the steel loses its toughness and fails in a brittle, rather than a ductile, manner. This characteristic usually is measured by means of a Charpy V-Notch impact test.[2.4] In this test, a standard notched specimen is subjected to an impact load by a swinging pendulum. The temperature of the specimen is varied, the energy absorbed by each specimen is recorded, and an energy-temperature transition curve (Figure 2.4) is plotted. From this curve, a transition temperature corresponding to some level of energy absorption (usually 15 or 20 foot-pounds) can be selected. The transition temperature is the temperature below which fractures are mostly brittle and above which fractures are mostly ductile.

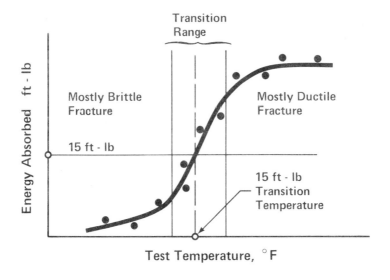

Figure 2.4
Energy-Temperature Transition Curve

Structural steels differ greatly in toughness. A fully killed, fine grain steel with a suitable chemical composition, or a specially heat-treated steel, will exhibit considerable toughness. Several tough steels have been developed for use in Canada, where low ambient temperatures are an inescapable design condition for exposed structures. Under low temperature conditions, a structural member with a severe notch or other stress raiser, subject to a significant tensile stress, may be susceptible to brittle fracture. Selection of a "notch tough" steel for this design condition will help to minimize the possibility of brittle fracture. Guidance in the selection of a suitable steel is provided elsewhere.[2.3, 2.8, 2.9]

Most steel structures are fabricated and erected with the aid of welding. Many structures are assembled with welds and bolts—but seldom with bolts only. Thus the weldability of the structural steel to be used is a design consideration. All structural steels are weldable in the sense that two pieces can be connected with a weld. However, the ease with which the welding can be accomplished, the cost, and the quality of the welds differ from steel to steel. Standard specifications[2.1, 2.10] provide information on those structural steels considered readily weldable, while other publications[2.3, 2.8] provide more details on the weldability of steel.

Toughness, weldability and corrosion resistance are important for this overpass.

Atmospheric corrosion resistance may be an important design consideration when structures are exposed to the weather. Special steels (CSA G40.21, grades 50A, 60A, 50R; ASTM A588) which eliminate the need for paint or other protective coatings under most atmospheric conditions have been developed.[2.1, 2.3, 2.8]

34

The modulus of elasticity (Young's modulus) for structural steel is practically constant. Values ranging from 29 000 ksi to 30 000 ksi are commonly used in design calculations. In CSA Standard S16.1-1974, a value of 29 000 ksi is assumed. In SI units, the modulus of elasticity is taken as 200 000 MPa. Poisson's ratio (ratio of transverse to longitudinal strain) is usually assumed to be 0.30 in the elastic range. The unit weight of steel is 490 pounds per cubic foot (7 850 kg/m^3 in SI) and the coefficient of thermal expansion, at atmospheric temperatures, is approximately 6.3 x 10^{-6} (11.3 x 10^{-6} in SI). The coefficient of expansion is the change in length, per unit of length, for a change of one degree of temperature.

2.5 Types of Structural Steel

In 1924, the first standard of the Canadian Standards Association (CSA) dealing with the design of steel buildings was published. Designated A16, this building standard contained a material specification for the type of steel to be used. This was mild steel with a specified minimum yield point of 27.5 ksi.

In 1940, mild steel was supplanted by medium structural steel, with a yield point of 33 ksi. Ultimately designated G40.4 by the CSA and A7 by the American Society for Testing and Materials (ASTM), this steel remained the basic structural steel for buildings and bridges for approximately twenty years.

In the early 1960's many new structural steels were introduced by steel mills in North America. These steels can be separated into five categories:

1. Carbon Steel—Carbon and manganese are the principal strengthening elements. The specified minimum yield point ranges from about 30 ksi to 45 ksi, and the specified minimum tensile strength from about 55 to 65 ksi. Typical carbon steels, widely used in Canada in the 1960's and early 1970's were:

    (a) CSA G40.8 "Structural Steels with Improved Resistance to Brittle Fracture",

    (b) CSA G40.12 "General Purpose Structural Steel",

    (c) ASTM A36 "Structural Steel".

2. High strength carbon steel—Adding carbon increases the steel strength but reduces ductility, toughness and weldability. For transmission towers and other structures where relatively light members are joined together by bolts, this steel has proven to be satisfactory. The specified minimum yield point ranges from 50 ksi to about 60 ksi, and the specified minimum tensile strength from about 70 to 85 ksi.

3. High strength low-alloy steel—The carbon content is kept low and strength is increased by adding alloys such as vanadium or columbium. The specified minimum yield point ranges from about 42 to 70 ksi, and the tensile strength from 65 to 80 ksi. Typical specifications covering steels in this category are:

    (a) ASTM A441 "High Strength Low-Alloy Structural Manganese Vanadium Steel",

(b) ASTM A572 "High Strength Low-Alloy Columbium—Vanadium Steels of Structural Quality".

4. Atmospheric corrosion resisting steel—This is a low-alloy type steel in which the alloying elements are chosen so that the long-term atmospheric corrosion resistance is at least four times that of plain carbon structural steel. Also known as "weathering steels", these steels are often left unpainted. The yield point is generally 50 ksi and the tensile strength about 70 ksi. A typical steel of this type, widely used for bridges in Canada in the late 1960's and early 1970's was CSA G40.11 "High Strength Low-Alloy Structural Steel".

5. High strength quenched and tempered steel—These are steels heat treated to develop high strength. They are generally weldable and tough, but special welding techniques are usually required. The specified minimum yield strength ranges between 80 and 100 ksi, with specified minimum tensile strengths between 105 and 135 ksi. A typical example is ASTM A514 "High-Yield-Strength, Quenched and Tempered Alloy Steel Plate Suitable for Welding".

Complex structures may use more than one type of steel.
(Photo courtesy Heavy Construction News)

The large variety of structural steels available has given the designer freedom to select the type of steel most suitable for his particular structure. At the same time however, the task is complicated by this very variety. Publications have been prepared[2.3, 2.8] which assist the designer in selecting the most suitable structural steel. Also, the Canadian Standards Association has developed a new type of steel standard which simplifies the designer's task of selection. This is described in Section 2.6.

2.6 Structural Steel Material Standards

In the mid-1960's the International Organization for Standardization (ISO) published document R630 "Recommended Standard for Structural Steels". This document listed steels of many different qualities and strength levels in one publication, and paved the way for rationalization and simplification of steel material standards existing in various countries. Thus, in 1968, the British Standards Institution published BS 4360 "Weldable Structural Steels"; in 1971 the Standards Association of Australia published A187 "Structural Steels, Weather-Resistant Weldable Grades" and A186 "Structural Steels, Ordinary Weldable Grades"; and in 1973 the Canadian Standards Association published G40.21 "Structural Quality Steels" and G40.20 "General Requirements for Rolled or Welded Structural Quality Steel". Other countries are considering the preparation of similar standards.

CSA G40.20 covers the testing, inspection, marking and delivery requirements for the G40.21 structural steels as well as the dimensional tolerances permitted for the various rolled and welded products. CSA G40.21 specifies chemical compositions, strength levels, methods of manufacture, methods of identification, etc., for the grades of steel covered by the standard.

All CSA Standards for structural steels that were in existence prior to the introduction of G40.20 and G40.21 have now been withdrawn. It is now only necessary for the designer to specify that the structural steel to be used shall be CSA Standard G40.21, grade 50T (or other suitable grade).

For more information, the Standard[2.1] and explanatory publications[2.3, 2.8] should be consulted. For convenience here Table 2-1 is provided. This table lists the grades of steel covered by G40.21 and G40.21M, the metric version of the Standard.

In Table 2-1, each grade of steel is identified by a number and a letter. The number is the specified minimum yield point of the thinnest plate and lightest section available in that grade of steel. (The yield point in some grades decreases for the larger plate or shape thicknesses.) The letter refers to the characteristics of the six types of steel available, as follows:

1. Type G—General construction steel
2. Type W—Weldable steels
3. Type T—Weldable low temperature steels
4. Type R—Atmospheric corrosion resistant structural steel
5. Type A—Atmospheric corrosion resistant structural steel with improved low temperature properties
6. Type Q—Quenched and tempered low-alloy steel plate.

More detailed tables dealing with steel materials are provided in Appendix A.

TABLE 2-1

CSA G40.21		CSA G40.21M	
Grade	Yield Point (ksi)	Grade	Yield Point (MPa)
33G	33	230G	230
50G	50	350G	350
60G	60	400G	400
38W	38	260W	260
*42W	42		
44W	44	300W	300
50W	50	350W	350
*55W	55	*380W	380
60W	60	400W	400
70W	70	480W	480
38T	38	260T	260
44T	44	300T	300
50T	50	350T	350
*55T	55	*380T	380
60T	60	400T	400
70T	70	480T	480
50R	50	350R	350
50A	50	350A	350
60A	60	400A	400
100Q	**100	700Q	**700

* Available in hollow structural sections only.

** Yield strength rather than yield point.

2.7 Structural Steel Products

Structural steel products are the basic ingredients from which structural members, such as beams and columns, are fabricated. A complete list of items used in buildings, which the Canadian structural steel fabricating industry considers to be covered by the term "structural steel" is contained elsewhere.[2.11]

The structural steel products of interest to designers can be divided into the following categories:

1. Flat rolled products—plate, flat bars, sheet and strip,
2. Sections—rolled shapes, rolled bar-size shapes and hollow structural sections,
3. Bolts,
4. Welding electrodes.

In broad terms, plate is flat-rolled steel over 8 inches wide and .230 inches or more in thickness; sheet is flat-rolled steel over 12 inches wide and less than .230 inches thick; strip is flat rolled steel less than 12 inches wide and less than .230 inches thick. More precise definitions are available elsewhere.[2.3]

High strength bolts, welded plate girders, rolled angles, plate and shapes are used in this bridge.

Rolled shapes are sections with flanges, having at least one dimension of the cross section 3 inches or greater; bar-size shapes have all dimensions less than 3 inches. Welded shapes are sections with flanges, produced by welding together two or more components. Hollow structural sections are hollow square, rectangular or round sections, produced by either hot forming or cold forming. Properties, dimensions and illustrations of all sections generally available in Canada are contained in the CISC Handbook of Steel Construction[2.12] and the CISC publication Properties of Structural Steel Sections.[2.13]

For convenience, tables from the Handbook referred to in this book are reproduced in Appendix A.

When designating structural steel products on drawings, it is desirable that a standard method of abbreviation be employed which will identify the product without reference to the manufacturer. In 1971, the Canadian Institute of Steel Construction approved the use in Canada of a new nomenclature for rolled shapes. This new nomenclature is incorporated in the list below.

Welded Wide Flange Shapes	WWF(M)39x163
W Shapes	W24x76
M Shapes	M8x37.7
Standard Beams (S Shapes)	S15x42.9
Standard Channels (C Shapes)	C9x13.4
Structural Tees	
—cut from WWF Shapes	WWT(M)11x141
—cut from W Shapes	WT5x10.5
—cut from M Shapes	MT4x9.25
Equal Leg Angles (leg dimensions x thickness, all in inches)	L3 x 3 x 1/4
Unequal Leg Angles (leg dimensions x thickness, all in inches)	L6 x 4 x 1/2
Plates (width x thickness, both in inches)	Pl. 18 x 1/2
Square Hollow Structural Sections (outside dimensions x thickness, both in inches; G40.20 class)	HSS—4 x 4 x .375 Class H
Round Hollow Structural Sections (outside dimensions x thickness, both in inches; G40.20 class)	HSS—4.5 OD x .250 Class H
Rectangular Hollow Structural Sections (outside dimensions x thickness, both in inches; G40.20 class)	HSS—8 x 4 x .375 Class H

The bolts most widely used in steel construction are those conforming to ASTM Standard A325 "High Strength Steel Bolts for Structural Steel Joints

Including Suitable Nuts and Plain Hardened Washers". These high-strength bolts are used extensively for connecting structural members at the job site, and to a lesser extent in the steel fabricator's shop. Under certain conditions it may be desirable to use a higher strength bolt, such as ASTM A490 "Quenched and Tempered Alloy Steel Bolts for Structural Steel Joints". In many structures, lower strength bolts, conforming to ASTM Standard A307 "Carbon Steel Externally and Internally Threaded Standard Fasteners" are suitable. Design standards[2.7] stipulate conditions under which these bolts cannot be used.

Welding electrodes are the rods or wire which are used to produce welds. They must conform to standards such as the CSA W48 series of standards on electrodes. Each electrode is suitable for use with a certain type of steel, using a particular type of welding equipment and specific welding procedures. Each electrode is designated by a code number which identifies the minimum tensile strength of the deposited weld metal, the welding positions for which the electrode is suitable, and the deposition characteristics of the electrode. The selection of the most suitable electrode to use in a given situation requires specialized knowledge of welding. Normally, this decision should be left to the fabricator, after consultation with the designer as to the required performance and service conditions.

Field welded splice in a large column.

References

2.1 Canadian Standards Association, "Structural Quality Steels", CSA G40.21, 1976, Rexdale, Ontario.

2.2 American Society for Testing and Materials "ASTM Book of Standards, Part 4", Philadelphia, Pennsylvania.

2.3 Canadian Institute of Steel Construction, "General Information on Structural Steel", Toronto, Ontario, 1975.

2.4 Canadian Standards Association, "General Requirements for Rolled or Welded Structural Quality Steel" CSA G40.20, 1976, Rexdale, Ontario.

2.5 Graham, R. R. Jr. et al "Glossary of Terms", Journal of the Structural Division, ASCE, Vol. 97, No. ST8, August, 1971.

2.6 Tall, L. et al "Structural Steel Design" p. 37, Ronald Press, New York, N.Y., 1974.

2.7 Canadian Standards Association "Steel Structures for Buildings—Limit States Design" CSA S16.1-1974, Rexdale, Ontario.

2.8 Kimball, W. A., "A Commentary on Structural Steel and CSA Standard G40.21M", Canadian Institute of Steel Construction, Toronto, Ontario, 1977.

2.9 Rolfe, S. T. and Barsom, J. M. "Fracture and Fatigue Control in Structures", Prentice-Hall, Inc., Englewood Cliffs, New Jersey, 1977.

2.10 Canadian Standards Association "Specification for Welded Steel Construction (Metal—Arc Welding)", CSA W59, 1977, Rexdale, Ontario.

2.11 Canadian Institute of Steel Construction "CISC Code of Standard Practice for Structural Steel for Buildings", Toronto, Ontario, 1970.

2.12 Canadian Institute of Steel Construction "Handbook of Steel Construction", Second Edition, Toronto, Ontario, 1976.

2.13 Canadian Institute of Steel Construction "Properties of Structural Steel Sections", Second Edition, Toronto, Ontario, 1976.

CHAPTER 3

TENSION MEMBERS

3.1 Introduction

Tension members are those structural elements which are subjected to direct axial loads which tend to elongate the members. They occur as components of trusses, hangers and cables for floors or roofs, in bracing systems, as tie rods, and similar members. The design of tension members is one of the simplest problems with which the structural engineer is faced. In limit states design, the basic requirement is simply that enough cross-sectional area be provided in order that the factored resistance of the member is equal to or greater than the factored load in the member.

Tension members are used in trusses.
(Photo courtesy Heavy Construction News)

In discussing the resistance of a tension member, it is pertinent to examine the qualitative behaviour of a typical member as the load on it is increased to the failure value. Figure 3.1(a) shows such a member and plots its behaviour in terms of the elongation response to load. Figure 3.1(b) shows an enlarged plot of the initial portion of this curve. Like a coupon of the same material, the initial portion of the curve shows an elastic response, that is, unloading of the member anywhere in this region will cause it to return to its original undeformed shape. Local yielding starts at a value less than the yield point of the material as obtained from a tension coupon, however. This is due to the inevitable eccentricity of load, dimensional variations in the cross-section, and the presence of residual stresses. Eventually, all the material in the cross-section reaches the yield point, terminating this region of "contained plastic flow". Deflections now will increase rapidly under no increase in load until the fibres start to strain-harden and the load again increases. Although this region of "unrestricted plastic flow" defines one limit of usefulness of the member, the member has considerable additional load-carrying capacity. The other limit of usefulness is that given by the ultimate resistance of the member. Both of these limits are used by CSA Standard S16.1 in establishing the criteria for tension members. As is the case for all members proportioned according to Limit States Design, the deformation of the tension member under the specified load must also be examined.

3.2 Tension Member Resistance

For the usual case, wherein the connections are made either by means of bolts or by welding, CSA Standard S16.1 requires (Clause 13.2(a)) that the resistance of a tension member be taken as the lesser of the following two cases:

(i) $T_r = \phi \, A_n \, F_y$ (3.1)

$\quad$ when $A_n/A_g \geqslant F_y/F_u$

$\quad\quad$ or

$T_r = \phi \, (F_u \dfrac{A_n}{A_g}) \, A_n$ (3.2)

$\quad$ when $A_n/A_g < F_y/F_u$

(ii) $T_r = 0.85 \, \phi \, A_n \, F_u$ (3.3)

The requirement given by Equation 3.3 follows directly from the examination of the behaviour of a typical tension member that was made using Figure 3.1. The member should be able to attain an ultimate load given by the product of the tensile strength of the material (F_u) and the least cross-sectional area of the member (A_n). As for all members, a performance factor (ϕ) is applied to the calculation of the resistance but an additional multiplier, 0.85, is included here. This is provided because there is no reserve of any

44

kind beyond the ultimate resistance; if a member were subjected to the load given by ϕ A_n F_u, it could be expected that fracture would result. This philosophy is consistent with past practice.

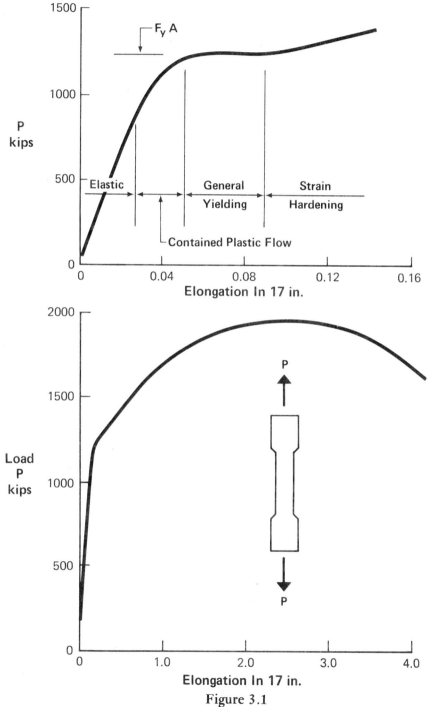

Figure 3.1
Load-Deformation Response of Tension Member (From Reference 2.6)

It was observed in Section 3.1 that a tension member will have a reserve of strength above the load which produces unrestricted plastic flow. Since the flow is "unrestricted", the deformations that result, although undefined, can be expected to be large if plastic flow occurs.

The capacity for distortion before failure is considered to be of importance in any structural assemblage as it allows for the re-distribution of forces as the structure proceeds towards its ultimate capacity.[3.1] The spread between yield strength and ultimate tensile strength has been very large for steels commonly used in the past. For CSA G40.21 44W steel, for example, these values are 44 ksi and 65 ksi (minimum), respectively. Usual member proportions will allow yielding before the ultimate strength is attained and failure of the member would be preceded by a great deal of distortion, a desirable feature. On the other hand, a steel such as ASTM A514 has a much lower spread between yield and ultimate strengths, the figures being 100 ksi and 115 ksi (minimum). If material is removed in the form of holes when making the end connections, the situation can easily arise wherein the ultimate strength of an A514 steel member is reached by tearing of the material through the least cross section before yielding is reached in the main portion of the member where no holes are present. If failure did occur, this means that it would happen suddenly and with little warning. In recognition of this, CSA S16.1 relates the criterion for member resistance based on unrestricted plastic flow (yield) to the relative proportions of the cross-section of the member.

If the ratio of net area to gross area (A_n/A_g) is greater than the ratio of the yield point of the member to its ultimate strength (F_y/F_u), then the member cross-section will reach yield on the gross cross-section prior to the time that the ultimate strength is reached at the net cross-section. Such a member would have considerable reserve of ductility if failure were to occur. Load could possibly be redistributed to other parts of the structure but, in any event, failure would be preceded by ample warning as the result of large deformations. In this case, the member resistance, as given by the yield level of usefulness, is taken directly as $\phi A_n F_y$.

On the other hand, if the criterion stated above is not met, failure would potentially occur by tearing through the net cross-section before any significant amount of yielding was present. In this case, a lower tensile resistance is permitted. It varies with the amount of ductility that might be expected, that is, with the ratio A_n/A_g.

In summary, the resistance of a tensile member is to be established as the lesser of the capacity based on yield load (Clause 13.2(a)(i)) and the capacity based on ultimate strength (Clause 13.2(a)(ii)). The yield load capacity is further distinguished as to the amount of ductility that might be expected to occur in members that use mechanical fasteners rather than welds. For most steels in common use today, Equation 3.1 will govern but all three possibilities must be examined.

Pin-connected members are used infrequently but, if they are required, the factored resistance is established as 75% of that of a tension member fastened by the usual structural fastener (Clause 13.2(b)). This reduction recognizes the greater non-uniformity of stress that occurs around a hole that is large relative to the material in which it is formed.

3.3 Design Requirements

In equation form, the basic design requirement can be expressed as

$$T_r \geqslant T_f \tag{3.4}$$

where T_f is the force in the member resulting from the factored loads and T_r is the factored tensile resistance of the member. The left-hand side of the equation contains the term A, the required cross-sectional area. This equation implies that all fibres of a cross-section are uniformly stressed, or, more precisely, that all fibres undergo the same elongation. Excluding for the moment the disturbing effects if holes are introduced in making the end connections, this assumption will generally be valid if the load axis is coincident with a longitudinal axis through the centre of gravity of the member. Unavoidable eccentricities do arise, however, such as is the case when only part of a member can be connected at its ends. Angles may be fastened along only one leg, for example. For usual member proportions and for static loadings, such minor eccentricities can generally be ignored as the ultimate capacity of the member is unaffected.[3.2] There may be cases where the load is definitely not coincident with the neutral axis of the member and the additional effect of the bending should then be considered.

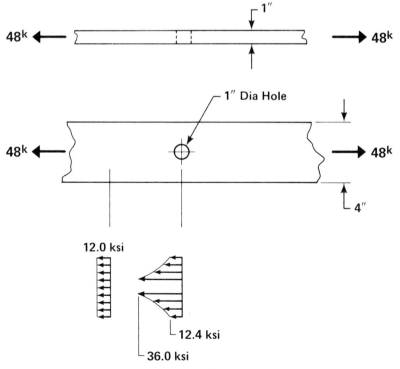

Figure 3.2
Theoretical Stress Distribution at a Hole

The introduction of holes for purposes of making end connections will result in local stresses considerably higher than a nominal stress calculated on the basis of the least area available to carry the load. For plates with widths at least four times the hole diameter, this increased stress will be about three times the nominal value.[3.3] As shown in Figure 3.2, the disturbance is highly localized. The situation is further complicated by the fact that such a hole is normally filled by a fastener. The fastener would be introducing a localized compressive stress into the plate adjacent to the region of theoretically high tensile stress.

Taking all of these factors into consideration, the effect of stress concentrations around holes is generally neglected in structural steel design when dealing with holes used for bolts. In these cases, the stress is assumed to be uniformly distributed over the area of a cross-section through one or more holes.

As already indicated, one notable exception to this rule is made when dealing with the substantially larger holes that are needed for pins in eyebars or in pin-connected plates.

The choice of section or shape to be used as a tension member is governed to a considerable extent by the type of end connection that will be used. Some of the sections available, exclusive of cables, are shown in Figure 3.3.

Round and flat bars are used infrequently today. In the sizes generally required, the stiffness of these members will be very low and they may sag under their own weight or that of workmen and maintenance personnel. Their small cross-sectional dimensions also mean high slenderness values and, as a consequence, they may tend to flutter under wind loads or vibrate under moving loads. Design Standards commonly place an upper limit on slenderness (ratio of unsupported length to least radius of gyration, L/r) to guard against these undesirable features. The CSA S16.1 requirement limits the slenderness ratio of tension members to 300. This requirement may be waived if the designer takes other steps to control possible sag, flutter, or vibration.

Angles, used singly or in multiples, are common tension members for light to medium loads. It is considered good practice to provide angles in pairs rather than singly. At least one axis of symmetry is then present and eccentricity in the end connection can be minimized. When angles or other shapes are used in this fashion, they should be interconnected at intervals to prevent rattling, especially when moving loads are present.

Larger tension loads may be carried by W or S-shapes, channels, or built-up sections. The built-up sections are also tied together either at intervals (batten plates) or continuously (lacing or perforated cover plates). Except when perforated cover plates are used, these ties are considered to not add load-carrying capacity in themselves but they do serve to provide rigidity and to distribute the load among the main elements.

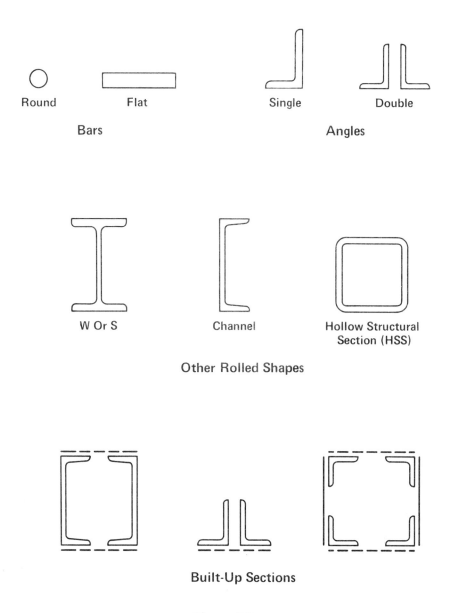

Round   Flat   Single   Double

Bars   Angles

W Or S   Channel   Hollow Structural
                                 Section (HSS)

Other Rolled Shapes

Built-Up Sections

Figure 3.3
Typical Sections Used as Tension Members

3.4 Effective Area of Tension Members

If the connection of a tension member is made using welds, such as shown in Figure 3.4, the full cross-sectional area of any chosen section is available for carrying load. The design can proceed directly in this case in accordance with the requirements of Equation 3.4. On the other hand, a connection made using bolts means that material has been removed from the cross-section in the form of holes. Only a portion of the cross-section is now available to carry load and this is termed the "net section".

49

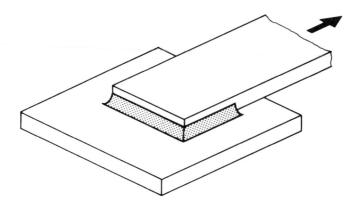

Figure 3.4
Tension Member with Welded End Connection

In setting forth the procedure for determination of the net section, it should be recognized that the hole used for a bolt is usually punched through the metal and is usually made one-sixteenth of an inch greater than the nominal diameter of the fastener. Since the punching process distorts the metal around the edges of the hole, an additional one-sixteenth of an inch on the nominal fastener diameter is assumed to be non-effective. Thus, a designer usually assumes that the diameter of a fastener hole is one-eighth of an inch greater than the actual fastener diameter. The area of metal removed as a result of the introduction of a given hole is then given by the product of this increased diameter times the thickness of material.

Consider fasteners laid out in a simple fashion, such as shown in the "lap" splice of Figure 3.5(a). Starting from plate A, it can be seen that the load is transferred in some manner into the six fasteners, then from the fasteners the load is transferred back into plate B. (Connection design is fully discussed in Chapter 10.) Plates A or B here represent a simple form of tension member. Intuitively, it could be expected that any failure of the tension member A, for example, would occur through a pair of fastener holes, such as shown in Figure 3.5(b). Experiment would confirm the result of the intuitive reasoning. If, for example, w = 8 in. and t = 1 in. then the "gross" cross-sectional area of the member is 8 sq. in. The area removed in the form of holes here is (7/8 + 1/8) in. x 1 in. x 2 holes = 2 sq. in. The "net" area available for carrying stress is thus (8−2) = 6 sq. in.

Carrying this illustration to its logical conclusion, the tensile capacity of member A can be determined. For G40.21 44W steel, F_y = 44 ksi and F_u = 65 ksi. Since the ratio of net to gross area (6/8 = 0.75) is greater than the ratio of yield to tensile strength (44/65 = 0.68), only Equations 3.1 and 3.2 need to be checked. Using ϕ = 0.90, Equation 3.1 gives a member resistance T_r = 0.90 x 6 sq. in. x 44 ksi = 238 kips and Equation 3.3 gives T_r = 0.85 x 0.90 x 6 sq. in. x 65 ksi = 298 kips. Applying the governing value, the factored member resistance is therefore 238 kips.

50

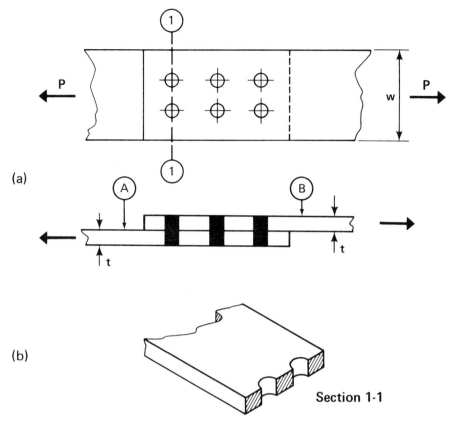

(a)

(b)

Figure 3.5
Tension Member — Lap Splice

In the preceding example, a cross-section of 6 sq. in. of material would be loaded to its maximum capacity if a load of 238 kips is applied. However, a cross-section of 8 sq. in. was provided for most of the length of the member. This means that 33% more cross-sectional area than is necessary is being used for a greater part of the member. While the ideal of 100% efficiency is not obtainable when mechanical fasteners are used, the designer might look for a more favorable fastener pattern. One alternative is shown in Figure 3.6. The net section which will provide the least area is no longer obvious and each possibility must be considered. Here, two cases are possible, a tearing of the plate across section 1-1 or through in a zig-zag fashion as in section 2-2.

Which of the two sections is critical depends not only upon the actual length of the section but also upon the stress conditions on each section. Although more exact formulae have been proposed, an adequately reliable and easily applied rule is the one specified by CSA S16.1 Clause 12.3.3—net width equals gross width minus the sum of all hole diameters in the chain plus a term $s^2/4g$ for each gauge in the chain. In equation form

$$w_{net} = w - \Sigma\, d + \Sigma\, \frac{s^2}{4g} \tag{3.6}$$

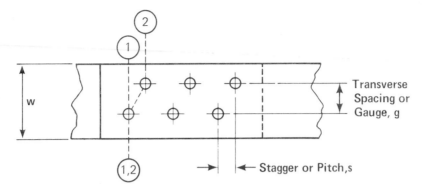

Figure 3.6
Tension Member — Staggered Fasteners

CSA Standard S16.1 further stipulates that the effective net section shall be limited to a maximum value of 85, 90, or 95% of the gross cross section, depending on the ratio of F_y to F_u of the material being used. These limitations are based on the results of tests on structural carbon[3.4] and high-strength steels.[3.5] The higher efficiencies are desirable not only from an economic point of view, but as discussed in Section 3.2, they may be used to promote yielding of the high strength steel member if ductility is considered to be of importance.

Referring again to Figure 3.6 and assuming values of w = 8 in., s = 3 in., and g = 5 in., the net widths are

Section 1-1: $\quad 8 - (\frac{7}{8} + \frac{1}{8})1 = 7.00$ in.

Section 2-2: $\quad 8 - (\frac{7}{8} + \frac{1}{8})2 + \frac{3^2}{4 \times 5}$

$$= 8 - 2.00 + 0.45 = 6.45 \text{ in.}$$

The latter governs and, for a plate thickness of 1 in. again, the effective net area is 6.45 sq. in. (For G40.21 44W steel, the 85% limitation applies and it is noted that this connection does not violate the limitation, that is, 0.85 x 8 > 6.45).

The efficiency of this connection is now 6.45/8.00 = 81%, a considerable improvement over that obtained with the previous fastener arrangement. The improvement does come at the expense of having to make a longer joint, however. The capacity of this member can now be established. Since A_n/A_g is still greater than F_y/F_u, only Equations 3.1 and 3.3 need to be checked.

$T_r = 0.90$ x 6.45 sq. in. x 44 ksi = 255 kips

or,

$T_r = 0.85$ x 0.90 x 6.45 sq. in. x 65 ksi = 321 kips

The capacity based on the yield load governs.

52

In some instances, a member may be connected by using fasteners in more than one plane. If the fasteners are staggered, such as those shown in Figure 3.7, the usual procedure is to develop the cross-section into an equivalent flat plate by revolving about the centrelines of the component parts. The critical net section can then be established by the procedure described for plates. An illustration of the calculations involved is given in Example 3.3.

Examples of net section calculations will also be found in Chapter 10.

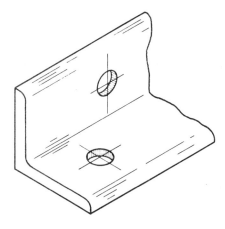

Figure 3.7
Net Section — Fasteners in More Than One Plane

3.5 Design Examples

The preceding sections have set out the basis of design of tension members. As has been noted, one of the main criteria affecting the design will be the connection details. If the end connection is to be made using welds, there generally is no resulting reduction in cross-section and the design of the member can proceed directly. When bolts are to be used, however, the design of the member is influenced by the amount of material removed in making the connection. In turn, the design of the connection itself cannot proceed without a knowledge of the shape to be used. As with most design problems, the engineer must work in a trial and error fashion until all relevant aspects have been satisfied.

Example 3.1

Given

Design the tension diagonal of an all-welded Pratt roof truss in which the chords are made from WT 10.5 x 41 sections. The factored load in the member under consideration is 142 kips and its length is 12 ft. Use G40.21 44W steel. (F_y = 44 ksi, F_u = 65 ksi).

Solution

Since welded end connections would be used, the net and gross areas of the cross-section will be equal (A) and only Equations 3.1 and 3.3 need to be examined.

$T_r = \phi A_n F_y = 0.90 \times 44 \text{ ksi} \times A = 39.6A$ (Governs)

or

$T_r = 0.85 \phi A_n F_u = 0.85 \times 0.90 \times 65 \text{ ksi} \times A = 49.7A$

(these resistances will be in kips when the area is given in sq. in.)

$T_r \geqslant T_f$ ⟋P

$39.6\, A \geqslant 142$

$A_{req'd} = 3.59 \text{ in.}^2$

As shown in Figure 3.8, it will be convenient to use a pair of angles, one welded on each side of the WT. Since there is no reduction in member area due to the connection, the selection of the angle sizes can be made directly. From Appendix A, p 321

Try 2—3 x 2 1/2 x 3/8 angles, long legs back to back.

$A_{prov.} = 3.84 \text{ in.}^2$ $r_{min.} = 0.93 \text{ in.}$

$\text{Max:} \ \dfrac{L}{r} = \dfrac{12 \times 12}{0.93} = 155 < 300$ (Satisfactory — CSA S16.1 Clause 10.2.2)

Use 2 - 3 x 2 1/2 x 3/8 angles as shown.

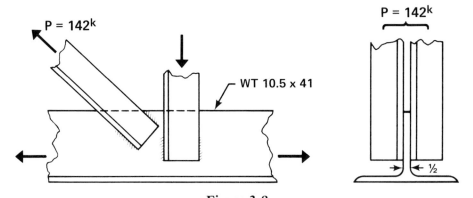

Figure 3.8
Tension Member — Welded End Connection — Example 3.1

Example 3.2

Given

Re-design the member of Example 3.1 assuming that fabrication will be made using 3/4 in. diameter high-strength bolts. Angles will be used for all members including the chords, as shown in Figure 3.9, and connections will be made using 3/8 in. thick gusset plates.

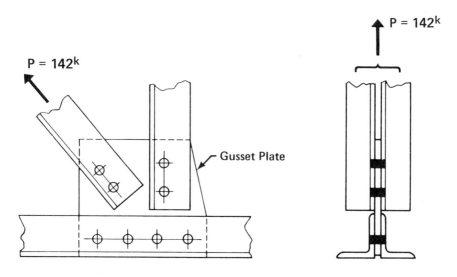

Figure 3.9
Tension Member — Bolted End Connection — Example 3.2

Solution

Assume that the factored resistance of the member will again be governed by

$$T_r = 39.6 \, A$$

where A is now the net cross-sectional area required. After the member has been designed, the possible application of Equation 3.2 will have to be checked. (From Example 3.1, it is known that Equation 3.3 will not govern.)

From $T_r \geqslant T_f$,

$$A_{net} \text{ req'd} = \frac{142}{39.6} = 3.59 \text{ in.}^2$$

Since angles with leg sizes less than 5 in. can accommodate fasteners only along one gauge line (Appendix A), the arrangement of fasteners will probably be like that shown in the figure.

Try 2—3 x 2 1/2 x 7/16 angles, long legs back to back. From the Appendix A, A_{gross} = 4.42 in.² and r_{min} = 0.92 in.

$$A_{holes} = (\frac{3}{4} + \frac{1}{8}) \times \frac{7}{16} \times 2 \text{ (one hole each angle)}$$

$$= 0.77 \text{ in.}^2$$

$$A_{net} \quad = 4.42 - 0.77 = 3.65 \text{ in.}^2 \qquad \text{(Satisfactory)}$$

55

Checking, $A_n/A_g = 0.825$ which is greater than the ratio F_y/F_u ($44/65 = 0.68$). The assumption that the resistance of the member is governed by Equation 3.1 is thus verified.

$$\text{Max.} \ \frac{L}{r} = \frac{12 \text{ x } 12}{0.92} = 157 < 300 \qquad \text{(Satisfactory)}$$

Use 2−3 x 2 1/2 x 7/16 angles as shown. The interconnection requirement for angles, Clause 18.2 of CSA S16.1, should be noted.

Example 3.3

Given

The lower chord of a large truss consists of two C 12 x 30 sections tied across the flanges with lacing bars. The critical section of the chord occurs just outside a panel point where it is necessary to splice the member. As shown in Figure 3.10, both web and flange plates are provided to transfer the stress from one section of the member to the other. Determine the allowable load of this member if the fasteners are 7/8 in. diameter and A441 steel is used throughout ($F_y = 50$ ksi, $F_u = 70$ ksi).

Solution

$$A_{gross}: \ 2-\text{C } 12 \text{ x } 30 = 2 \text{ x } 8.82 = 17.64 \text{ in.}^2 \qquad \text{(Appendix A)}$$

$A_{holes}:$ Section 1. $w_n = (12 + 3.17 + 3.17) - (0.51 \text{ x } 2) -$
$$3 \left(\frac{7}{8} + \frac{1}{8}\right) = 14.32 \text{ in.}$$

Section 2. $w_n = (12 + 3.17 + 3.17) - (0.51 \text{ x } 2) -$
$$5\left(\frac{7}{8} + \frac{1}{8}\right) + \frac{3^2}{4 \text{ x } 4.24} + 0 + 0 +$$
$$\frac{3^2}{4 \text{ x } 4.24} = 13.38 \text{ in.} \qquad \text{(Governs)}$$

Section 3. $w_n = (12 + 3.17 + 3.17) - (0.51 \text{ x } 2)$
$$- 4\left(\frac{7}{8} + \frac{1}{8}\right) + \frac{3^2}{4 \text{ x } 4.24} + 0 + 0$$
$$= 13.85 \text{ in.}$$

$A_{net} = (13.38 \text{ x } 0.51) = 6.82 \text{ in.}^2$ per channel or, 13.64 in.^{2} total.

$A_n/A_g = 13.64/17.64 = 0.77$

For A441 steel

$$F_y/\text{T.S.} = 0.71 \quad A_n/A_g > F_y/F_u$$

Therefore,

$$T_r = 0.90 \times 13.64 \text{ in.}^2 \times 50 \text{ ksi} = 614 \text{ kips} \qquad \text{(Governs)}$$

or

$$T_r = 0.85 \times 0.90 \times 13.64 \text{ in.}^2 \times 70 \text{ ksi} = 730 \text{ kips}$$

and the factored resistance of this member is 614 kips.

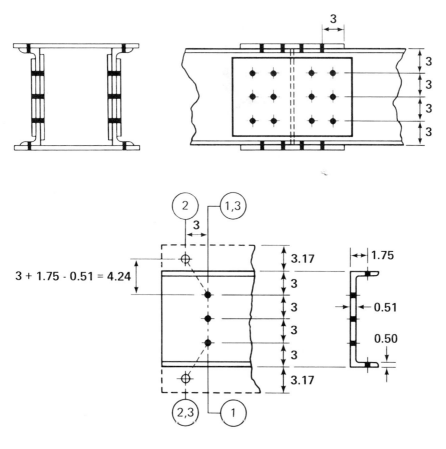

Figure 3.10
Tension Member Splice — Example 3.3

3.6 Eyebars and Cables

Eyebars were used rather extensively in the past, particularly as tension members in bridges. The sections are usually made from plate with a hole drilled at each end in an enlarged section. Pins are then used to make the connection. As noted in Section 3.2, the factored resistance of pin-connected members is appreciably lower than that permitted in members where mechanical fasteners or welds are used. CSA Standard S16.1 permits $T_r = 0.75 \, \phi \, A_n \, F_y$ and stipulates a number of other requirements as to

57

dimensions and details (see CSA S16.1 Clause 12.4). These requirements also apply to pin-connected plates or to pins in built-up members. Pin-connected members are seldom used today.

In contrast to the use of eyebars, cables are being used more in recent years than formerly. They continue to be used in modern suspension bridges, of course, but are also finding use in longspan structures such as aircraft hangers, in cable-suspended and cable-supported roofs for auditoriums, and in building frames which are formed by suspending all floors from a central core.[3.6]

The Papineau-Leblanc Bridge, near Montreal, is the longest cable-stayed bridge in North America.

Cables are generally classified as either strand or rope. Strand consists of an arrangement of individual wires laid helically around a centre wire. It is used for tension members where flexibility or bending is not a major requirement. The term "bridge strand" is used to denote the best-quality strand rather than the end use of the product.

Wire rope is made by laying a number of strands, as described above, around a central core. These strands are also laid on helically and the core may be fibre rope, another steel strand, or a small wire rope. "Bridge rope" refers again to the quality rather than to the use of the rope.

Because both rope and strand are made of a multiplicity of individual wires, the first applications of load will cause an appreciable amount of non-recoverable deformation as these individual wires seat themselves. In almost all structural applications, prestretching of the cable will be called for so that this non-elastic deformation is removed before installation of the cables. The manufacturer then provides information about the modulus of elasticity of the cable along with the metallic core area and the minimum ultimate tensile load. The modulus can be expected to be appreciably less than that associated with a solid steel section of the same area.

Terminal fittings for cables are made using either zinc-poured sockets or by a pressed-on assembly (swaging). The fittings are usually supplied such that the tensile strength of the cable can be developed before any yielding occurs in the end fitting. The end connection is made using pins or heavy hex nuts. Details of cable strengths and fittings may be obtained from manufacturers' catalogues. More information on design is available in other published literature.[3.7, 3.8]

Example 3.4

Given

A cable-supported roof of 100 ft. span consists of a series of parallel cables with a sag of 10 ft. The uniformly applied load (per foot of horizontal projection of the cable) is 120 lb. This is made up of 40 lb./ft. dead load and 80 lb./ft. live load. Choose a suitable cable.

Solution

Using the criteria for factored loads given in Clause 7.2 of the Standard, and assuming that the importance factor for the structure should be 1.0, the factored load is (1.25 x 40 lb./ft.) + (1.5 x 80 lb./ft.) = 170 lb./ft. Consideration of the equilibrium conditions for half the cable will establish that the maximum tension in the cable corresponding to this factored load is 22.9 kips.

Since the cable will pass over saddles and then down to anchorages at the edge of the roof or to the ground, rope will be preferred to strand because of its flexibility. From catalogues,[3.6] the breaking strength of a 1/2 in. diameter 6 x 7 WSC bridge rope is 23.0 kips. This rope consists of six strands with seven wires per strand and it has a wire strand core. The metallic area of the rope is 0.119 sq. in. and it weighs 0.42 lb./ft. If prestretched, it will have a minimum modulus of elasticity of 20×10^3 ksi.

References

3.1   Frankland, J. M., "Physical Metallurgy and Mechanical Properties of Materials: Ductility and the Strength of Metal Structures", J. of the Engineering Mechanics Division, ASCE, Vol. 86, No. EM6, December, 1960.

3.2   Gibson, G. J. and B. T. Wake, "An Investigation of Welded Connections for Angle Tension Members", Welding J. N.Y., Vol. 21, 1942.

3.3   Timoshenko, S. P., and J. N. Goodier, "Theory of Elasticity, 2nd ed.", McGraw-Hill, New York, N.Y.

3.4   Schultz, F. W., "Effective Net Section of Riveted Joints", Proceedings, 2nd Illinois Structural Engineering Conference, University of Illinois, Urbana, November, 1952.

3.5   Kulak, G. L., and J. W. Fisher, "A514 Steel Joints Fastened by A490 Bolts", Journal of the Structural Division, ASCE, Vol. 94, No. ST 10, October, 1969.

3.6   "Cable Roof Structures", Booklet 2318 Bethlehem Steel Company, Bethlehem, Pa.

3.7   Scalzi, J. B. and McGrath, W. K., "Mechanical Properties of Structural Cables", Journal of the Structural Division, ASCE, Vol. 97, No. ST12, December, 1971.

3.8   Merritt, F. S., "Structural Steel Designers' Handbook", 1972, McGraw-Hill, New York, N.Y.

CHAPTER 4

AXIALLY LOADED COMPRESSION MEMBERS

4.1 Introduction

Compression members are those members in a structure which are subjected to loads tending to decrease their lengths. Compression members are used as the vertical load-resisting elements of a building structure, called columns; as the posts which resist the compressive components of a load in a truss; as bridge piers; and as the load resisting elements in many other situations.

Heavy welded columns are often used in tall buildings.

In a building structure, forces and moments are transmitted to the columns through beams at each floor or roof level in the structure. In some cases the arrangement of members will be such that the net bending

61

moments acting at the ends of the column are zero. In this situation the column is required to resist a load acting concentric to the original longitudinal axis of the member and is termed an axially loaded column or simply a column. This will be the case treated in this chapter. If the net end moments are not zero the member will be subjected to an axial load and to bending moments along its length. This type of member is termed a beam-column and will be treated in Chapter 7.

An example of an axially loaded column is shown schematically in Figure 4.1. The centroidal axis of the member is shown by a broken line in the figure. The axial load, C, to be resisted by the member is equal to the sum of the beam shears, $V_1 + V_2$. The net moment, M, to be resisted by the column is a result of the end moments, M_1 and M_2, developed by the beams and the difference in beam end shears, $V_1 - V_2$, acting through the depth of the column, d. For the member shown in Figure 4.1 the net end moment is assumed to be zero; this could be the case, for example, if the end moments and shears developed by the two beams were equal. Where the beams are not connected rigidly to the column, the beams would not develop significant end moments and any moment to be resisted by the column would be due to the difference in end shears. In many such cases the net moment is small and the member is designed as an axially loaded column.

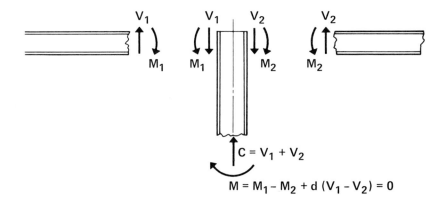

Figure 4.1
Force Transfer — Axially Loaded Column

Unlike the member subjected to tension, the column is designed on the assumption that its gross cross-sectional area will be effective in resisting the applied load. Bolts are often used to connect the column to adjacent members. As the load is applied the member will contract. It is assumed that the action of the bolts is such that they will replace the material removed for the holes.

When a steel member is subjected to an increasing axial load its stiffness decreases gradually as the maximum load carrying capacity is approached. Eventually the member cannot resist an increase in the applied force; at this stage the member is said to have failed. The attainment of the maximum load carrying capacity may be a result of local failure in the plates making up the cross-section (for example the flange or web plates in a wide-flange section) or overall failure of the column. The design relationships developed later in this chapter are based on the assumption that failure will be an overall column type of failure. To ensure that this will always be the case, the width-to-thickness ratios of the plate elements of the cross-section must be limited so that the plates will not buckle locally before the column fails as a unit. For example, the projecting width-to-thickness ratio of the flange plate of a wide-flange type section is limited in CSA Standard S16.1 to $100/\sqrt{F_y}$ and the clear web depth-to-thickness ratio to $255/\sqrt{F_y}$. If the plate width-to-thickness ratios must exceed these values the column cannot be designed on the assumption of overall failure.[4.1] These provisions are summarized in Figure 4.2 and are discussed in more detail in Chapter 6. In the example problems used in this chapter it will be assumed in most cases that the plate elements meet the limitations. This will generally be the case for rolled sections of steel having yield stress levels less than 65 ksi.

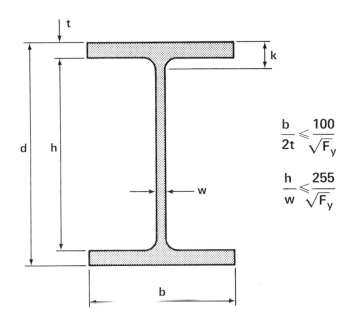

$$\frac{b}{2t} \leq \frac{100}{\sqrt{F_y}}$$

$$\frac{h}{w} \leq \frac{255}{\sqrt{F_y}}$$

Figure 4.2
Cross-Section Nomenclature

4.2 Strength of Steel Columns

The maximum strength of a steel column depends, to a large degree, on the member length. For discussion, steel columns can be conveniently classified as short, intermediate or long members. Each class has associated with it a characteristic type of behaviour and therefore different techniques must be used to assess the maximum strength.

A short column is loosely defined as a member which can resist a load equal to the yield load, C_y. The yield load is defined as the product of the cross-sectional area of the column, A, and the yield stress level, σ_y ($C_y = A\sigma_y$). In this case, the maximum strength of the member is governed only by the yield stress of the steel.

For longer columns, on the other hand, failure is accompanied by a rapid increase in the lateral deflection. If the member is extremely slender the load at which this increased deflection takes place is not sufficient to significantly yield the member. Thus the maximum load is not a function of the material strength but rather depends on the bending stiffness of the member, and its length.

Columns falling into the intermediate range are more complex to analyze but also are most common in steel structures. For intermediate length columns failure is also characterized by a rapid increase in the lateral deflection, but only after some portions of the column cross-section have yielded. Yielding is initiated first in those portions of the cross-section having large compressive residual stresses. The failure in this case is termed inelastic instability and the maximum strength of the column depends not only on the bending stiffness and length but also on the yield stress level of the steel, the distribution of residual stress over the cross-section, and the magnitude of the initial imperfections in the columns.

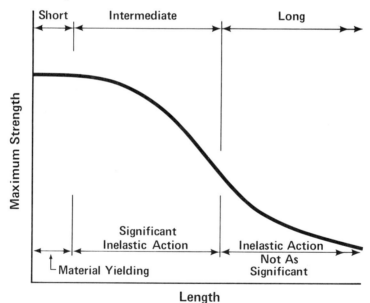

Figure 4.3
Strength of Steel Columns

Figure 4.3 shows schematically the relationship between the maximum strength of a column and its length. The three classes of columns are shown in the figure together with the characteristic marking the attainment of maximum strength. In the Sections following, the determination of the maximum strength will be discussed in detail.

4.3 Behaviour of Cross-Section

The stress-strain curve obtained from a tension test performed on a steel specimen is shown in Figure 2.2. A very similar curve would be obtained from a compression test performed on a suitable specimen. Theoretically, because the applied load on a column is distributed uniformly over the cross-sectional area, the average stress versus average strain curve for a short column should also be similar to Figure 2.2.

If a short length of wide-flange column is subjected to an axial compressive load, however, the stress-strain curve differs from that obtained from a small coupon. The average stress-strain curve for a short column is shown in Figure 4.4 where the applied load has been divided by the yield stress and the resulting strain by the yield strain.[4.2] The term σ/σ_y, plotted on the vertical axis is equivalent to the ratio C/C_y. The first significant difference between the curves of Figure 2.2 and 4.4 becomes apparent at Load No. 15 (Figure 4.4) when the σ-ϵ curve for the short column deviates from the elastic straight line relationship.

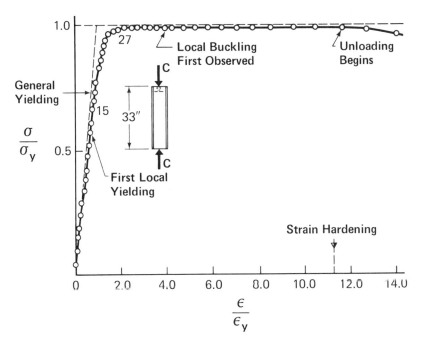

Figure 4.4
Stub Column Stress-Strain Relationship

The reason for the early yielding lies in the presence of residual strains in the short column. These strains are parallel to the longitudinal axis of the member and are typically distributed over the cross-section as shown in Figure 4.5(a). The residual strains develop as a result of the rolling and cooling process. As the structural member comes off the rolls it is allowed to cool in air. The flange tips cool more quickly than the areas adjacent to the

65

flange-to-web junctions, and gain strength and stiffness in the process. Then when the central portions of the flanges and the web cool, the material is restrained by the stiffer areas near the flange tips. The result is a set of residual strains as shown in Figure 4.5(a); the flange tips are subjected to compressive strains, the remainder of the section to tensile strains.[4.2]

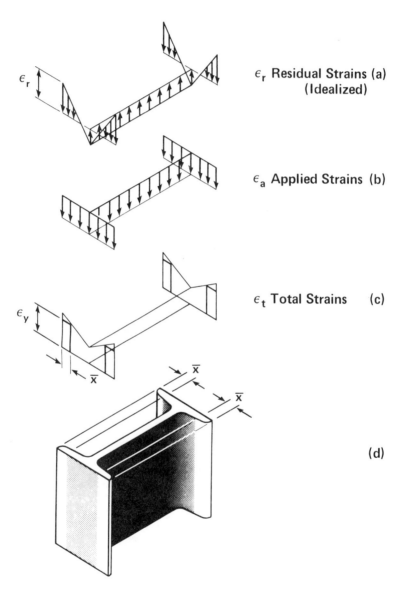

ϵ_r Residual Strains (a)
(Idealized)

ϵ_a Applied Strains (b)

ϵ_t Total Strains (c)

(d)

Figure 4.5
Residual and Applied Strains

An applied load produces a uniform strain distribution over the cross-section as shown in Figure 4.5(b). As the load is increased, the magnitude of the total strain, $\epsilon_t = \epsilon_a + \epsilon_r$, eventually exceeds the yield strain, ϵ_y, as shown in Figure 4.5(c). On additional loading, the yielded areas are ineffective since an increase in the magnitude of the applied strain does not produce a corresponding increase in stress. In addition, the width of the yielded area, $\bar{x}$, increases, causing the section to be even more ineffective. This process corresponds approximately to the portion of the σ-ϵ curve between load numbers 15 and 27 (Figure 4.4). Once the applied strain exceeds the maximum tensile residual strain by an amount ϵ_y, the entire cross-section will have yielded and the applied load will be equal to the so-called yield load, C_y = $A\sigma_y$. This stage corresponds approximately to Load No. 27 on the curve of Figure 4.4.

In accordance with the stress-strain curve of Figure 2.2 the load should increase above C_y due to the presence of strain-hardening. However, in compression, as the applied strain is increased the plates composing the cross-section begin to exhibit large local deflections and the load carrying capacity of the cross-section begins to decrease. Thus for a column, the maximum load carrying capacity is in fact governed by the strength of the cross-section and can never exceed the yield load.

4.4 Behaviour of Columns—Buckling Strength

While the strength of the cross-section is dependent on the yield stress level, the strength of an actual column is, to some extent, independent of the material strength. A column of length L is shown in Figure 4.6. The column is subjected to a load C and is pinned at either end. The pinned connections are assumed to be incapable of resisting a bending moment. The column cross-section is shown in Section A.A. In the following development it will be assumed that the cross-section is free to translate in the x direction only so that this motion will tend to bend the member about its weak axis (the y axis). The moment of inertia about the y axis will be denoted by I and the material has a modulus of elasticity, E.

As the member is loaded, it will remain in a straight position, provided that it is free from imperfections of load or geometry. If it is then forced into the position shown by the full line in Figure 4.6(a) and then the forcing agency is removed, it will return to the straight position. As the load is increased, a stage will eventually be reached at which the member will no longer return to the straight position. At this value of the load, C_{cr}, the member remains in equilibrium in the deflected position and a free body diagram is shown in Figure 4.6(b).

Summing moments at the cut section produces an expression for the moment, M

$$M = C x \tag{4.1}$$

The internal resisting moment is also related to the curvature by:[4.3]

$$M = -EI \frac{d^2 x}{dz^2} \tag{4.2}$$

Combining Equations 4.1 and 4.2 results in the basic differential equation:

$$EI \frac{d^2 x}{dz^2} + Cx = 0 \qquad (4.3)$$

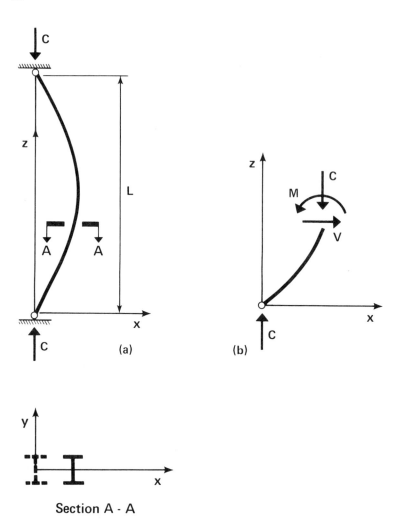

Section A - A

Figure 4.6
Column Buckling

The solution of Equation 4.3 results in an expression for the deflected shape:

$$x = A \sin \sqrt{\frac{C}{EI}} \, z + B \cos \sqrt{\frac{C}{EI}} \, z \qquad (4.4)$$

where constants A and B are evaluated by considering the boundary conditions at the member ends. For instance the deflection x must be zero at z = 0 and at z = L.

From these conditions, B = 0 and:

$$\sqrt{\frac{C}{EI}} \, L = n\pi \tag{4.5}$$

Solving Equation 4.5 the load, C_{cr}, required to hold the member in a deflected shape is given by:

$$C_{cr} = n^2 \pi^2 \frac{EI}{L^2} \tag{4.6}$$

where n = 0, 1, 2, 3. . . . .A value of n = 0 implies that there is no load on the member; values of n = 2, 3. . . .imply that an external agency is used to hold the column in a straight position for the load associated with n = 1 and thus the higher values are not relevant to the physical problem. The critical load is given by:

$$C_{cr} = \frac{\pi^2 EI}{L^2} \tag{4.7}$$

At the instant before buckling (or bifurcation, the change from the straight to the deflected equilibrium position) the average stress on the cross section is:

$$\sigma_{cr} = \frac{C_{cr}}{A} = \frac{\pi^2 EI}{AL^2} = \frac{\pi^2 E}{(L/r)^2} \tag{4.8}$$

Where r is the radius of gyration for bending about the y axis and L/r is termed the slenderness ratio of the member.

The development of Equation 4.8 assumes that the resisting moment of the cross-section is assumed to be given by Equation 4.4, that is, the expression is valid only as long as the load does not induce yielding in the cross-section prior to buckling. This means that the applied stress, σ_{cr} must be less than $E(\epsilon_y - \epsilon_r)$ since at this value of stress, yielding will be initiated in the cross-section as a result of the strains produced by the applied load adding to the residual strains in the cross-section (see Figure 4.5).

Figure 4.7 plots the average stress, σ, versus the deflection at midspan, x(L/2) for a column failing after elastic buckling. The column remains straight (or returns to the straight position after disturbance) as long as the stress is below that given by Equation 4.8; however, at the critical stress the deflection is that given by Equation 4.4 with z = L/2:

$$x(L/2) = A \sin \sqrt{\frac{C}{EI}} \, \frac{L}{2} \tag{4.9}$$

where the coefficient A has not been determined but is not zero. Thus, at the critical stress the deflection increases as shown by the full horizontal line in Figure 4.7.

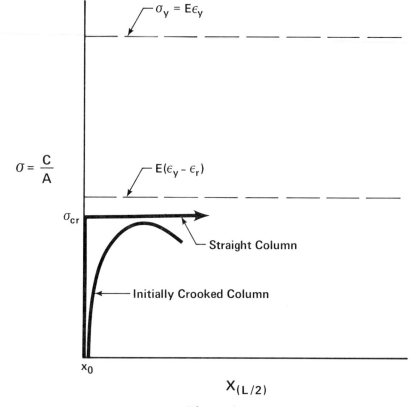

Figure 4.7
Load-Deflection Relationship — Long Column

As the slenderness ratio of a column is reduced, the critical value of the average stress is increased until the member will yield under the applied stress before buckling. Yielding will start in those portions of the cross-section having high compressive residual stresses.

The residual strain distribution is shown in Figure 4.5(a). The distribution is idealized with high compressive strains at the flange tips and tensile strains at the flange-to-web junctions and in the web. The uniform compressive strain distribution, produced as a result of the applied load, is shown in Figure 4.5(b) and the total strain picture (the algebraic sum at each point in the cross-section) is plotted in Figure 4.5(c). The peak strain values occur at the flange tips as shown and now exceed the yield strain. The extent of yielding over the cross-section is shown in Figure 4.5(d). The flanges are yielded over a length $\overline{x}$ extending in from the flange tips; the extent will depend on the magnitude of the applied load.

The strain history for a yielded element of the cross-section is shown in Figure 4.8. The total compressive strain is made up of the residual strain plus the strain due to the applied load, and is sufficient to bring the material to a point A in Figure 4.8. If the column is now subjected to an additional compressive strain the material will continue to deform at the yield stress as

70

shown by the horizontal arrow in this figure. If, however, the incremental strain is tensile, the material will unload elastically along the line shown by the inclined arrow.

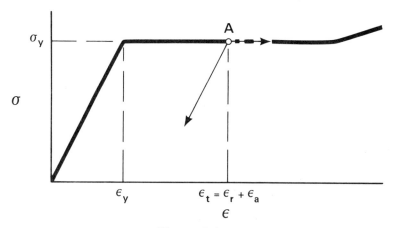

Figure 4.8
Strain Reversal in Yielded Zone

The deformation on buckling results in a bending type motion so that the incremental strains would appear to be those shown in Figure 4.9(a) for the elastic buckling case. However, Shanley has shown by a series of careful experiments that when a column buckles in the inelastic range the initial motion is accompanied by an increase in load.[4.4] In this situation, the strain distribution is that shown in Figure 4.9(b), with all elements of the cross-section subjected to an increase in compressive strain.

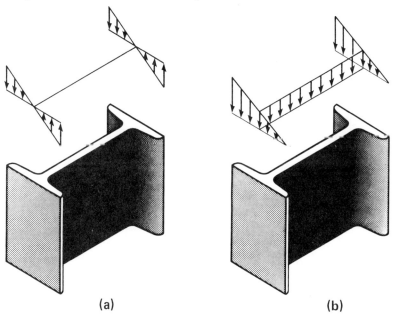

(a)   (b)

Figure 4.9
Strains Induced by Buckling

The load-deformation curve for the initially straight column is shown in Figure 4.10, with the applied stress plotted against the midspan deformation. As the member continues to deform in its buckled shape, the load (stress) increases to its maximum value and then drops off. During this process the cross-section continues to yield. The maximum stress is not much greater than the stress at the instant of buckling.

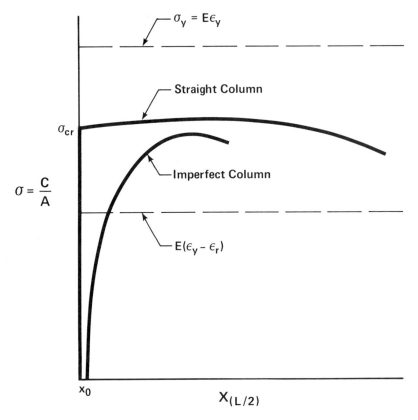

Figure 4.10
Load-Deflection Relationship — Intermediate Column

Returning to an examination of the cross-section, if all elements are subjected to an increase in compressive strain at the instant of buckling then those areas which were yielded at the instant before buckling will not accept an increased stress during buckling and will not contribute to the internal bending moment. In fact, the internal resisting moment will depend on the portion of the cross-section which remains elastic, the portion shown cross-hatched in Figure 4.5(d). The resisting moment would then be given by Equation 4.2 but with the moment of inertia replaced by the moment of inertia of the elastic portion of the cross-section, I_e. Following through the same derivation as before, the critical buckling stress is now given by:

$$\sigma_{cr} = \frac{\pi^2 E}{(L/r_e)^2} \tag{4.10}$$

72

where the radius of gyration, r, in Equation 4.8 has been replaced by

$$r_e = \sqrt{I_e/A} \qquad (4.11)$$

The value of r_e would depend on the buckling stress, as well as the magnitude and distribution of the residual strain pattern and on the proportions of the cross-section.

4.5 Behaviour of Actual Columns

A real column does not behave exactly as described in the previous section. Due to unavoidable disturbances during the rolling and cooling process, the real column will not be perfectly straight. If, for example, the out-of-straightness at mid-height of the column (in the x direction) is x_o then as soon as the column is loaded the external bending moment at mid-span will be Cx_o. In this situation, buckling does not occur. However, the extra bending moment will cause additional deflections, and, as the average stress is increased, the load-deflection curve will take the shape shown by the lower curves in Figure 4.7 or 4.10. As the average stress approaches the critical value, the deflection will increase rapidly and produce large bending moments. These in turn will lead to inelastic action and eventual unloading of the member.

For the member shown in Figure 4.6(a), the internal bending moment in the presence of an initial imperfection is given by:

$$M = -EI\left(\frac{d^2x}{dz^2} - \frac{d^2x_o}{dz^2}\right) \qquad (4.12)$$

since the internal moment develops only as a result of the curvatures induced after the load is applied. The resulting equilibrium equation (replacing Equation 4.3) is:

$$EI\left(\frac{d^2x}{dz^2} - \frac{d^2x_o}{dz^2}\right) + Cx = 0 \qquad (4.13)$$

Assuming that the initial imperfection is in the form of a sine wave, and applying the boundary conditions the deflection at mid-height of the column can be expressed as:

$$x(L/2) = \frac{x_o}{1 - C/C_{cr}} \qquad (4.14)$$

Equation 4.14 is plotted as the initial portion of the lower curve in Figure 4.7 and is valid until yielding is initiated in the member. The magnitude of the initial imperfection, x_o, is restricted by CSA Standard S16.1, and for slender members the maximum load carrying capacity is not greatly reduced by the presence of initial imperfections.

73

For columns of intermediate length the situation is more serious, however. As the axial load is increased, the internal moment is given by Equation 4.12 until yielding occurs in the member. The strain distribution over the cross-section would be obtained by superimposing the distributions of Figure 4.5 (a and b) and Figure 4.9(a) reflecting the influence of residual strains, axial force and bending moment, respectively.

At any specific loading stage, yielding will have occurred at various locations in the cross-section, where the total strain exceeds the yield strain. The yielded zone will extend from the mid-height of the member over a length which depends on the shape of the column cross-section. Corresponding to the yielded patterns, a stress distribution exists on each cross-section that must be sufficient to hold in equilibrium the axial force, C, and the bending moment, Cx. As the load is increased the yielded zones grow and the corresponding stress distributions change to maintain these equilibrium relationships.

At some stage of loading it is no longer possible to maintain equilibrium under an increasing axial load. This point marks the maximum load carrying capacity for an initially imperfect column and corresponds to the peak of the lower curve of Figure 4.10. As the member is deformed beyond this stage equilibrium cannot be maintained unless the load is reduced. Since the yielded condition changes continually during the loading history, the stiffness values required to determine the deflected shape of the member, and thus the maximum load carrying capacity, also change. The actual calculation of the maximum strength is accomplished by a numerical integration procedure which is similar to that described in more detail in Section 7.5 for beam-columns.

For columns of intermediate length the extent of yielding before the maximum strength is attained is significant. Thus the interaction of the residual strains with those additional strains caused by axial load and bending can influence the maximum strength. Since the additional strains corresponding to bending are initially triggered by initial imperfections the interaction of these two variables (residual strain pattern and magnitude of initial imperfection) results in a wide scatter in column strengths for intermediate columns.

4.6 Design of Columns

To reflect the influences described above and to provide a convenient tool for design, CSA Standard S16.1 describes the maximum strength of a column by means of a four-part equation depending on the non-dimensional slenderness factor

$$\lambda = \frac{KL}{r} \sqrt{\frac{F_y}{\pi^2 E}} \tag{4.15}$$

The factored compressive resistance, C_r, is given by:

$$0 \leqslant \lambda \leqslant 1.0 \quad C_r = \phi A F_y (1.035 - 0.202\,\lambda - 0.222\,\lambda^2) \tag{4.16a}$$

$$1.0 < \lambda \leqslant 2.0 \quad C_r = \phi A F_y (-0.111 + 0.636\,\lambda^{-1} + 0.087\,\lambda^{-2}) \tag{4.16b}$$

$$2.0 < \lambda \leqslant 3.6 \quad C_r = \phi A F_y (0.009 + 0.877\,\lambda^{-2}) \tag{4.16c}$$

$$3.6 < \lambda \qquad C_r = \phi A F_y\,\lambda^{-2} = \phi A \left[\frac{286000}{(\frac{KL}{r})^2} \right] \tag{4.16d}$$

In Equation 4.15, r denotes the radius of gyration of the cross-section and L denotes the member length. The radius of gyration is calculated for the axis about which bending takes place and L/r is termed the slenderness ratio. The factor K is called the effective length factor, the calculation of which will be examined in detail in Chapter 5. The specified minimum yield stress is denoted by F_y. To account for the expected variations in material properties and cross-sectional dimensions, the compressive resistance contains the performance factor, ϕ. The derivation of the performance factor for axially loaded columns will be described in Section 4.7.

Column slenderness affects column strength.
(Photo courtesy Heavy Construction News)

Referring to the previous sections, the ranges of applicability for the various parts of Equation 4.16 do not coincide with the slenderness factors for short, intermediate and long columns used for the purpose of discussion. Some comparisons can be made, however. For example, a short column would be contained in the lower end of the range covered by Equation 4.16(a). For values of λ less than approximately 0.25 (corresponding to $\dfrac{KL}{r}$ $= 20$ for a steel with $F_y = 44$ ksi) the compressive resistance, excluding the performance factor, will be within 3% of C_y. For the commonly used steels, slender members can be thought of as those having slenderness factors greater than 2.0 (corresponding to $\dfrac{KL}{r} = 161$ for $F_y = 44$ ksi) although there is no definite dividing line between slender and intermediate members. For intermediate members, the compressive resistance is given by Equations 4.16(a) and (b) while for slender members Equation 4.16(c) is generally appropriate. Equation 4.16(d) applies only to the high strength steels.

For extremely slender members the maximum strength is highly sensitive to changes in both the end conditions and initial imperfections and such members cannot safely be designed using Equations 4.16. For this reason CSA Standard S16.1 limits the maximum slenderness ratio for compressive members to $\dfrac{KL}{r} = 200$ (corresponding to $\lambda = 2.5$ for $F_y = 44$ ksi).

4.7 Performance Factor for Columns

In general, the performance factor, ϕ, is used to reduce the nominal value of the compressive resistance to account for the possibility of under-strength material, underrun in the cross-sectional dimensions, and variations in workmanship. As applied to axially loaded columns, the variations in material strength and cross-sectional dimensions can be expected to have similar effects on columns of different slenderness ratios. As discussed earlier, however, the influences of variations in column out-of-straightness and residual strain distribution are more severe for intermediate length columns.[4.5]

The equations used to predict the compressive resistance (Equation 4.16) for CSA Standard S16.1 have been adjusted to reflect the increased uncertainty in the prediction of the ultimate strength of intermediate columns.[4.6] For this reason the performance factor, ϕ, can be held constant at 0.90 over the entire range of slenderness ratios. This procedure results in a relatively uniform probability of failure for columns of differing slenderness.

4.8 Summary and Design Examples

The design provisions of the Canadian Standards Association are shown in Figure 4.11 for steel having $F_y = 44$ ksi. This curve plots the compressive resistance (C_r/ϕ) divided by the cross-sectional area versus the slenderness ratio of the member. The equivalent slenderness factors are shown near the bottom of the figure. The provisions depicted in Figure 4.11 are based on the assumption that failure will involve bending about one of the major axes

76

of the cross-section. This will be the axis associated with the larger slenderness ratio. In sections having only one axis of symmetry (or in asymmetrical sections) the possibility also exists that failure will be accompanied by both bending and twisting of the cross-section and may occur at a reduced load.[4.7] For these sections the compressive resistance should be based on a consideration of the actual failure modes as discussed in References 4.4 and 4.7.

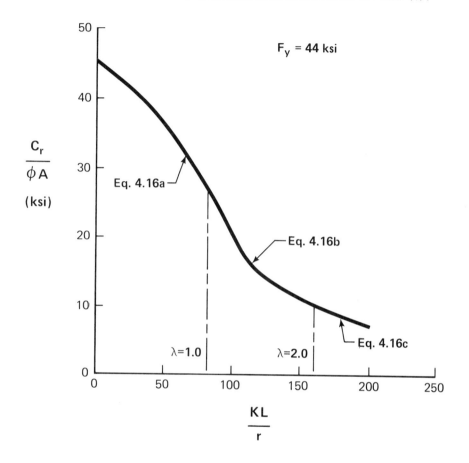

Figure 4.11
Compressive Resistance

The column strength relationship shown in Figure 4.11 is thought to be applicable to most of the sections in common use in Canada.[4.4] For other types of sections it is suggested that relationships recommended by the Structural Stability Research Council may be applicable.[4.4] For example, stress-relieved sections, G40.20 Class H hollow structural sections and a few specific sections having high yield stress levels (100 ksi) could be designed in such a way as to permit higher capacities.[4.8] On the other hand, many heavy sections, G40.20 Class C hollow structural sections and welded sections fabricated from universal mill plates should be designed for a smaller capacity than that corresponding to Figure 4.11.[4.4]

In Canada many H-section columns are now made by welding together three plate components. The flange-to-web welds induce large residual stresses which are tensile in the vicinity of the weld and compressive near the flange tips. In some cases the compressive stresses are much higher than normally occur in rolled shapes, which can result in a section with reduced strength. Studies have indicated that welded H-shapes which have flange edges flame-cut are preferable to those having flange edges rolled, as is the case if unsheared universal mill plate is used. The flame cutting process induces tensile rather than compressive residual stresses at the edges of the plate. For this reason the Standard notes that welded H-shapes should have flame-cut flanges and may then be designed using the relationship contained in CSA Standard S16.1.

The examples which follow treat the analysis (a checking process) and design of axially loaded pin-ended columns.

As in Chapter 3, the examples will be solved using basic principles; however, in many cases tabulated values may be used to reduce the number of computations involved. The values of $\sqrt{\dfrac{F_y}{\pi^2 E}}$, for example, are given as a part of Clause 13.3.1 of Reference 4.1. In addition, many convenient tables are included in Reference 4.9. Following the working of each example problem, the alternative solutions using tabulated values will be outlined briefly.

Example 4.1

Given

A W10x49 section of G40.21 44W steel (F_y = 44 ksi) is used as a pedestal with a length of 3'-6". Determine the factored compressive resistance.

Solution

The cross-sectional properties of the W10x49 shape are listed in Appendix A as:

$$A = 14.4 \text{ in.}^2 \qquad r_x = 4.35 \text{ in.} \qquad r_y = 2.54 \text{ in.}$$

The slenderness ratios are computed assuming the effective length factor K = 1.0, as:

$$\frac{L}{r_x} = \frac{12 \times 3.5}{4.35} = 9.7$$

$$\frac{L}{r_y} = \frac{12 \times 3.5}{2.54} = 17 \qquad \text{(Governs)}$$

The compressive resistance is dependent on the larger slenderness ratio, L/r_y = 17. Using Equation 4.15:

$$\lambda = \frac{L}{r}\sqrt{\frac{F_y}{\pi^2 E}} = 17\sqrt{\frac{44}{\pi^2 \times 29000}} = 0.20$$

Since $\lambda < 1.0$ the column falls within the limit of applicability of Equation 4.16(a) and the factored compressive resistance is:

$$C_r = \phi A\, F_y\, (1.035 - 0.202\,\lambda - 0.222\,\lambda^2)$$

$$= 0.90 \times 14.4 \times 44(1.035 - 0.202 \times 0.20 - 0.222 \times 0.20^2)$$

$$= 562 \text{ kips}$$

Using the CISC Manual,[4.9] the value of the unit factored compressive resistance (C_r/A) corresponding to a slenderness ratio $L/r = 16.5$, and a yield stress of 44 ksi is given on page 4.9. Information on yield stress values for various steels is given in Reference 4.10. In addition, the factored compressive resistances for the W10x49 section are tabulated directly on page 4.35.

Example 4.2

Given

A W10x49 section of G40.21 44W steel (F_v = 44 ksi) with a length of 36'-0" is used as a temporary support. Determine the factored compressive resistance of the member.

Solution

The cross-sectional properties of the W10x49 shape are listed in Appendix A:

$$A = 14.4 \text{ in.}^2 \qquad r_x = 4.35 \text{ in.} \qquad r_y = 2.54 \text{ in.}$$

Assuming an effective length factor K = 1.0, the slenderness ratios are computed as:

$$\frac{L}{r_x} = \frac{36 \times 12}{4.35} = 99$$

$$\frac{L}{r_y} = \frac{36 \times 12}{2.54} = 170 \qquad\qquad \text{(Governs)}$$

The compressive resistance is dependent on the larger slenderness ratio, L/r_y = 170. According to Equation 4.15 the slenderness factor is:

$$\lambda = \frac{KL}{r}\sqrt{\frac{F_y}{\pi^2 E}} = 170\sqrt{\frac{44}{\pi^2 \times 29000}} = 2.1$$

Since $2.0 \leqslant \lambda \leqslant 3.6$ the member falls within the limit of applicability of Equation 4.16(c) and the factored compressive resistance is:

$$C_r = \phi A F_y \, (0.009 + 0.877 \, \lambda^{-2})$$

$$= 0.90 \times 14.4 \times 44 \, (0.009 + 0.877 \times 2.1^{-2})$$

$$= 119 \text{ kips}$$

Using the CISC Manual[4.9] the factored compressive resistance for the W10x49 section is tabulated directly on page 4.35. For extremely slender members (those having $\lambda > 3.6$ but $\dfrac{KL}{r} < 200$) the compressive resistance is given by Equation 4.16(d) and does not depend on the yield stress of the steel. For most of the commonly used steels, columns normally encountered in building construction will not fall in this range.

Example 4.3

Given

A W10x49 section of G40.21 44W steel ($F_y = 44$ ksi) is used as a column with a length of 20'-0". Determine the compressive resistance.

Solution

The cross-sectional properties of the W10x49 shape are listed in Appendix A:

$$A = 14.4 \text{ in.}^2 \qquad r_x = 4.35 \text{ in.} \qquad r_y = 2.54 \text{ in.}$$

Assuming an effective length factor $K = 1.0$, the slenderness ratios are computed as:

$$\frac{L}{r_x} = \frac{20 \times 12}{4.35} = 55$$

$$\frac{L}{r_y} = \frac{20 \times 12}{2.54} = 94 \qquad \qquad \text{(Governs)}$$

The compressive resistance is dependent on the larger slenderness ratio, $L/r_y = 94$. The corresponding slenderness factor is given by Equation 4.15:

$$\lambda = \frac{KL}{r} \sqrt{\frac{F_y}{\pi^2 E}} = 94 \sqrt{\frac{44}{\pi^2 \times 29000}} = 1.2$$

Since $1.0 \leqslant \lambda \leqslant 2.0$ the member falls within the limits of applicability of Equation 4.16(b) and the factored compressive resistance is:

$$C_r = \phi AF_y\,(-0.111 + 0.636\,\lambda^{-1} + 0.087\,\lambda^{-2})$$

$$= 0.90 \times 14.4 \times 44\,(-0.111 + 0.636 \times 1.2^{-1} + 0.087 \times 1.2^{-2})$$

$$= 280 \text{ kips}$$

Using the CISC Manual[4.9] the factored compressive resistance for the member is again tabulated directly on page 4.35.

Example 4.4

Given

A W12x190 section of G40.21 50A steel (F_y = 50 ksi) is used as a main member. The column has a length of 15'-0" and is assumed to be pin-connected at either end. The cross-section is built-up by welding two plates, each 11" x 3/4", to the outside faces of the flanges. The column is braced at mid-height to prevent movement in the x direction only. Determine the compressive resistance. The column is shown in Figure 4.12.

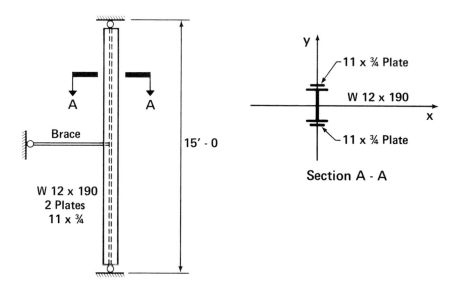

Figure 4.12
Structural Arrangement — Example 4.4

Solution

The cross-sectional properties of the W12x190 section are listed in Appendix A:

A = 55.9 in.^{2}	I_x = 1890 in.^{4}	I_y = 590 in.^{4}
r_x = 5.81 in.	r_y = 3.25 in.	d = 14.38 in.

Before the compressive resistance can be determined the properties of the built-up section must be computed. The calculation of I_x involves the I_x value for the W shape and the contribution of the two plates. This second contribution is the sum of the moments of inertia of the plates about their own centroidal axes and the transfer term to shift the calculations to the centroidal axis of the complete section. The moments of inertia of the two plates about their own centroidal axes are relatively small and would normally be ignored.

$$I_x = I_x \text{ (W)} + I_x \text{(plates)} + A\text{(plates)}(\frac{d + t}{2})^2$$

$$= 1890 + 2 \times \frac{11}{12} \times 0.75^3 + 2 \times 11 \times 0.75 \, (\frac{14.38 + 0.75}{2})^2$$

$$= 2840 \text{ in.}^4$$

$$I_y = I_y \text{ (W)} + I_y \text{(plates)}$$

$$= 590 + 2 \times 0.75 \times \frac{11^3}{12}$$

$$= 756 \text{ in.}^4$$

$$A = A \text{ (W)} + A\text{(plates)}$$
$$= 55.9 + 2 \times 0.75 \times 11$$
$$= 72.4 \text{ in.}^2$$

$$r_x = \sqrt{\frac{I_x}{A}} = \sqrt{\frac{2840}{72.4}} = 6.26 \text{ in.}$$

$$r_y = \sqrt{\frac{I_y}{A}} = \sqrt{\frac{756}{72.4}} = 3.23 \text{ in.}$$

The slenderness ratios are computed as in the previous examples except that the brace at mid-height is used to reduce the length for buckling about the y axis of the section

$$\frac{L_x}{r_x} = \frac{15 \times 12}{6.26} = 29 \qquad\qquad\qquad \text{(Governs)}$$

$$\frac{L_y}{r_y} = \frac{15 \times 12}{2 \times 3.23} = 28$$

The use of bracing to prevent movement in the x direction has reduced the L/r_y value so that the compressive resistance may be computed on the basis of L/r_x = 29. The corresponding slenderness factor is given by Equation 4.15:

$$\lambda = \frac{KL}{r} \sqrt{\frac{F_y}{\pi^2 E}} = 29 \sqrt{\frac{50}{\pi^2 \times 29000}} = 0.38$$

Since $0 \leqslant \lambda \leqslant 1.0$ the member falls within the range of slenderness factors appropriate to Equation 4.16(a) and the factored compressive resistance is:

$$C_r = \phi AF_y \,(1.035 - 0.202\,\lambda - 0.222\,\lambda^2)$$
$$= 0.90 \text{ x } 72.4 \text{ x } 50\,(1.035 - 0.202 \text{ x } 0.38 - 0.222 \text{ x } 0.38^2)$$
$$= 3010 \text{ kips}$$

In this example the unit factored compressive resistances tabulated in the CISC Manual[4.9] on page 4.9 could again be used to compute the factored compressive resistance once the governing slenderness ratio has been computed. The compressive resistances of built-up shapes are not tabulated directly.

Example 4.5

Given

A brace consists of two angles 3 1/2 x 2 1/2 x 5/16 placed with long legs back to back as shown in Figure 4.13. The two angles are separated by 1/4 inch thick gusset plates at both ends but will be interconnected to act as a unit. The member is G40.21 44W steel ($F_y = 44$ ksi) and is 12'-0" in length. The ends are assumed to be pin-connected. Determine the factored compressive resistance.

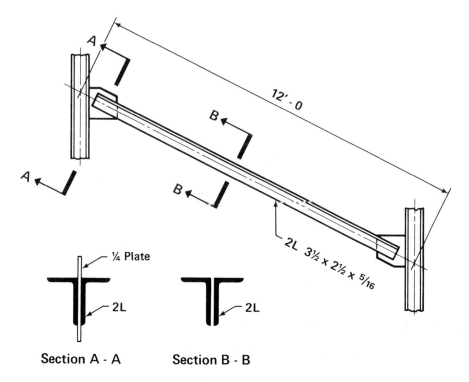

Figure 4.13
Structural Arrangement — Example 4.5

Solution

The cross-sectional properties for the double angle member are listed in Appendix A:

$$A = 3.56 \text{ in.}^2 \qquad r_x = 1.11 \text{ in.} \qquad r_y = 1.05 \text{ in.} \qquad \text{(Two angles)}$$

For the case of members built-up of single angles, the width-to-thickness ratios are more restrictive than for wide flange shapes. The limiting plate width-to-thickness ratio to prevent premature local buckling of an angle is stipulated in CSA Standard S16.1, Clause 11.3 as:

$$75/\sqrt{F_y}$$

The critical leg is the 3 1/2 inch length.

$$\text{Actual } \frac{b}{t} = \frac{3.5}{0.313} = 11.2$$

$$\text{Allowable } \frac{b}{t} = \frac{75}{\sqrt{36}} = 12.5$$

Since the width-to-thickness ratio of the critical leg is less than the limiting value the compressive resistance may be based on the overall member strength. The slenderness ratios are computed as:

$$\frac{L}{r_x} = \frac{12 \times 12}{1.11} = 130$$

$$\frac{L}{r_y} = \frac{12 \times 12}{1.05} = 137 \qquad\qquad \text{(Governs)}$$

The compressive resistance will be governed by the L/r_y value of 137. It should be noted that the thickness of the gusset plate separates the long legs of the two angles. Thus, the thicker the plate, the larger will be r_y. This property is given in Appendix A for several thicknesses of gusset plates. The slenderness factor corresponding to $L/r_y = 137$ is given by Equation 4.15:

$$\lambda = \frac{KL}{r}\sqrt{\frac{F_y}{\pi^2 E}} = 137\sqrt{\frac{44}{\pi^2 \times 29000}} = 1.7$$

Since $1.0 \leqslant \lambda \leqslant 2.0$ the member falls within the range encompassed by Equation 4.16(b) and the factored compressive resistance is:

$$C_r = \phi A F_y \left(-0.111 + 0.636\,\lambda^{-1} + 0.087\,\lambda^{-2}\right)$$

$$= 0.90 \times 3.56 \times 44 \left(-0.111 + 0.636 \times 1.7^{-1} + 0.087 \times 1.7^{-2}\right)$$

$$= 41 \text{ kips}$$

In the design of double angle struts, advantage can be taken of the tabulated values in the CISC Manual.[4.9] For columns composed of double angles of G40.21 44W steel and for certain specific arrangements the compressive resistance may be determined directly from tables such as those provided on pages 4-88 to 4-117 of the CISC Manual.

Research performed on compression members composed of double angles has shown that the design of such members can be based on the provisions developed for the W shapes.[4.11] For double angle columns the lateral torsional strength is not significantly below the flexural strengths.

Example 4.6

Given

A column is to be designed to resist a factored load of 3200 kips. The length of the member is 12'-0" and the ends are assumed to be pin-connected. The column is to be of G40.21 44W steel.

Solution

The determination of the compressive resistance cannot proceed without a knowledge of the cross-section to be used. Thus the design procedure becomes a trial and checking process; a particular cross-section is assumed, the factored compressive resistance is determined and then checked against the factored load on the member.

The trial section selected is a W14x342 shape. As explained in Chapter 2, the specified minimum yield stress of a section (rolled to certain specifications) depends on the thickness of the flange and web plates. The shapes are classified into five groups in CSA Standard G40.20.[4.8] The W14x342 section is classified as a Group 4 shape (relatively thick flange and web plates) and the yield stress for this group is F_y = 40 ksi.

The cross-sectional properties of the W14x342 shape are listed in Appendix A:

$$A = 101 \text{ in.}^2 \qquad r_x = 6.97 \text{ in.} \qquad r_y = 4.23 \text{ in.}$$

The slenderness ratios are computed as:

$$\frac{L}{r_x} = \frac{12 \times 12}{6.97} = 21$$

$$\frac{L}{r_y} = \frac{12 \times 12}{4.23} = 34 \qquad \text{(Governs)}$$

The compressive resistance will be governed by the L/r_y value of 34. The corresponding slenderness factor is given by Equation 4.15:

$$\lambda = \frac{KL}{r} \sqrt{\frac{F_y}{\pi^2 E}} = 34 \sqrt{\frac{40}{\pi^2 \times 29000}} = 0.40$$

Since $0 \leqslant \lambda \leqslant 1.0$ the member falls within the range encompassed by Equation 4.16(a) and the factored compressive resistance is:

$$C_r = \phi AF_y \, (1.035 - 0.202\,\lambda - 0.222\,\lambda^2)$$

$$= 0.90 \times 101 \times 40 \, (1.035 - 0.202 \times 0.40 - 0.222 \times 0.40^2)$$

$$= 3340 \text{ kips}$$

Since $3340 > 3200$, the W14x342 will adequately resist the load. The next lighter section, the W14x320, might also be checked. As in the previous examples, use of the tabulated values would considerably reduce the computational effort involved.

References

4.1 Canadian Standards Association, CSA Standard S16.1-1974, "Steel Structures for Buildings—Limit States Design", Canadian Standards Association, Rexdale, Ontario, 1974.

4.2 WRC-ASCE Joint Committee, "Plastic Design in Steel, A Guide and Commentary", 2nd. Edition, American Society of Civil Engineers, New York, 1971.

4.3 McGuire, W., "Steel Structures", Prentice-Hall Inc., Englewood Cliffs, New Jersey, 1968.

4.4 Structural Stability Research Council, "Guide to Stability Design Criteria for Metal Structures", 3rd Edition, B. G. Johnston Editor, John Wiley and Sons, New York, 1976.

4.5 Bjorhovde, R., "A Probabilistic Approach to Maximum Column Strength", Proceedings of the Conference on Safety and Reliability of Metal Structures, American Society of Civil Engineers, November, 1972.

4.6 Galambos, T. V., and Ravindra, M. K., "Tentative Load and Resistance Factor Design Criteria for Steel Buildings", Research Report No. 18, Civil and Environmental Engineering Department, Washington University, St. Louis, 1973.

4.7 Galambos, T. V., "Structural Members and Frames", Prentice-Hall, Inc. Englewood Cliffs, New Jersey, 1968.

4.8 Canadian Standards Association, CSA Standard G40.20, "General Requirements for Rolled or Welded Structural Quality Steel", Canadian Standards Association, Rexdale, Ontario, 1976.

4.9 "Limit States Design Steel Manual", Canadian Institute of Steel Construction, Toronto, Ontario, 1977.

4.10 Canadian Standards Association, CSA Standard G40.21, "Structural Quality Steels", Canadian Standards Association, Rexdale, Ontario, 1976.

4.11 Nuttall, N. J. and Adams, P. F., "Buckling Strength of Double Angle Struts", Structural Engineering Report No. 30, University of Alberta, Edmonton, 1970.

CHAPTER 5

THE EFFECTIVE LENGTH CONCEPT

5.1 Introduction

In the previous chapter design provisions were developed on the assumption that both ends of the column were completely free to rotate as the column reached its ultimate strength. This situation would arise, for example, if the girders were attached to the columns through web connections, as illustrated in Figure 5.1(a). As the member is deformed, the rotation of the column end will not induce a corresponding rotation of the girder, thus the column will act as if it were pin ended.

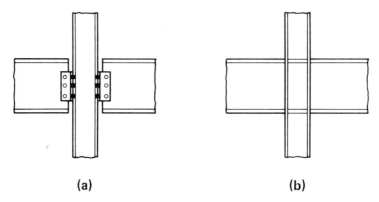

(a)   **(b)**

Figure 5.1
Beam-to-Column Connections

Where continuous construction is used, however, the girder-to-column connections are rigid as illustrated in Figure 5.1(b). In this situation the column end rotations occurring during the bending motion will induce corresponding rotations in the girder ends. Bending moments will be developed at the connections which restrain the motion of the column and increase its strength.

In order to use the design rules developed for a pin ended column in situations where a column is restrained at its ends, the actual length of the column L, is replaced (in Equation 4.15) by its effective length KL; that is, the length between points of inflection (points of zero bending moment) on the buckled shape.[5.1] Thus the buckling strength of an ideal column with the actual length and restraining conditions is equal to that for a similar pin ended column having the appropriate effective length. For simplicity the ideal column is used in the development of the model for the effective length and the concept is then applied to real columns having initial imperfections.

5.2 Effect of Rotational Restraint on Column Strength

If the column end connections are able to resist bending moments, the strength of the column will be increased significantly above that of the equivalent pin ended member. Three simple cases are shown in Figure 5.2.

The first is a pin ended member having the buckling load given by Equation 4.7:

$$C_{cr} = \frac{\pi^2 EI}{L^2}$$

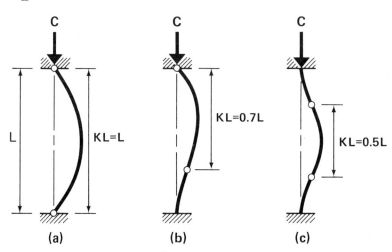

Figure 5.2
Buckled Shapes — Sway Prevented

The second column has its lower end clamped so that rotation cannot occur. The buckling load, in this situation is[5.2]

$$C_{cr} = 2.05 \frac{\pi^2 EI}{L^2}$$

The buckling load can also be expressed in terms of the effective length, KL, defined as the length of the equivalent pin ended column. For the case shown in Figure 5.2(b), KL = 0.7L and

$$C_{cr} = \frac{\pi^2 EI}{(KL)^2} = \frac{\pi^2 EI}{(0.7L)^2} = \frac{2.05 \, \pi^2 EI}{L^2}$$

If both ends are clamped, the effective length becomes 0.5L, as shown in Figure 5.2(c), and the buckling load is increased to:

$$C_{cr} = \frac{\pi^2 EI}{(KL)^2} = \frac{\pi^2 EI}{(0.5L)^2} = \frac{4.0 \, \pi^2 EI}{L^2}$$

In an actual building frame the ends of the columns will not be clamped but rather will be restrained by the bending action of the members connected to them. A typical frame is shown schematically in Figure 5.3. The X-bracing system is assumed to resist the lateral loads acting on the frame.

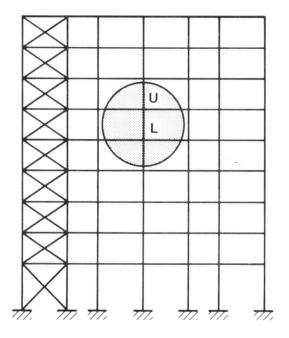

Figure 5.3
Braced Frame

To consider the buckling strength of column UL, this portion of the frame has been isolated in Figure 5.4. The dashed lines show the position of this portion of the frame before loads are applied. If the loads are applied symmetrically the beams will deform but the columns will remain relatively straight.

At the instant of buckling, the additional deformations of the column and adjacent members are shown by the full lines in Figure 5.4. It is assumed in this discussion that buckling will occur in the plane of the frame shown; in an actual structure the possibility of buckling in the perpendicular direction must also be considered. Assuming that all columns in the frame are designed with approximately the same safety index, it is reasonable to assume that the column sections above and below UL buckle along with UL. During the buckling motion the ends of the columns rotate through an angle θ_U (or θ_L); it is assumed that the beam ends are also forced through this same rotation.

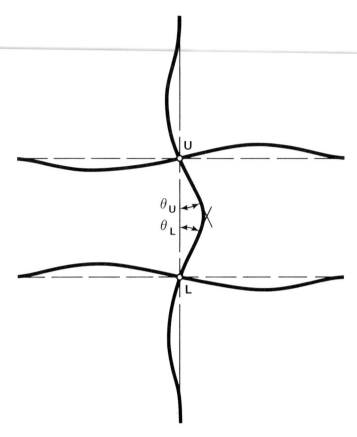

Figure 5.4
Isolated Column — Sway Prevented

Assuming that both ends of the girder are forced through equal and opposite rotations, θ_U, a resisting moment, M_{UG}, will be developed at the beam-to-column connection equal to[5.3]

$$M_{UG} = \frac{2EI_g}{L_g} \theta_U \qquad (5.1)$$

where E is the modulus of elasticity and I_g and L_g are the moment of inertia of the beam about its axis of bending, and the beam length, respectively.

The other beams at the joint would develop similar moments and resist the rotation of the column ends during buckling. The beams at a particular joint would provide resistance to the column above and below that joint. Assuming that the resistance to buckling is in proportion to the stiffness, I_c/L_c of the column considered, then the net resisting moment, M_U, acting on the column will be:

$$M_U = \frac{(I_c/L_c)}{\Sigma(I_c/L_c)} \times 2E \, \theta_U \, \Sigma(I_g/L_g) = \frac{2EI_c}{G \, L_c} \theta_U \qquad (5.2)$$

where G is defined as:

$$G = \frac{\Sigma(I_c/L_c)}{\Sigma(I_g/L_g)} \qquad (5.3)$$

in which Σ indicates a summation for all members rigidly connected to the joint and lying in the plane in which buckling is being considered. I_c is the column moment of inertia and L_c is its length.

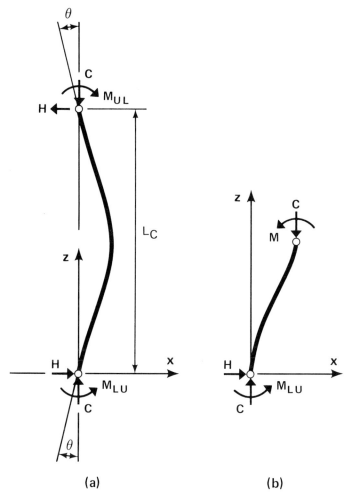

Figure 5.5
Free Body Diagram — Sway Prevented Column

The forces acting on column UL are shown in Figure 5.5(a) and the corresponding free body diagram in Figure 5.5(b). The differential equation of equilibrium no longer corresponds to that for the pin ended column but now must account for the presence of the end moments and shears. The solution to the equation can be expressed as[5.1]

91

$$\frac{G_U G_L}{4} \left(\frac{\pi}{K}\right)^2 + \left(\frac{G_U + G_L}{2}\right)\left(1 - \frac{\pi/K}{\tan \pi/K}\right) + 2\frac{\tan \pi/2K}{\pi/K} = 1 \qquad (5.4)$$

where G_U and G_L are defined in Equation 5.3 for joints U and L, respectively, and K is the effective length factor of the column considered, defined as the ratio of the effective length to the actual length.

Equation 5.4 is not in a form directly suitable for design use but has been plotted as a nomograph, as shown in Figure 5.6.[5.1] The nomograph is entered with specific values of G_U and G_L and the straight line joining these two values determines the value of K. For the example shown in the figure $G_U = 2.0$, $G_L = 0.4$ and $K = 0.75$. If both G_U and G_L are zero the implication is that the beams are infinitely stiff as compared to the columns $\Sigma(I_g/L_g) \gg \Sigma(I_c/L_c)$ (Equation 5.3), so that no rotation of the column end will occur during buckling. In this case the buckled shape would correspond to that shown in Figure 5.2(c) and the effective length factor, K, is 0.5.

If both G_U and G_L are infinite the implication is that the beams have no rotational stiffness and thus the column end can rotate freely during the buckling motion. For this case $\Sigma(I_g/L_g) \ll \Sigma(I_c/L_c)$ in Equation 5.3 and the effective length factor is 1.0. The buckled shape corresponds to that of the pin ended column shown in Figure 5.2(a). If one value of G is zero and the other infinite, the column corresponds to that shown in Figure 5.2(b) with an effective length factor of 0.7.

The value of G given by Equation 5.3 is a measure of the effective rotational restraint delivered by the beams to the column during the buckling motion. However, a special situation exists at the connection of the column end to the foundation. If the connection has been designed to resist a bending moment and the foundation is fairly rigid, then rotation of the column end is restrained during buckling and the effective value of I_g is infinite (G equal to zero). In fact some rotation will always occur and to compensate for this G is normally taken as 1.0 for this type of foundation condition.

Where the connection at the foundation is not designed to resist a bending moment, the foundation will offer little rotational restraint to the column and the effective value of I_g is zero. (This corresponds to an infinite value of G). To compensate for the fact that some small rotational restraint will be offered even in this case, G is commonly taken as 10.0.

In the derivation of Equation 5.4 the columns and beams were assumed to behave elastically.[5.1] In fact, this will only be true for relatively long columns; for stockier columns failure occurs only after considerable inelastic action and the effective length computations discussed above will not be strictly valid. In addition, it is possible that beams in the structure will be deformed inelastically before buckling occurs. Nevertheless, primarily because of its simplicity, the effective length approach is also used for columns which fail after inelastic action has occurred.

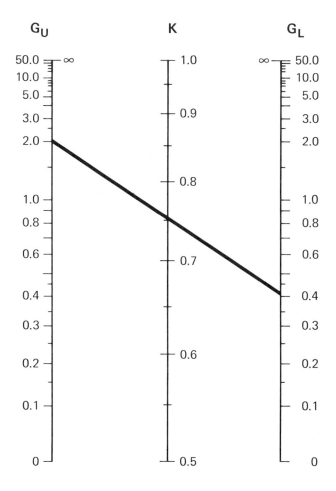

G_U K G_L

Sidesway Prevented

Figure 5.6
Nomograph — Sway Prevented

5.3 Design Examples

The following design examples were chosen primarily to illustrate the calculation of effective length. Once the effective length (and the corresponding effective slenderness ratio) has been determined the calculation of the load carrying capacity proceeds in a manner similar to that illustrated in the examples of Chapter 4.

Although the effective length has been developed in terms of the elastic buckling strength of the member, the design of an axially loaded column is based on the maximum strength of an initially imperfect column. Any restraint to the rotation of the ends of the member does, however, provide an increase in the ultimate strength as well as an increase in the buckling capacity. For this reason the effective length is used for the design relationship for axially loaded columns in Equations 4.15 and 4.16.

Example 5.1

Given

A W10x49 section of G40.21 50W steel (F_y = 50 ksi) is used as a column with a 12'-0" storey height. The column is shown in Figure 5.7 together with the rigidly connected framing members. The connection at the foundation is not designed to resist moment. Determine the factored compressive resistance of the member.

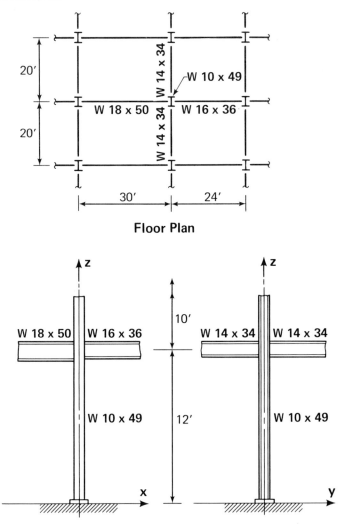

Figure 5.7
Structural Arrangement — Example 5.1

Solution

The effective lengths for buckling about the two principal axes must be determined. As a first step, consider buckling in the xz plane, and compute the relative stiffnesses at the lower and upper ends of the column according to Equation 5.3:

$$G = \frac{\Sigma(I_c/L_c)}{\Sigma(I_g/L_g)}$$

The base plate connection at the lower end of the column is not designed to resist moment and therefore the foundation offers little resistance to the end rotation of the column. Theoretically, $G_L = \infty$ but it is common practice to use:[5.4]

$$G_L = 10.0$$

Now:

$$G_U = \frac{\Sigma(I_c/L_c)}{\Sigma(I_g/L_g)}$$

The W10x49 column extends above as well as below the floor girders. At the instant of buckling the two column sections bend about their weak (y-y) axes. The moment of inertia about the y-y axis for a W10x49 is given in Appendix A as 93.0 in.[4]

$$\Sigma(I_c/L_c) = \frac{93.0}{12 \times 12} + \frac{93.0}{10 \times 12} = 1.4$$

The beams bend about their strong (x-x) axes as the column buckles. For a W18x50 from Appendix A, $I_{x-x} = 802$ in.[4] and for a W16x36, $I_{x-x} = 447$ in.[4].

$$\Sigma(I_g/L_g) = \frac{802}{30 \times 12} + \frac{447}{24 \times 12} = 3.8$$

$$G_U = \frac{\Sigma(I_c/L_c)}{\Sigma(I_g/L_g)} = \frac{1.4}{3.8} = 0.37$$

From the nomograph, Figure 5.6, $K_y = 0.78$ and from Appendix A, $r_y = 2.54$ for the W10x49 section. The effective slenderness ratio, $\dfrac{K_y L}{r_y}$, for buckling in the xz plane is thus

$$\frac{K_y L}{r_y} = \frac{0.78 \times 12 \times 12}{2.54} = 44$$

Next, the possibility of buckling in the yz plane should be considered. The relative stiffnesses at the lower and upper ends of the column are computed as before.

$$G_L = 10$$

$$G_U = \frac{\Sigma(I_c/L_c)}{\Sigma(I_g/L_g)}$$

For buckling in the yz plane the column sections above and below the joint bend about their strong (x-x) axes. The moment of inertia about this axis for a W10x49 section is taken from Appendix A as 273 in.^{4}.

$$\Sigma(I_c/L_c) = \frac{273}{12 \times 12} + \frac{273}{10 \times 12} = 4.2$$

At the instant of buckling the W14x34 beams also bend about their strong axes. For W14x34, $I_{xx} = 340$ in.^{4}.

$$\Sigma(I_g/L_g) = \frac{340}{20 \times 12} + \frac{340}{20 \times 12} = 2.8$$

$$G_U = \frac{\Sigma(I_c/L_c)}{\Sigma(I_g/L_g)} = \frac{4.2}{2.8} = 1.5$$

From the nomograph, Figure 5.6, $K_X = 0.87$ and from Appendix A, $r_X = 4.35$ for the W10x49 section. The effective slenderness ratio, $\dfrac{K_X L}{r_X}$, for buckling in the yz plane is thus:

$$\frac{K_X L}{r_X} = \frac{0.87 \times 12 \times 12}{4.35} = 29$$

Since $\dfrac{K_y L}{r_y} > \dfrac{K_X L}{r_X}$, failure of the column will be accompanied by bending

about the y-y axis and the compressive resistance will be computed using an effective slenderness ratio of 44. From this point on the determination of the factored compressive resistance follows the steps outlined in Chapter 4 and only the results of the calculations will be shown. Note that in the equations for column strength developed in Chapter 4, the actual length or slenderness ratio is replaced by the effective length or slenderness ratio. For a steel having $F_y = 50$ ksi and for a governing slenderness ratio $K_y L/r_y = 44$ the slenderness factor is calculated from Equation 4.15:

$$\lambda = 0.58$$

Since $0 \leqslant \lambda \leqslant 1.0$ the member falls within the limits of applicability of Equation 4.16(a) and with a cross-sectional area of 14.4 in.^{2} from Appendix A, the factored compressive resistance for the member is:

$$C_r = 545 \text{ kips}$$

As in the examples of Chapter 4, the tabulated values in the CISC Manual[5.4] could be used to reduce the computational effort once the effective slenderness ratio is determined.

96

Example 5.2

Given

Compute the effective slenderness ratio, K_yL/r_y, for a W14x342 column if the structural arrangement is that shown in Figure 5.8. It is assumed in this example that buckling about the strong axis of the column is prevented by continuous bracing in the yz plane.

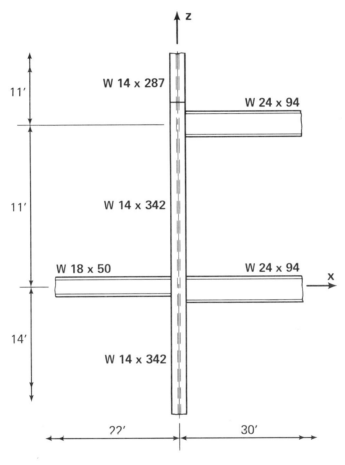

Figure 5.8
Structural Arrangement — Example 5.2

Solution

As the column buckles the column sections are bent about their weak (y-y) axes. For the W14x342, $I_{y-y} = 1810$ in.[4] and for the W14x287, $I_{y-y} = 1470$ in.[4] as given in Appendix A. The beams are rigidly connected to the columns and will be bent about their strong (x-x) axes. For the W18x50, $I_{x-x} = 802$ in.[4] and for the W24x94, $I_{x-x} = 2690$ in.[4]. The relative stiffnesses are given by Equation 5.3:

$$G_L = \frac{\Sigma(I_c/L_c)}{\Sigma(I_g/L_g)} = \frac{\dfrac{1810}{11 \times 12} + \dfrac{1810}{14 \times 12}}{\dfrac{802}{22 \times 12} + \dfrac{2690}{30 \times 12}} = 2.3$$

$$G_U = \frac{\Sigma(I_c/L_c)}{\Sigma(I_g/L_g)} = \frac{\dfrac{1470}{11 \times 12} + \dfrac{1810}{11 \times 12}}{\dfrac{2690}{30 \times 12}} = 3.3$$

From the nomograph, Figure 5.6, $K_y = 0.88$ and from Appendix A, $r_y = 4.23$ for the W14x342 section. The effective slenderness ratio for buckling in the xz plane is:

$$\frac{K_y L}{r_y} = \frac{0.88 \times 11 \times 12}{4.23} = 27$$

5.4 Effective Lengths of Columns in Unbraced Frames

In the previous sections the effective length of a column has been established by assuming that during the buckling motion the upper end of the column does not translate laterally with respect to the lower end. In practice this is approximately the case when shear walls or bracing systems are provided so as to restrict translational movements. The bracing system must be designed to resist the applied lateral loads on the structure as well as the additional forces produced by the sway of the structure. (See also Section 5.6).

In many cases, however, for architectural or other reasons, bracing systems or shear walls are not available to restrict the movement of frames in a building and the lateral forces produced by the sway of the structure must be resisted by the flexural action of the beams and the columns in the frame. In this case the ends of the column are assumed to translate, for the calculation of the effective length, and the strength of the column is severely reduced.

Consider the columns shown in Figure 5.9; in all three cases the upper end is free to translate laterally during the buckling motion. The column shown in Figure 5.9(a) is clamped to prevent rotation at both the upper and lower ends. On buckling the deformed shape has zero slope at the two ends and a point of inflection at mid-height. As shown, the effective length is equal to the actual length of the column and the buckling load is given by:

$$C_{cr} = \frac{\pi^2 EI}{(KL)^2} = \frac{\pi^2 EI}{L^2}$$

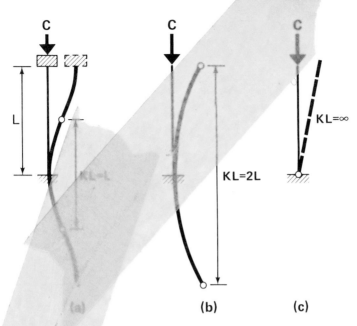

Figure 5.9
Buckled Shapes — Sway Permitted

If the rotational restraint is removed from the top end of the column, the resulting member is similar to a flagpole and on buckling deforms as shown in Figure 5.9(b). The buckled shape can be visualized as one half of a pin ended column (see Figure 5.2(a)), and the effective length KL = 2.0L. The buckling load is:

$$C_{cr} = \frac{\pi^2 EI}{(KL)^2} = \frac{\pi^2 EI}{(2L)^2} = \frac{0.25 \, \pi^2 EI}{L^2}$$

Finally, if the rotational restraint is removed from both ends the member becomes unstable as shown in Figure 5.9(c) and the effective length is infinite; the buckling load will be zero.

The above three examples illustrate the importance of rotational restraint in an unbraced frame. The effective length of a column in such a frame will vary from 1.0L, if both ends are clamped against rotation, to infinity, if both ends are pinned. Thus, the buckling strengths of columns in an unbraced frame will be much less than the strengths of otherwise equivalent columns in a braced frame.

As discussed previously, the column ends in an actual structure would not be completely clamped (or completely free) but would be restrained by the bending action of adjacent members. For example, the column UL of the unbraced frame shown in Figure 5.10 is isolated in Figure 5.11 with the members framing into either end. The dashed lines show the position of the member before loading and the solid lines represent the additional deformations caused by the buckling motion. Again it is assumed for this discussion that buckling will occur in the plane of the frame.

99

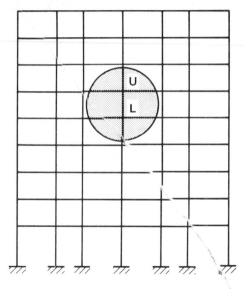

Figure 5.10
Unbraced Frame

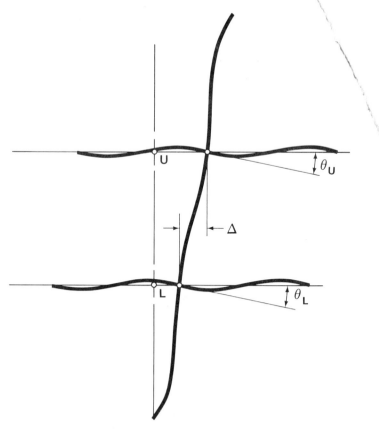

Figure 5.11
Isolated Column — Sway Permitted

Assuming the columns above and below UL buckle along with column UL, the buckled shape of the structure will be as shown in Figure 5.11, with the additional column end rotations denoted as θ_U and θ_L at the upper and lower joints, respectively, and Δ denoting the translational movement of joint U with respect to joint L. Since all columns in the frame must translate at the instant of buckling, the assumption is made that both girder ends rotate through the angle, θ_U, in the same sense.[5.1] Following the reasoning of the previous section, the end moment developed by the girder at U during this motion:

$$M_{UG} = \frac{6EI_g}{L_g}\theta_U \qquad (5.5)$$

Similar moments will be developed by the other beams attached to the column. Assuming further that the resisting moment at a joint is divided between the column above and the column below the joint in proportion to their stiffnesses, the resisting moment acting on the column under consideration is:

$$M_U = \frac{6EI_c}{G L_c}\theta_U \qquad (5.6)$$

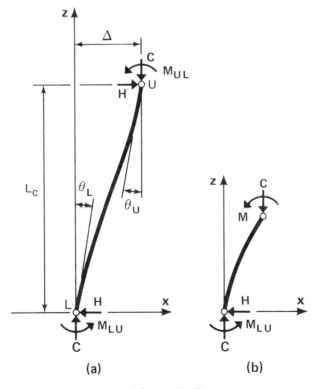

Figure 5.12
Free Body Diagram — Sway Permitted Column

The forces acting on the column are those shown in Figure 5.12(a) and the corresponding free body diagram is shown in Figure 5.12(b). The differential equation expressing equilibrium of this segment is the same as that for the restrained column in the braced frame. However, the physical boundary conditions are different. For the column in the unbraced frame the deflection is zero at the origin but has a value Δ at the upper end of the column $(x_{(0)} = 0; x_{(L)} = \Delta)$. An additional condition is that at the upper end of the column the shear is equal to zero. This implies that the buckled column receives no support from other columns in the frame (presumably these too are on the verge of buckling), an assumption which is generally conservative.

Using the conditions described above, the solution to the differential equation may be expressed as[5.1]

$$\frac{G_U G_L (\pi/K)^2 - 36}{6(G_U + G_L)} = \frac{\pi K}{\tan \pi/K} \tag{5.7}$$

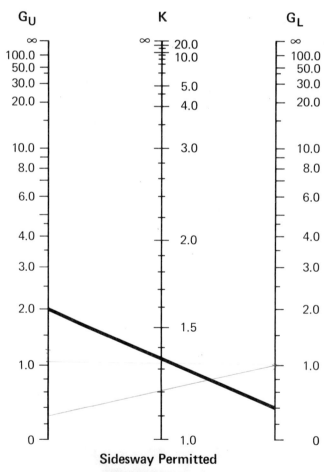

Sidesway Permitted

Figure 5.13

Nomograph — Sway Permitted

This equation is not convenient for design and has been plotted in nomograph form in Figure 5.13. The nomograph is entered for specific values of G_U and G_L and the straight line joining these two values determines the effective length K. For the example shown in the figure, $G_U = 2.0$, $G_L = 0.4$ and K = 1.35. For comparison, in a braced frame and for the same values of G_U and G_L, K = 0.75 (See Figure 5.6). In Figure 5.13 if both G_U and G_L are infinite, K is also infinite. This implies that the beams provide no rotational restraint and is the case shown in Figure 5.9(c). If the beams at both ends of the column are infinitely stiff, G = 0 and the value of the effective length is K = 1.0, corresponding to Figure 5.9(a). If one value of G is zero and the other is infinite, K = 2.0, corresponding to Figure 5.9(b).

5.5 Design Examples

The example below illustrates the calculation of the effective length of a column for a frame in which the lateral forces are to be resisted by the flexural action of the girders and columns in the structure. Only the effective lengths will be computed; the computation of the compressive resistance then follows the steps outlined in Example 5.1.

Example 5.3

Given

A W10x49 section of G40.21 50W steel ($F_y = 50$ ksi) is used as a column with a 12'-0" storey height. The column is shown in Figure 5.7 together with the rigidly connected framing members. The connection at the foundation is not designed to resist moment and the structure must rely on the flexural stiffnesses of the frames to resist translation in both the x and y directions. Determine the effective slenderness ratio of the column for buckling in both the xz and yz planes.

Solution

For buckling in the xz plane, the relative stiffnesses at the top and bottom of the column have been computed in Example 5.1 as:

$G_L = 10$

$G_U = 0.37$

From the nomograph, Figure 5.13, $K_y = 1.75$. The effective slenderness ratio, $K_y L / r_y$, for buckling in the xz plane is:

$$\frac{K_y L}{r_y} = \frac{1.75 \times 12 \times 12}{2.54} = 99$$

For buckling in the yz plane the relative stiffnesses at the top and bottom of the column have also been determined in Example 5.1 as:

$$G_L = 10$$

$$G_U = 1.5$$

From the nomograph, Figure 5.13, $K_X = 2.0$. The effective slenderness ratio, $K_X L/r_X$, for buckling in the yz plane is:

$$\frac{K_X L}{r_X} = \frac{2.0 \times 12 \times 12}{4.35} = 66$$

A comparison of these results with the results of Example 5.1 shows the advantage of providing a bracing system to resist the lateral forces. The slenderness ratios computed for the column in the unbraced frame are 99 and 66 for buckling in the xz and yz planes respectively. For the braced frame (see Example 5.1) the corresponding slenderness ratios were 44 and 29.

5.6 Compensation for the Effect of Translation

In the previous sections, procedures for the calculation of the effective length factor were based either on the assumption that translation is prevented entirely (Section 5.2) or that translation will occur without external restraint (Section 5.4). For structures of the usual proportions, however, translation of adjacent floor levels will occur under the applied loads, both in unbraced structures and in structures containing vertical trusses or shear walls.[5.5] Thus it would initially appear that every column should be designed with an effective length based on the assumption that translation will occur.

However, a comparison of Figures 5.5 and 5.12 reveals a more meaningful distinction between the two cases, a distinction which can be used to decide whether to classify the structure as sway (translation) permitted or sway prevented for the purpose of computing an effective column length. For the column shown in Figure 5.12 the algebraic sum of the two end moments (M_{UL} and M_{LU}), must be equal to the moment produced by the horizontal reaction, HL_c, plus that caused by the axial load acting through the sway displacement, $P\Delta$. In the sway prevented condition, shown in Figure 5.5, this latter term, the so-called $P\Delta$ effect, need not be included.

The increased moments produced by the $P\Delta$ term in the sway permitted condition (Figure 5.12) enter into the differential equation expressing the equilibrium of the column and thus affect the solution, Equation 5.7. It is implied that the increased moments are resisted by the bending action of the column and its adjacent girders. On the other hand for the column shown in Figure 5.5, the $P\Delta$ effects are ignored. Since all structures will sway to some extent, the implication in this case is that the effects caused by the $P\Delta$ term are resisted by parts of the structure other than the columns and girders under consideration.

104

Thus, if the PΔ effects are to be resisted by the column and girders under consideration, the column must be designed using an effective length based on the sway permitted condition (Nomograph, Figure 5.13). If the PΔ effects are to be assigned to some other portion of the structure, the column under consideration may be designed on the basis of an effective length based on the sway prevented condition (Nomograph, Figure 5.6). In this latter case the PΔ effects must be computed and assigned to other portions of the structure. The calculation of the PΔ effects will be discussed further in Chapter 7, which deals with the design of beam columns.

Sway effects are important in slender structures like the Chateau Champlain, Montreal.

References

5.1 Structural Stability Research Council, "Guide to Stability Design Criteria for Metal Structures", 3rd Edition, B. G. Johnston Editor, John Wiley & Sons, Inc. New York, 1976.

5.2 McGuire, W., "Steel Structures", Prentice-Hall Inc., Englewood Cliffs, New Jersey, 1968.

5.3 "Structural Steel Design", 2nd Edition, L. Tall, Editor, Ronald Press Company, New York, 1974.

5.4 "Limit States Design Steel Manual", Canadian Institute of Steel Construction, Toronto, Ontario, 1977.

5.5 Adams, P. F., "The Design of Steel Beam-Columns", Canadian Steel Industries Construction Council, Willowdale, Ontario, April, 1974.

CHAPTER 6

BEAMS

6.1 Introduction

Beams are the members in a structure which resist loads primarily through flexure. In a building structure, generally the beams (or girders) are horizontal members, spanning between adjacent columns and supporting the loads delivered by the floor or roof system. Beams may also appear in an inclined position as stringers for stairways, ramps, etc., or may be used to support heavy machinery, pipelines or ductwork. Although beams may be required to resist torsional moments in some situations, generally the framing scheme is such that torsion is minimized and the primary loading results in bending of the member. The problem of torsional action will not be considered in this chapter.[6.1]

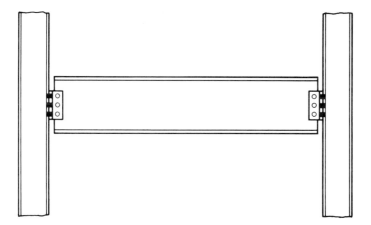

Figure 6.1
Simply Supported Beam

Beams may be joined to their supporting columns by simple or rigid connections. A simple connection is designed to resist shear only; in this case the connection is assumed to act like a roller or hinged support. Figure 6.1 illustrates schematically a simply supported beam attached to the adjacent columns. The web connections are designed to transmit the beam reactions to the column and are capable of sustaining relatively large rotations without developing significant moments. In other situations the designer may wish to connect the beam using a moment resisting connection, thus achieving a continuous design. In this case the moment developed at the end of the beam is shared by the connected members. Figure 6.2 illustrates a rigid framing scheme in which the girder is attached to the adjacent columns by connections which have been designed to transmit both moment and shear.

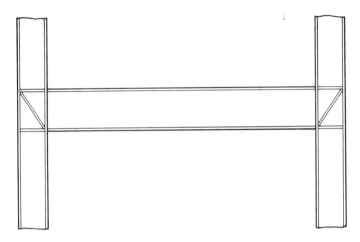

Figure 6.2
Continuous Beam

In a light building structure, the elements supporting floor or roof slabs may be open web joists—a light type of truss. The open web steel joist is an extremely common element in building construction and one that requires careful attention in both the design and production stages. These elements are normally selected from information provided by the manufacturer and the responsibilities of both designer and manufacturer are delineated in Reference 6.2. In other cases, the beams may be rolled or welded sections, usually wide flange shapes. For longer spans or unusual loads built-up plate girders may be designed. This chapter will concentrate mainly on rolled and standard welded sections. Chapter 9 contains a discussion of the problems associated with plate girders.

A beam or girder is designed primarily on the basis of its flexural strength. Holes in the cross-section would tend to reduce this strength. However, tests on beams have shown little reduction, even in sections having as much as 15% of the flange area removed. CSA Standard S16.1 therefore, provides that the presence of fastener holes, constituting 15% or less of the gross area of a flange, may be ignored (Clause 15.1). Larger openings, such as those required for duct work, etc., must be considered in design. The associated problems are beyond the scope of this text.[6.3]

6.2 Moment-Curvature Relationships for Beams

A small element of beam subjected to a bending moment, M, is shown in Figure 6.3(a). Under the action of the applied moment strains will develop in the cross-section that are assumed to vary linearly from zero at the neutral axis to a maximum at the extreme fibre, as shown in Figure 6.3(b). For the positive bending moment shown the top fibres will be in compression, the bottom fibres in tension. The curvature, κ, is the angle change between the original and deformed positions of the cross-section. From elementary strength of materials, if the member behaves elastically:[6.4]

$$\kappa = M/EI = \epsilon/y \tag{6.1}$$

From the stress-strain curve of Figure 2.3, if the maximum strain in the cross-section is less than the yield strain, ϵ_y, the stress distribution is also linear ($\sigma = E\epsilon$) and is that shown by line 1 in Figure 6.3(c). However, when the maximum strain exceeds ϵ_y the stress cannot increase above σ_y, the yield stress, and thus yielding must begin to penetrate from the extreme fibres towards the interior of the cross-section, as shown by line 2 in Figure 6.3(c).

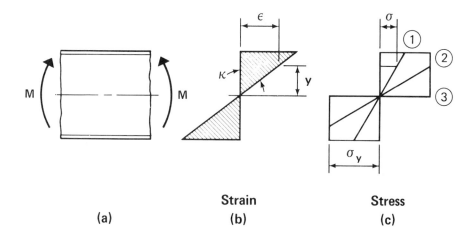

Strain   Stress
(a)   (b)   (c)

Figure 6.3
Strain and Stress Distributions

The strains will continue to increase until the cross-section is fully plastified (theoretically this requires an infinite strain). At this stage the full plastic moment, M_p, has been developed and the stress distribution corresponds to that shown by line 3 in Figure 6.3(c). The plastic moment M_p, is computed by summing the moments caused by the forces on each fibre (at a stress σ_y) to obtain:

$$M_p = \sigma_y Z \tag{6.2}$$

The plastic modulus, Z, represents the first moment of the area of the tension and compression zones about the neutral axis. Although theoretically an infinite strain is required for the section to reach M_p, in most wide-flange shapes approximately 98% of M_p is attained at strains of twice ϵ_y[6.5]

The relationship between moment and curvature is plotted as the solid curve in Figure 6.4. In this figure M_y represents the yield moment, that is, the moment corresponding to the attainment of the yield strain in the extreme fibre:

$$M_y = \sigma_y S \qquad (6.3)$$

where S denotes the section modulus (S = 2I/d).

Figure 6.4 represents the M-κ relationship as the moment is increased on the beam element. For moment values below M_y, the relationship is elastic and the slope of the M-κ curve is equal to EI. Above M_y, yielding begins to penetrate through the flanges and the section "softens". The stress distribution at this stage corresponds to that shown by line 2 in Figure 6.3(c). As the section continues to deform, the moment closely approaches M_p.

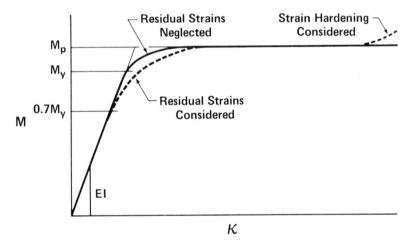

Figure 6.4
Moment-Curvature Relationship

This moment-curvature relationship must be modified to take into account the residual strains which are present in the rolled or welded cross-section. The residual strains are shown (idealized) in Figure 4.5(a). When the applied bending moment reaches a value of 0.7 M_y, the total strains in the tips of the compression flange will reach ϵ_y (assuming that the maximum residual strain is 0.3 ϵ_y).[6.5] If additional bending moment is applied, the flange tips will be ineffective in accepting the increased stresses and thus larger strains than those anticipated will be necessary to develop the required resisting moment. This gradual yielding will modify the behaviour described above and the resulting M-κ relationship will be that shown by the dashed line in Figure 6.4. Since the residual stresses are themselves in equilibrium, the full value of M_p will still be attained by the section.

The second factor which will modify the behaviour of the cross-section is strain-hardening of the material. As shown in the stress-strain curve of Figure 2.2, strain hardening will occur in the cross-section when the strains are approximately 10 to 12 times the yield strain. The corresponding stresses will be above σ_y and the resisting moment developed by the cross-section will increase above M_p as again shown by the dashed portion of Figure 6.4.

6.3 Load-Deflection Relationships for Beams

The moment-curvature relationship reflects only the behaviour of a short element of beam length. To predict the behaviour of a complete member the curvatures corresponding to a given bending moment distribution must be integrated to determine the slopes and deflections.

For example, the beam shown in Figure 6.5(a) is assumed to be subjected to a concentrated load, P. The mid-span moment is denoted as M_O and at the stage of loading shown is greater than M_y. The bending moment distribution is shown in Figure 6.5(b) and the corresponding curvature distribution in Figure 6.5(c). The curvatures shown are determined from the M-κ relationship of Figure 6.4.

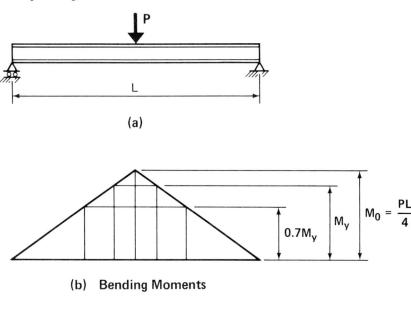

(a)

(b)   Bending Moments

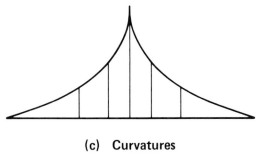

(c)   Curvatures

Figure 6.5
Bending Moment and Curvature Distributions

111

The mid-span deflections, Δ, are computed by the second moment-area principle and are plotted in Figure 6.6 as a function of the corresponding mid-span moments. The response of the beam is initially elastic until the mid-span moment is equal to 0.7 M_y. At this point yielding is initiated in the beam and the central portion "softens". As the load is increased yielding penetrates through the flanges and spreads along the member length in accordance with the curvature distribution of Figure 6.5(c). On further deformation, the maximum moment increases above M_p due to strain hardening of the material.

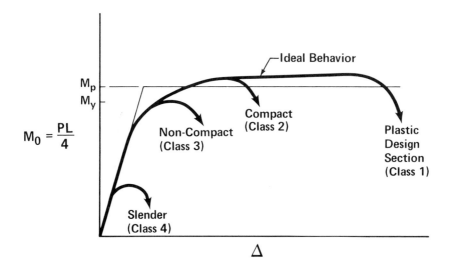

Figure 6.6
Load-Deflection Relationships

The upper solid curve in Figure 6.6 represents the ideal response and the moment capacity would continue to increase as shown were it not for two unpleasant occurrences which have not been included in the predictions. The first of these is local buckling. In a beam, local buckling of the compression flange is of primary concern although web buckling can also be of importance, particularly in built-up plate girders. The second factor, which can change the behaviour of the beam drastically, is the occurrence of lateral buckling. This is the onset of large out-of-plane (or lateral) deflections of the compression flange between points of lateral support.[6.5]

6.4 Flange Local Buckling and its Consequences

The plates composing the member cross-section may be visualized as columns, interconnected at the junction points. The compression flange column, for example, would be subjected to a load equal to the sum of the stresses acting on the flange plate. A plan view of the compression flange is shown schematically in Figure 6.7(a) where the stresses are those computed by the flexure theory.

The compression flange is assumed to be braced so that lateral deflections of the flange plate are prevented (this will be discussed below). The web plate is assumed to be stocky enough to prevent vertical buckling in most cases.[6.1] Thus the buckling mode consists of a twisting motion of the flange, together with a rotation of the web plate. The original cross-section and the buckled shape are shown in Figure 6.7(b).

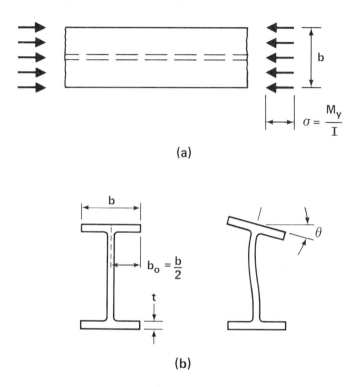

(a)

(b)

Figure 6.7
Flange Buckling Considerations

At the critical moment, the flange simply twists about the flange-to-web junction. At this stage the cross-section is unsymmetric and further deformation produces a rapid reduction in moment capacity. The driving force behind the buckling motion consists of the component of stress on the plate which produces a twisting moment, T, once the plate assumes the buckled position.[6.6]

$$T = \sigma(bt)\frac{b^2}{12}\frac{d\theta}{dx} \qquad (6.4)$$

where $\dfrac{d\theta}{dx}$ represents the rate of change of the angle of twist along the length of the beam. The torque resisting the motion is produced primarily by the St. Venant (or uniform) torsional moment developed in the plate and is given by:

$$T_R = JG\frac{d\theta}{dx} = \frac{1}{3}bt^3\, G\,\frac{d\theta}{dx} \qquad (6.5)$$

113

where G represents the torsional rigidity of the material and J the St. Venant torsional constant. Since the plate must be in equilibrium in the deflected shape, the external and resisting torques are equal, thus:

$$\frac{b}{2t} = \sqrt{G/\sigma}$$ (6.6)

Equation 6.6 can be used to restrict the plate width-to-thickness ratio, b/2t, so that the cross-section can develop the desired moment resistance before local buckling occurs. In Figure 6.6, the curve shown as characteristic of Class 1 Sections represents ideal behaviour for a beam. The moment resistance reaches M_p and increases slightly as the beam continues to deflect. For Class 1 Sections the factored moment resistance is specified in CSA Standard S16.1, Clause 13.5.1 as:

$$M_r = \phi M_p = \phi Z F_y$$ (6.7)

Eventually, after a significant amount of inelastic deflection has occurred, local buckling of the flange may occur, leading to a decrease in moment capacity. In this case the maximum stress in the member is equal to the yield stress, but yielding has penetrated completely through the flange thickness and the material stiffness has been correspondingly reduced. The value of G in this yielded condition is taken as approximately 3000 ksi and the corresponding value of b/2t from Equation 6.6 is $54/\sqrt{\sigma_y}^{6.5}$. The above limitation is expressed in CSA Standard S16.1, Clause 11.2 in terms of a restriction on the half flange width (or overhanging width) $b_o = b/2$, and the specified minimum yield stress F_y, as:

$$\frac{b_o}{t} \leqslant 54/\sqrt{F_y}$$ (6.8)

The Class 1 section must not only develop a moment resistance equal to the plastic capacity of the member but must maintain this resistance through relatively large inelastic deformations. This will enable the complete structure to redistribute bending moments and reach the load-carrying capacity anticipated on the basis of a plastic analysis. The implications of this requirement are discussed further in Section 6.14.

The limiting width-to-thickness ratios specified for Class 2 Sections are less restrictive than those for Class 1 since the requirements for large inelastic deformations do not exist. The moment resistance developed by the Class 2 Section is equal to that of the stockier Class 1 Section, however, and CSA Standard S16.1-1974 specifies the moment resistance for both types of sections as that given in Equation 6.7. Tests on steel beams have shown that if

$$b_o/t \leqslant 64/\sqrt{F_y}$$ (6.9)

the member will be capable of developing the full plastic moment capacity.[6.8] This restriction is included in CSA Standard S16.1, Clause 11.2. The moment-deflection curve for the member would be similar to that shown for compact or Class 2 Sections in Figure 6.6, with the section buckling locally once M_p has been attained.

114

The width-to-thickness limits for Class 3 Sections are again less restrictive than those for Class 2. Referring to Figure 6.6, the plates composing the cross-section should be capable of allowing the member to develop a moment resistance equal to the yield moment, M_y, and in this condition the stress in the extreme fibre will be equal to the yield stress, σ_y. In general the plate will behave elastically at this stage although some deterioration due to the large compressive residual stresses in the flange tips may be expected. Using $G = 11,200$ ksi for steel in the elastic range, Equation 6.6 becomes:

$$\frac{b}{2t} = \frac{106}{\sqrt{\sigma_y}} \qquad (6.10)$$

If the value of b/2t exceeds that given by Equation 6.10, local buckling will occur before the moment resistance reaches M_y. After a reduction to account for the residual stress effect, the limitation contained in Equation 6.10 is expressed in CSA Standard S16.1, Clause 11.2 as:

$$\frac{b_o}{t} \leqslant 100/\sqrt{F_y} \qquad (6.11)$$

If the compression flange of the member meets this limit the behaviour should be that depicted by the curve for non-compact or Class 3 Sections in Figure 6.6.

The factored moment resistance specified for a Class 3 Section in CSA Standard S16.1, Clause 13.5.2 is:

$$M_r = \phi M_y = \phi S F_y \qquad (6.12)$$

Sections having plate components that are too slender to meet the requirements for Class 3 Sections are classified as Class 4 Sections. As shown in Figure 6.6 this type of section buckles locally at a moment less than M_y and the moment resistance is a function of the width-to-thickness ratios of the plates composing the section.[6.1]

Clause 13.5.3 of CSA Standard S16.1-1974 divides Class 4 Sections into three categories. The first category contains those sections having both flange and web plates falling within Class 4. This type of section is designed to the requirements of CSA Standard S136-1974, using the material properties appropriate to the structural steel specified.[6.9]

The second category contains those sections having flanges meeting the requirements of Class 3 but having webs so slender as to place the section in Class 4. This type of section is designed according to the requirements of Clause 15 of CSA Standard S16.1-1974, which bases the moment resistance on a consideration of the redistribution of load carrying capacity between the portion of the web in compression, and the compression flange. This type of member is discussed in detail in Chapter 9.

For those Class 4 Sections having web plates meeting the Class 3 requirements but slender compression flanges exceeding Class 3 limits, the moment resistance is governed by local buckling of the compression elements and is given by SF_{cr}. The term F_{cr} is the critical stress for local buckling and is a function of the type of compression element considered.[6.10] The factored moment resistance is specified in CSA Standard S16.1-1974, Clause 13.5.3 as:

$$M_r = \phi S F_{cr} \qquad\qquad (6.13)$$

Workmen connect a beam to its supporting columns.

6.5 Web Buckling and Slenderness Limits

Depth-to-thickness limits for webs serve the same purpose as the width-to-thickness ratios prescribed for beam flanges. The individual elements comprising a cross-section must be able to carry the forces imposed upon them until the strength of the overall cross-section has been attained. This is conveniently, and with reasonable accuracy, done by limiting the width-to-thickness values of the individual elements of the cross-section. As described above, CSA Standard S16.1-1974 does this by referring to Class 1 through Class 4 Sections (respectively, plastic design sections, compact sections, non-compact sections and slender sections).

116

Web buckling under the action of a bending moment is not generally a problem in beams of normal proportions.[6.10] This is primarily because the stress condition on the web plate is much less severe than that on the compression flange. In addition, most of the resistance to moment is developed by the flange plates; thus even if the web does buckle the reduction in moment capacity is not severe.

For Class 1 Sections, the web plate must accept strains which are sufficient to allow the flange to become fully yielded. In order to achieve this condition the h/w ratio is limited for beams in CSA Standard S16.1-1974, Clause 11.2 to:

$$h/w \leqslant 420/\sqrt{F_y} \tag{6.14}$$

where h denotes the clear depth of web between flanges for built-up sections or the clear distance between flanges minus the fillet radius at each flange for rolled sections, and w denotes the web thickness.

The requirements of Equation 6.14 were developed for plastically designed structures. The web slenderness requirements are not as stringent for Class 2 and Class 3 Sections, where the strength and stability requirements are less severe. CSA Standard S16.1-1974 thus adopts more liberal requirements for Class 2 (compact) and Class 3 (non-compact) sections, in Clause 11.2, respectively:[6.11, 6.12]

$$h/w \leqslant 520/\sqrt{F_y} \tag{6.15}$$

$$h/w \leqslant 690/\sqrt{F_y} \tag{6.16}$$

For class 4 Sections, having slender webs, the slenderness of the web must be limited so that the flange cannot deflect locally by buckling into the web. This will be discussed in Chapter 9.

The limiting width-to-thickness ratios are summarized for each class of section in Table 6.1.

TABLE 6.1
Width-To-Thickness Limits

Class	Flange	Web
Class 1	$b_o/t \leqslant 54/\sqrt{F_y}$	$h/w \leqslant 420/\sqrt{F_y}$
Class 2	$b_o/t \leqslant 64/\sqrt{F_y}$	$h/w \leqslant 520/\sqrt{F_y}$
Class 3	$b_o/t \leqslant 100/\sqrt{F_y}$	$h/w \leqslant 690/\sqrt{F_y}$
Class 4	- - - -	- - - -

6.6 Performance Factor—Laterally Supported Members

In CSA Standard S16.1-1974 the moment resistance of a section is multiplied by a performance factor ϕ to obtain the factored moment resistance. This factored moment resistance is then matched against the effects (bending moments) produced by the factored loads. The performance factor, ϕ is taken as 0.90 for members subjected to flexure. The purpose of the performance factor is to take into account the variability of material properties, dimensions, and workmanship. Galambos and Ravindra have examined the results of three series of tests on Class 1 Sections subjected to various loading conditions and as a result have suggested a value of ϕ = 0.89 for this type of section.[6.13] On this basis the value of ϕ = 0.90 used for laterally supported members in CSA Standard S16.1-1974 at the present time appears to be reasonable.

6.7 Design Examples

In the examples which follow, it is assumed that the members are braced laterally so that their capacities are limited by local buckling. Only the flexural capacities will be considered in these examples. Other factors, such as deflection, bracing spacing, shear, etc., play a major part in beam design and will be illustrated later in this chapter.

Example 6.1

Given

A W12x36 beam of G40.21 44W steel (F_y = 44 ksi) spans 24'-0" and is connected to columns at either ends by means of standard web connections. Compute the uniformly distributed factored load that the member can resist.

Solution

The cross-section dimensions and properties are tabulated in Appendix A:

$$Z_x = 51.6 \text{ in.}^3 \qquad\qquad b = 6.57 \text{ in.}$$
$$d = 12.24 \text{ in.} \qquad\qquad t = 0.540 \text{ in.}$$
$$w = 0.305 \text{ in.}$$

As a first step the actual plate proportions will be checked against the limiting values for a Class 2 section.

$$\text{Actual Flange } \frac{b}{2t} = \frac{6.57}{2 \times 0.54} = 6.09$$

The allowable flange width-to-thickness ratio is calculated according to Equation 6.9 as:

$$\frac{64}{\sqrt{F_y}} = \frac{64}{\sqrt{44}} = 9.65$$

Although CSA Standard S16.1 permits the h/w ratio for rolled beams to be computed using the clear distance between flanges minus the fillet radius at each flange, for simplicity here the more conservative clear distance between flanges will be used for "h".

$$\text{Approximate web } \frac{h}{w} = \frac{d - 2t}{w} = \frac{12.24 - (2 \times 0.54)}{0.305} = 36.6$$

The allowable web depth-to-thickness ratio is given by Equation 6.14 as:

$$\frac{420}{\sqrt{F_y}} = \frac{420}{\sqrt{44}} = 63.3$$

Since both the flange and web meet the prescribed limitations, the member is a Class 2 or compact section and is capable of developing the plastic moment capacity. It will be assumed throughout that the example members are not intended for use in a plastically designed structure and thus it will not be necessary to meet the requirements for Class 1 Sections.

For a Class 2 Section the factored moment resistance is given by Equation 6.7 as:

$$M_r = \phi F_y Z = 0.90 \times 44 \times 51.6 = 2040 \text{ inch kips}$$

The maximum moment produced by the factored loading is $\frac{wL^2}{8}$, where w denotes the uniformly distributed factored load in kips per foot and L represents the span of the beam. For a satisfactory design:

$$M_r \geqslant \frac{wL^2}{8}$$

$$2040 \geqslant w \times \frac{24 \times 24 \times 12}{8}$$

$\therefore w \leqslant 2.4$ kips per foot

As in the previous chapters, the tables contained in the CISC Manual [6.14] can be used to greatly simplify the calculations. For example the factored moment resistance is tabulated on page 5-112 for the W12x36 section and the factored load capacity on page 5-126.

Example 6.2

Given

A beam is to be selected to span 36'. The bending moment diagram has been obtained from an analysis of the structure and is shown in Figure 6.8. The member is to be of G40.21 44W steel ($F_y = 44$ ksi).

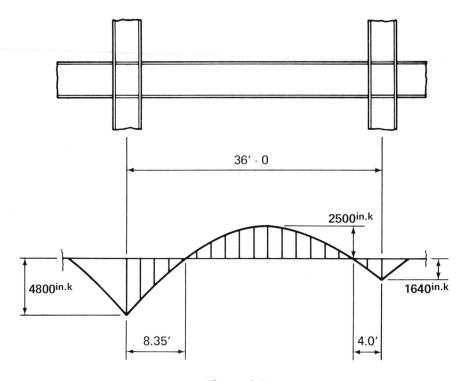

Figure 6.8
Bending Moment Diagram — Example 6.2

Solution

Before the moment resistance can be determined, the plate width-to-thickness ratios for the section must be known. Most rolled sections at least meet the requirements for Class 2 (for the carbon or low alloy steels), however, and this knowledge can be used to initiate the design.

The factored moment resistance is computed from Equation 6.7, assuming that the member to be selected is a Class 2 Section:

$$M_r = \phi M_p = \phi Z_x F_y$$

The required plastic modulus for the member is determined on the basis of the maximum bending moment over the length of the member due to the factored loads (Figure 6.8):

$$Z_x \text{ (required)} = \frac{M_{max}}{\phi F_y}$$
$$= \frac{4800}{0.90 \times 44} = 121 \text{ in.}^3$$

Many factors enter into the selection of the member; these will be discussed as they arise in this chapter. One possible member which has a plastic modulus meeting that required is used in the following calculations.

Try W21 x 55, $Z_x = 126$ in.^{3} $p\ 308$

The plate proportions must now be checked to ensure that the member does meet the requirements for a Class 2 Section and the factored moment resistance used above is correct. The cross-section dimensions are given in Appendix A:

$$d = 20.80 \text{ in.} \qquad\qquad t = 0.522 \text{ in.}$$
$$b = 8.22 \text{ in.} \qquad\qquad w = 0.375 \text{ in.}$$

Actual Flange $\dfrac{b}{2t} = \dfrac{8.22}{2 \times 0.522} = 7.87$

The limiting width-to-thickness ratio for a Class 2 Section is given by Equation 6.9 as:

$$\frac{64}{\sqrt{F_y}} = \frac{64}{\sqrt{44}} = 9.65$$

The approximate web $\dfrac{h}{w} = \dfrac{d-2t}{w} = \dfrac{20.80 - (2 \times 0.522)}{.375} = 52.7$

The allowable web depth-to-thickness ratio is given by Equation 6.15 as:

$$\frac{520}{\sqrt{F_y}} = \frac{520}{\sqrt{44}} = 78.4$$

Since both plate slenderness ratios are within the allowable limits, the section is included in Class 2 and thus the assumed moment resistance is correct. The W21x55 section will be used. The W18x60 section will also be satisfactory for this situation. Since this member is heavier than the W21x55 it normally would not be used. However, where the additional depth of the 21 inch section would create problems the heavier shallower section might be selected.

The Beam Selection Tables contained in the CISC Manual[6.14] may be used to great advantage in the member selection process. For example the most economical sections that will provide a factored moment resistance greater than 400 ft-kips are listed on page 5-110.

6.8 The Effect of Shear on Beam Strength

In the selection procedure described above the influence of the shear force was ignored. The presence of a shear force should theoretically reduce the flexural strength of the cross-section, however, it is impossible to separate this "weakening" influence from the increase in strength produced through strain-hardening. In fact, experiments have shown that beams tested under relatively high shear forces will develop moment capacities which are approximately 15% greater than beams tested under pure moment (zero shear) conditions.[6.8] However, in cases where the web of the member is

121

completely yielded under the action of the shear force, web buckling develops before the full plastic moment capacity has been attained. Thus the strength of the beam is reduced below its capacity under pure bending. The primary problem then is to prevent premature shear yielding of the member.[6.5]

Where steel is subjected to a combined stress condition, the yield stress in shear, τ_y, is normally approximated by the Von Mises value:[6.5]

$$\tau_y = \sigma_y / \sqrt{3} \qquad\qquad (6.17)$$

or in terms of the specified minimum yield stress:

$$\tau_y = 0.58\, F_y \qquad\qquad (6.18)$$

Noting that the major portion of the shear in a wide-flange member is carried by the web, the factored shear resistance is expressed in CSA Standard S16.1-1974, Clause 13.4.1 as:

$$V_r = \phi A_w F_s \qquad\qquad (6.19)$$

where A_w represents the shear area, equal to d x w, the gross cross-sectional area of the web and F_s is taken as 0.66 F_y. Note that the effective value of the shear yield stress, F_s, has been increased above the value given in Equation 6.18 to account for the beneficial effects of strain-hardening.

If the web is relatively slender, it will buckle under the action of the shear forces before it is completely yielded. In this case the shear resistance is reduced from that given by Equation 6.19. This will be covered in Chapter 9, in connection with plate girders. For the rolled and standard welded shapes Equation 6.19 may be used provided that, as specified in CSA Standard S16.1-1974, Clause 13.4.1:

$$\frac{h}{w} \leqslant 167 \sqrt{\frac{k_v}{F_y}} \qquad\qquad (6.20)$$

In Equation 6.20, k_v is a shear buckling coefficient and has a value of 5.34 for an unstiffened web.[6.10] The restriction imposed by Equation 6.20 ensures that shear buckling will not occur before the web is completely yielded.

Example 6.3

Given

Check the W21x55 beam of Example 6.2 for shear. The maximum shear force caused by the factored loads is 120 kips.

Solution

The dimensions of the W21x55 section are given in Appendix A:

$$d = 20.80 \text{ in.} \qquad t = 0.522 \text{ in.} \qquad w = 0.375 \text{ in.}$$

$$A_w = 7.80$$

As a first step the clear web depth-to-thickness ratio is computed

$$\frac{h}{w} = \frac{d - 2t}{w} = \frac{20.80 - (2 \times 0.522)}{0.375} = 52.7$$

The allowable web slenderness ratio, according to Equation 6.20, is:

$$167 \sqrt{\frac{k_v}{F_y}} = 167 \sqrt{\frac{5.34}{44}} = 58.2$$

Since the actual h/w is less than the limit specified, premature shear buckling is precluded. Shear yielding will limit the strength of the member and Equation 6.19 will be used to compute the factored shear resistance.

$$V_r = \phi A_w F_s = 0.90 \times 7.80 \times 0.66 \times 44 = 204 \text{ kips}$$

Since the actual shear force produced by the factored loads is less than the factored shear resistance, the W21x55 is adequate in shear. As a general note shear normally governs the design of rolled or standard welded sections only when the member is used over an extremely short span or is subjected to a large concentrated load. Other potentially dangerous situations may occur where a part of the cross-section is removed for some reason.

6.9 Limitations on Deflection

The deflections of a structure are a measure of its general serviceability. If the deflections of the girders are relatively large cracking may be expected in the floor or roof slabs. Similarly, excessive lateral deflections under wind loading are a sign that cracking of partitions and annoying vibrations may be expected.

The deflections of floor girders are limited for several reasons. If the deflections are unusually large the occupants may be affected directly; desks and filing cabinets may not operate properly. In extreme cases, the sag of the girder may be visible to the observer, creating an undesirable impression. If the beam or girder supports a plastered ceiling the deflections of the member may cause cracking of the plaster. Similar distress may occur in brick walls, rigid partitions, piping, etc. In these cases the non-structural elements are incorporated in the structure during construction. It is usual therefore, to limit the deflections under live load only so that non-structural damage does not occur. For roof girders, similar restrictions have been formulated.

The permissible deflection of a member depends on the nature of the non-structural materials supported by the structure. In many cases, information, based either on test results or on the manufacturer's recommendations, will be available for guidance. In the absence of such information Appendix I of CSA Standard S16.1-1974 recommends limits for both vertical and lateral deflections caused by the specified live loads. For example, the recommended maximum vertical deflections are:

INDUSTRIAL TYPE BUILDINGS

Due to:

Live Load	Simple span members supporting inelastic roof coverings	$\dfrac{1}{240}$ of span
Live Load	Simple span members supporting elastic roof coverings	$\dfrac{1}{180}$ of span
Live Load	Simple span members supporting floors	$\dfrac{1}{300}$ of span
Maximum Wheel Loads (no impact)	Simple span crane runway girders for crane capacity of 25T and over	$\dfrac{1}{800}$ of span
Maximum Wheel Loads (no impact)	Simple span crane runway girders for crane capacity under 25T	$\dfrac{1}{600}$ of span

ALL OTHER BUILDINGS

Live Load	Simple span members of floors and roofs supporting construction and finishes susceptible to cracking	$\dfrac{1}{360}$ of span
Live Load	Simple span members of floors and roofs supporting construction and finishes not susceptible to cracking	$\dfrac{1}{300}$ of span

It is important to note that the deflections considered are those corresponding to the specified load levels not the factored loads. Deflections must be checked at the specified load levels to ensure that the building will be serviceable but, except as discussed in Chapter 11, deflections do not generally influence the strength of the structure.

The deflections caused by dead loads may be computed in unusual cases and if significant, may be counteracted by cambering the member. In this process, a preset deflection (opposite in sense to that caused by the applied loads) is built into the member. Cambering may be achieved by cold bending. This is usually practical only for smaller members. For larger members cambering is done by heating one flange of the member either locally or uniformly along the length.[6.15] Cambering is not usually necessary in building structures having small or moderate spans.

In the past, the restrictions on deflections due to static loads have been sufficient in most cases to guard against the problems associated with moving loads, such as the vibrations induced by dancing in school auditoria. However, as higher strength steels become more common and as the trend toward longer span beams continues it is likely that in the future a dynamic analysis will be necessary for unusual loading situations.

Deflection limitations minimize serviceability problems.

Example 6.4

Given

The W12x36 beam considered in Example 6.1 spans 24'-0" and is subjected to a specified dead load of 0.5 kips per foot and a specified live load of 1.2 kips per foot. Calculate the dead and live load deflections and check to see that the member is satisfactory. It is assumed that the member supports an asphaltic roof membrane in an industrial building.

125

Solution

As shown in Example 6.1, the W12x36 member can safely support a factored uniformly distributed load of 2.4 kips per foot.

The cross-sectional properties for the W12x36 section are listed in Appendix A:

$I_X = 281$ in.^{4}

The maximum deflection formula is given on page 5-120 of the CISC Handbook.[6.16] The deflection due to dead load is:

$$\Delta_{DL} = \frac{5}{384} \frac{wL^4}{EI} = \frac{5 \times 0.5 \times 24^4 \times 1728}{384 \times 29\ 000 \times 281} = 0.46 \text{ inches}$$

The deflection due to live load is:

$$\Delta_{LL} = \frac{5}{384} \frac{wL^4}{EI} = \frac{5 \times 1.2 \times 24^4 \times 1728}{384 \times 29\ 000 \times 281} = 1.10 \text{ inches}$$

The allowable live load deflection for a beam supporting an asphaltic roof is given by CSA Standard S16.1-1974 in Appendix I as:

$$\Delta \leqslant \frac{L}{240} \leqslant \frac{24 \times 12}{240} \leqslant 1.20 \text{ inches}$$

Since the actual live load deflection is approximately 1.10 inches, less than the limit, the member is satisfactory. Under normal circumstances a member of this length would not be cambered.

In the calculation of deflections the tables in the CISC Manual may also be utilized. The actual deflections of the member under various loading conditions may be computed by using the tables on pages 5-98 and 5-99.

6.10 Laterally Unbraced Beams

It has been assumed thus far that the strength of the beam is dependent on the local buckling capacity of its plate elements. In most cases this assumption is valid. However, if the beam is laterally unsupported the strength may be governed instead by lateral buckling of the complete member.

A plot of the relationship between the applied moment, M, and the resulting mid-span deflection, Δ, for a member of length, L, is shown in Figure 6.9. The member, shown in the inset to the figure, is subjected to end moments producing a uniform bending moment distribution over the length of the span. Lateral supports are assumed to be present at the ends of the member so that the laterally unbraced length is equal to the span.

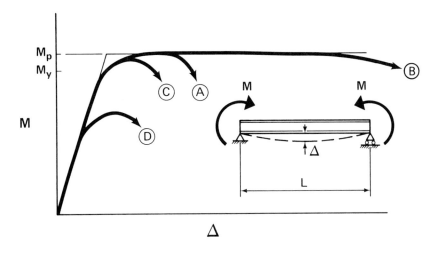

Figure 6.9
Moment-Deflection Relationships

At low values of M, the member will respond elastically. However, as the moment is increased yielding will occur due to the strains produced by the applied moment and the residual strains in the cross-section. Further increases in the applied moment will result in general yielding over the cross-section as the moment approaches M_p.

Figure 6.10 depicts the movement of the cross-section during this loading process. As the member is loaded the cross-section moves vertically from its initial position. At some stage of loading, however the cross-section may twist and bend about its weak axis; lateral buckling has occurred. Lateral buckling may occur at any stage during the loading history: after the member has reached M_p, as shown by curves A and B in Figure 6.9; between M_y and M_p, as shown by curve C; and even at moments below M_y, as shown by curve D. The lateral buckling capacity of the member depends on its unbraced length and on a variety of cross-sectional properties.

Lateral buckling of a beam is analogous to flexural buckling in a column in that both represent ideal situations. The actual beam will contain imperfections so that lateral deflections will be present even before loading. These deflections will be amplified as the moment is increased, and as the critical value is approached, the deflections will grow rapidly. The moment capacity may increase slightly beyond this stage, then drop off rapidly as inelastic action, produced by the out-of-plane motion of the beam, decreases its resistance.

Just as in the case of axially loaded columns, laterally unbraced beams can be conveniently classified into stocky, intermediate and slender members. Figure 6.11 shows schematically the relationship between the moment causing lateral buckling, M_{cr}, and the length, L, which represents the distance between points of positive lateral support.

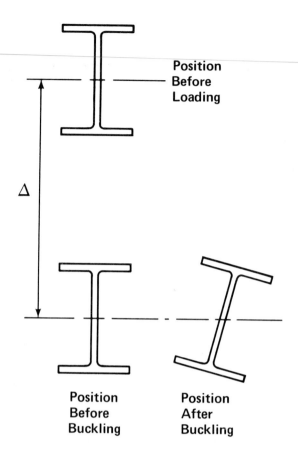

Δ

Position
Before
Loading

Position
Before
Buckling

Position
After
Buckling

Figure 6.10
Lateral-Torsional Buckling Motion

A stocky beam is defined as a beam which is able to reach its local buckling capacity before lateral buckling occurs. The local buckling capacity has been determined in the previous sections as M_p for a compact section and M_y for a non-compact member. On the other hand, a slender beam buckles laterally before the member yields. The important section properties, which are used to determine the lateral buckling strength, may be computed on the basis of full elastic action. For the intermediate member, the bending moment at the instant before lateral buckling is sufficient to cause portions of the member to yield (the yielding is a result of the strains due to the applied moment adding to the residual strains), thus the resistance of the member to both lateral and twisting motions is reduced.

The resistance of the member to lateral bending depends upon the weak axis bending stiffness of the cross-section, EI_y. The resistance to a twisting motion can be broken into two portions. One portion is termed the St. Venant resistance and is a function of the stiffness term, $G\,J$, where G represents the modulus of torsional rigidity and J is the St. Venant torsional

128

constant for the section. For a section such as the wide flange shape, $J = \frac{1}{3}\Sigma$

ℓt^3 where ℓ and t represent the length and thickness, respectively, for each plate and the summation extends over all plates in the cross-section. The St. Venant torsional resistance is generated by shear stresses developed by the rotation of adjacent cross-sections and is discussed in more detail in texts on strength of materials.[6.4]

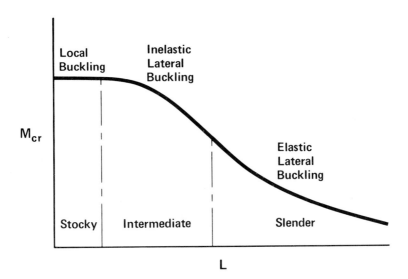

Figure 6.11
Beam Failure Modes

The second component of resistance to twisting, the warping resistance, is developed by cross-bending of the flanges. As the beam twists, the cross-section rotates about its centroidal axis and this motion induces lateral bending strains in the flanges. These strains result in the development of flange bending moments and accompanying shear forces acting in the plane of each flange. The couple produced by the shear forces at a particular section makes up the warping torsional resistance and is a function of $C_W = I_y (d-t)^2/4$, where C_W is the warping constant for the section.

For a beam subjected to end moments producing a constant bending moment distribution, and having simply supported boundary conditions, the moment at which lateral buckling will occur is given by:[6.6]

$$M_u = \frac{\pi}{L}\sqrt{EI_y G J + (\frac{\pi E}{L})^2 I_y \frac{I_y(d-t)^2}{4}} \qquad (6.21)$$

Equation 6.21 is conservative for most actual situations since the bending moment distribution is not likely to be uniform and since the connections between the beams and the supporting columns will provide some degree of restraint.

129

By approximating the various cross-sectional properties (neglecting the bending contribution of the web) and substituting for E and G, the critical moment for I shaped sections is expressed in CSA Standard S16.1-1974, Clause 13.6.1 as:

$$M_u = S \sqrt{\sigma_1^2 + \sigma_2^2}$$ (6.22)

where:

$$\sigma_1 = \frac{20\ 000}{Ld/A_f}$$ (6.23)

$$\sigma_2 = \frac{250\ 000}{(L/r_t)^2}$$ (6.24)

In the above equations, A_f denotes the area of one flange and r_t is the radius of gyration about the y axis of a tee section made up of the compression flange and one-sixth of the web.

Equation 6.21 (or 6.22 for I-shaped members) provides a reasonable estimate of the moment at which lateral buckling will occur, provided that the strains in the member are less than the yield strain at the instant before buckling. Thus Equation 6.21 is accepted as the basis for the design of slender members.

Due to the presence of relatively large residual stresses in the flange tips, yielding will occur when the applied moment reaches approximately two-thirds of the local buckling capacity of the member, M_p or M_y. This implies that the maximum residual stress is approximately one-third of the yield stress. Equation 6.21 is thus valid until M_u reaches $\frac{2}{3} M_p$, for Class 1 or 2 sections, or $\frac{2}{3} M_y$, for Class 3 or 4 sections.

For slender Class 1 or 2 sections (when $M_u \leqslant \frac{2}{3} M_p$) and for slender Class 3 and 4 sections (when $M_u \leqslant \frac{2}{3} M_y$) CSA Standard S16.1-1974 specifies in Clause 13.6.1 that the factored moment resistance is:

$$M_r = \phi M_u$$ (6.25)

where

$$M_u = \frac{\pi}{\omega L} \sqrt{EI_y G J + (\frac{\pi E}{L})^2 I_y \frac{I_y(d-t)^2}{4}}$$ (6.26a)

or for I shaped members:

$$M_u = \frac{S}{\omega} \sqrt{\sigma_1^2 + \sigma_2^2}$$ (6.26b)

130

Equation 6.26 is similar to Equation 6.21 except that an equivalent moment factor, ω, has been included in the expression. For members subjected to uniformly distributed transverse loads $\omega = 1.0$ but for members subjected to a moment gradient, $\omega \leqslant 1.0$ and reflects the fact that the loading conditions may not be as severe as that assumed in the derivation of the equation. Four of the many possible cases that may arise in practice are illustrated in Figure 2-18 of Reference 6.14. The equivalent moment factor, ω depends on the loading condition, conditions of lateral support and the moment gradient. Where transverse loads are applied between points of lateral support

$$\omega = 1.0 \tag{6.27a}$$

Where transverse loads are not applied between points of lateral support:

$$\omega = 0.6 + 0.4 \frac{M_{f1}}{M_{f2}} \tag{6.27b}$$

but

$$\omega \geqslant 0.4 \tag{6.27c}$$

where M_{f1} and M_{f2} are the smaller and larger bending moments at the two points of lateral support. The ratio M_{f1}/M_{f2} is positive for members bent in single curvature and negative for members bent in double curvature. The application of the equivalent moment factor for beam-columns will be discussed in Chapter 7.

For more stocky members when M_u is above $\frac{2}{3} M_p$ (for Class 1 or 2 sections) or $\frac{2}{3} M_y$ (for Class 3 or 4 sections), the assumptions made in deriving the elastic buckling expressions are no longer valid as the compression flange has been considerably weakened by yielding at the flange tips. Empirically, the factored moment resistance is therefore reduced in Clauses 13.6.1 and 13.6.2 of CSA Standard S16.1-1974 to:

$$M_r = 1.15 \phi M_p (1 - \frac{0.28 M_p}{M_u}) \tag{6.28}$$

for Class 1 or 2 sections or

$$M_r = 1.15 \phi M_y (1 - \frac{0.28 M_y}{M_u}) \tag{6.29}$$

for Class 3 or 4 sections.

Regardless of the results of the lateral buckling calculations (Equations 6.28 and 6.29), in no case may the moment resistance exceed that based on local buckling. Thus $M_r \leqslant \phi M_p$ for Class 1 and 2 sections (Equation 6.7) and

$M_r \leqslant \phi M_y$ or $\phi S\, F_{cr}$ for Class 3 and 4 sections, respectively. (Equations 6.12 and 6.13).

These provisions are summarized in Figure 6.12 where the moment resistance is plotted against the unbraced length for a W21x55 section of G40.21 44W steel. For members having an unbraced length greater than approximately 17.8 feet the moment resistance is given by Equation 6.25. For members having unbraced lengths between 9.3 feet and 17.8 feet the moment resistance is given by Equation 6.28 and for shorter members, those having lengths less than 9.3 feet, lateral buckling is not a problem and the moment resistance is given by Equation 6.7, based on local buckling.

As indicated in Figure 6.10, the movement of the cross-section during the buckling motion is characterized by the lateral deflection of the top (compression) flange and a rotation of the cross-section. During the motion the tension flange remains relatively straight. A laterally braced point, therefore, is a location at which the buckling type of motion is prevented. The compression flange might be held laterally by the floor or roof slab attached to the beam flange. Alternately, framing members at right angles to the beam would provide lateral support. If two members are joined by a standard end plate or angle connection, it is generally assumed that the shape of the cross-section at the connection point will be maintained and thus movement of the compression flange of the braced member will be prevented. This problem is discussed further in Chapter 11.

In cases where it is impossible to brace the compression flange directly, the brace may be attached to the tension flange. A stiffener is then required to prevent distortion of the cross-section and, in addition, the bracing member and its connection must possess sufficient flexural stiffness to prevent rotation of the member cross-section.

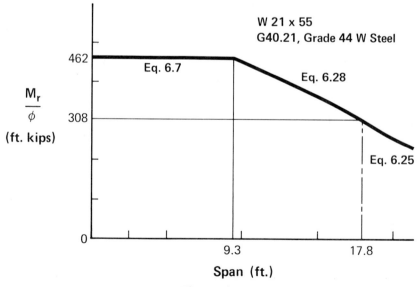

Figure 6.12
Bending Strength W21x55 Member

132

6.11 Performance Factor—Laterally Unsupported Beams

In CSA Standard S16.1-1974 the performance factor, ϕ, is taken as 0.90 for members which fail due to lateral buckling. More recent studies indicate that, theoretically, ϕ, should be taken as 0.84 for members failing by elastic lateral buckling and would vary with the cross-sectional shape and the unbraced length for members buckling laterally after portions of the cross-section have yielded.[6.6, 6.13] The values recommended for a W24x76 section, for example, having a specified minimum yield stress of 50 ksi, range from 0.88 for a slenderness ratio, L/ry = 34, to 0.83 for L/ry = 113.[6.13]

CSA Standard S16.1-1974 would, at first glance, seem to be slightly unconservative when compared with the above recommendations, especially for the intermediate range of slenderness ratios. On the other hand, in another respect the requirement of the Standard may well be conservative due to the assumptions regarding boundary conditions. Although the Standard specifies that the unbraced length, L, is to be taken as the length of the beam between supports, it is logical in some cases to take L as the distance between points of contraflexure on the laterally buckled shape of the compression flange. In other cases, however, when yielding of adjacent spans may have reduced the restraint, a more complex procedure is recommended.[6.17] In view of the difficulty in assessing the various situations the Standard does not specify any adjustment for end restraint.

Example 6.5

Given

Tables may be easier!

The W12x36 beam of Example 6.1 spans 24'-0" and is subjected to a uniformly distributed load. What value of the factored load can the member resist if it is unbraced laterally except at the supports.

Solution

The dimensions and section properties for the W12x36 are listed in Appendix A, with the torsional constants taken from page 5-152 of Reference 6.14.

d = 12.24 in.	t = 0.540 in.
b = 6.57 in.	w = 0.305 in.
Z_x = 51.6 in.^{3}	J = 0.85 in.^{4}
I_y = 25.5 in.^{4}	$\dfrac{I_y}{4}(d-t)^2$ = 873 in.^{6}
S_x = 45.9 in.^{3}	$= C_w$

The properties of the compression flange tee are computed below for illustration, even though the critical moment will be computed using the more basic equations.

$A_f = bt = 6.57 \times 0.54 = 3.55$ in.^{2}

$A_t = A_f + \dfrac{1}{6} A_w = (6.57 \times 0.54) + \dfrac{1}{6} \times 0.305\,(12.24 - 2 \times 0.54)$

$\qquad = 4.12$ in.^{2}

$I_t = \dfrac{b^3 t}{12} + \dfrac{1}{6}(d - 2t)\,\dfrac{w^3}{12}$

$\qquad = \left(\dfrac{6.57^3 \times 0.54}{12}\right) + \dfrac{1}{6} \times (12.24 - 2 \times 0.54) \times \dfrac{0.305^3}{12}$

$\qquad = 12.7$ in.^{4}

$r_t = \sqrt{\dfrac{I_t}{A_t}} = \sqrt{\dfrac{12.7}{4.12}} = 1.76$ in.

The plate slenderness ratios for the W12x36 were checked in Example 6.1. The member is a Class 2 section and the factored moment resistance for a Class 2 member of G40.21 44W steel (F_y = 44 ksi) based on local buckling is computed according to Equation 6.7 as:

$\qquad M_r = \phi Z F_y = 0.90 \times 51.6 \times 44 = 2040$ inch kips

The critical moment, based on the assumption that failure will be accompanied by elastic lateral buckling can be computed using either Equation 6.26(a) or 6.26(b). Using Equation 6.26(a), with E = 29000 ksi and G = 11200 ksi, the critical moment is:

$$M_u = \frac{\pi}{wL}\sqrt{EI_y\,G\,J + \left(\frac{\pi E}{L}\right)^2 I_y\,\frac{I_y(d-t)^2}{4}}$$

$$= \frac{\pi}{1.0 \times 24 \times 12}\sqrt{29000 \times 25.5 \times 11200 \times 0.85 + \left(\frac{\pi \times 29000}{24 \times 12}\right)^2 \times 25.5 \times 873}$$

$\qquad = 1050$ inch kips

Alternatively, using Equation 6.26(b) M_u = 1020 inch kips, slightly conservative for this section. If the critical moment given by Equation 6.26 is greater than $\dfrac{2}{3} M_p$ for a Class 2 section the moment resistance is reduced to account for inelastic action.

$\dfrac{2}{3} M_p = \dfrac{2}{3} \times Z\,F_y = \dfrac{2}{3} \times 51.6 \times 44 = 1510$ inch kips

Since $M_u < \dfrac{2}{3} M_p$ no reduction is required and the factored moment resistance is computed according to Equation 6.25 as:

134

$M_r = \phi M_u = 0.90 \times 1050 = 945$ inch kips

The actual bending moment (maximum) is $\frac{1}{8}\,wL^2$. For a satisfactory design:

$$M_r \geqslant \frac{1}{8}\,wL^2$$

$$945 \geqslant \frac{1}{8}\,w \times 24 \times 24 \times 12$$

$w \leqslant 1.1$ kips per foot.

The factored load carrying capacity for the unbraced member is 1.1 kips per foot whereas, if the member had been braced laterally, the factored load would have been 2.4 kips per foot (Example 6.1). Thus the absence of lateral support has reduced the carrying capacity of the member significantly.

The tabulated values in the CISC Manual[6.14] may be used to reduce the computational effort involved in the design of laterally unsupported beams. For example the Beam Selection Tables contained on pages 5-108 to 5-115 of Reference 6.14, tabulate the factored moment resistance for different laterally unsupported lengths.

Example 6.6

Given

use table first, much easier.

Select a member of G40.21 44W steel ($F_y = 44$ ksi) to span 24'-0" as a simply supported beam. The member is not supported laterally except at the ends and must safely carry a factored uniformly distributed load of 2.4 kips per foot.

Solution

This problem is simply an inverted form of Example 6.1. In order to achieve a solution a member first must be selected, then checked. Since the moment resistance depends on the proportions of the cross-section, general rules for selecting members are difficult to formulate. In the absence of design tables such as those given in the CISC Manual[6.14] a trial and error procedure is necessary. Since these tables cover only members of Grade 44W steel the more general procedure will be illustrated.

From the computations of Example 6.5 it is evident that the W12x36 will not be adequate. A heavier section will be selected and checked.

Try W12x50

The dimensions and section properties for the W12x50 section are listed in Appendix A with the torsional properties taken from page 5-152 of reference 6.14.

$$d = 12.19 \text{ in.} \qquad\qquad t = 0.641 \text{ in.}$$
$$b = 8.08 \text{ in.} \qquad\qquad w = 0.371 \text{ in.}$$
$$Z_x = 72.5 \text{ in.}^3 \qquad\qquad I_y = 56.4 \text{ in.}^4$$

$$J = 1.79 \text{ in.}^4 \qquad\qquad \frac{I_y}{4}(d-t)^2 = 1880 \text{ in.}^6$$

The plate slenderness ratios are first computed to determine whether the member meets the restrictions for a Class 2 section.

$$\text{Actual flange } \frac{b}{2t} = \frac{8.08}{2 \times 0.641} = 6.30$$

The allowable flange width-to-thickness ratio is given by Equation 6.9:

$$\frac{64}{\sqrt{F_y}} = \frac{64}{\sqrt{44}} = 9.65$$

$$\text{Approximate web } \frac{h}{w} = \frac{d-2t}{w} = \frac{12.19 - (2 \times 0.641)}{0.371} = 29.5$$

The allowable web depth-to-thickness ratio is given by Equation 6.15:

$$\frac{520}{\sqrt{F_y}} = \frac{520}{\sqrt{44}} = 78.4$$

Since the flange and web slenderness ratios are within the specified limits the cross-section is classified as Class 2 and the factored moment resistance, based on the local buckling strength, is given by Equation 6.7:

$$M_r = \phi Z_x F_y = 0.90 \times 72.5 \times 44 = 2870 \text{ inch kips}$$

The critical moment based on the assumption that failure will be accompanied by elastic lateral buckling is calculated according to Equation 6.26(a):

$$M_u = \frac{\pi}{\omega L}\sqrt{EI_y\,GJ + (\frac{\pi E}{L})^2\, I_y\, \frac{I_y(d-t)^2}{4}}$$

$$= \frac{\pi}{1.0 \times 24 \times 12}\sqrt{29000 \times 56.4 \times 11200 \times 1.79 + \left(\frac{\pi \times 29000}{24 \times 12}\right)^2 \times 56.4 \times 1880}$$

$$= 2270 \text{ inch kips}$$

(Note M_u = 2130 inch kips using Equation 6.26(b))

For a Class 2 section, if $M_u > \frac{2}{3} M_p$ the moment capacity must be based on a reduced critical moment to account for the effects of inelastic action.

136

$$\frac{2}{3} M_p = \frac{2}{3} Z_x F_y = \frac{2}{3} \times 72.5 \times 44 = 2120 \text{ inch kips}$$

Since $2270 > 2120$ the factored moment resistance is calculated from Equation 6.28:

$$M_r = 1.15 \, \phi M_p \, (1 - \frac{0.28 \, M_p}{M_u})$$

$$= 1.15 \times 0.90 \times 72.5 \times 44 \, (1 - \frac{0.28 \times 72.5 \times 44}{2270})$$

$$= 2000 \text{ inch kips}$$

As a final check, the factored moment resistance must be based on the more critical failure mode for the member. Thus the smaller of the two factored moment resistances predicted by Equations 6.7 and 6.28 will be used.

$$\therefore M_r = 2000 \text{ inch kips}$$

The actual bending moment on the member is $wL^2/8 = 1/8 \times 2.4 \times 24 \times 24 \times 12 = 2070$ inch kips. Although the factored moment resistance is less than the effect of the factored loads, the difference is not significant and the design will be considered satisfactory.

Using the tables on page 5-108 to 5-115 of the CISC Manual[6.14] the member can be selected with ease. The maximum bending moment is first computed as $wL^2/8 = (2.4 \times 24^2)/8 = 173$ ft. kips. The tables are then scrutinized for the lightest section that will provide at least this factored moment resistance with an unbraced length of 24'-0"

Example 6.7

Given

tables easier.

The W21x55 section used in Example 6.2 is assumed to be supported laterally along the top flange by the attachment of the floor deck. Is additional bracing required in the negative moment region?

Solution

The W21x55 is a Class 2 section in G40.21 44W steel (See Example 6.2). The factored moment resistance, based only on local buckling considerations, is calculated from Equation 6.7:

$$M_r = \phi Z_x F_y = 0.90 \times 126 \times 44 = 4990 \text{ inch kips}$$

Since the maximum bending moment produced by the factored loads is 4800 inch kips, as shown in Figure 6.8, the W21x55 section will be satisfactory in these regions where the member can develop its fully braced capacity. The bending moment values and the locations of points of inflection are shown on the diagram of Figure 6.8. One potentially critical area is that

137

adjacent to the left support. In order for the W21x55 section to be satisfactory without additional bracing of the bottom (compression) flange, the section must develop a factored moment resistance of at least 4800 inch kips over an unbraced length of 8.35 feet.

The dimensions and section properties for the W21x55 section are listed in Appendix A with the torsional properties taken from page 5-149 of Reference 6.14.

$$d = 20.80 \text{ in.} \qquad\qquad t = 0.522 \text{ in.}$$

$$b = 8.22 \text{ in.} \qquad\qquad w = 0.375 \text{ in.}$$

$$Z_x = 126 \text{ in.}^3 \qquad\qquad J = 1.24 \text{ in.}^4$$

$$I_y = 48.3 \text{ in.}^3 \qquad\qquad \frac{I_y}{4}(d-t)^2 = 4970 \text{ in.}^6$$

$$= C_w$$

The length of the member between points of lateral support is 8.35 x 12 = 100 in. The critical moment, based on the assumption that failure will be accompanied by elastic lateral buckling of the unbraced length, is calculated from Equation 6.26(a):

$$M_u = \frac{\pi}{\omega L}\sqrt{EI_y \, G J + (\frac{\pi E}{L})^2 \, I_y \, \frac{I_y(d-t)^2}{4}}$$

$$= \frac{\pi}{1.0 \times 100}\sqrt{29000 \times 48.3 \times 11200 \times 1.24 + \left(\frac{\pi \times 29000}{100}\right)^2 \times 48.3 \times 4970}$$

$$= 14700 \text{ inch kips}$$

(Note M_u = 12800 inch kips using Equation 6.26(b)).

For a Class 2 section, if $M_u > \frac{2}{3}M_p$ the factored moment resistance must be based on Equation 6.28, which accounts for inelastic action.

$$14700 > \frac{2}{3}M_p$$

$$> \frac{2}{3} \times 126 \times 44$$

$$> 3700$$

$$\therefore M_r = 1.15 \, \phi M_p \, (1 - \frac{0.28 \, M_p}{M_u})$$

$$= 1.15 \times 0.90 \times 126 \times 44 \, (1 - \frac{0.28 \times 126 \times 44}{14700})$$

= 5130 inch kips

However, since this value is greater than that predicted using Equation 6.7, the smaller value governs the design and:

M_r = 4990 inch kips

Since the factored moment resistance is greater than the actual maximum bending moment, the W21x55 will be satisfactory without additional bracing. The member is assumed to be braced laterally at the two ends and in the central positive moment region, by the floor slab.

The use of the tabulated values on page 5-110 of the CISC Manual[6.14] would greatly aid in the solution of this problem. The value, L_u, tabulated in these tables (L_u = 9.3 feet for the W21x55) represents the greatest unbraced length over which the moment resistance based on local buckling can be developed. Thus, as the actual unbraced length is less than L_u, no reduction in strength is anticipated.

6.12 Concentrated Loads and Reactions

Beams subjected to concentrated loads (including reactions) may require special consideration. In the usual framing schemes concentrated loads are transferred to a beam through web connections. A typical situation is illustrated in Figure 6.1 showing a beam framing into a column member. The reaction from the beam is resisted as a concentrated load by the column. However, in the beam itself, the reaction is distributed over the depth of the web.

In other situations, however, a concentrated load may be delivered to one of the flanges and provision must be made for its transfer into the web. The arrangement shown in Figure 6.13 illustrates two such cases; the concentrated load, P, delivered to the top flange and the reaction, R, which is resisted by the bottom flange at the support point. The danger here is that a large compressive force in the web may lead to yielding of the material and to web crippling.

If it is assumed that the load or reaction is distributed uniformly over the length of the bearing plate, N, and spreads at an angle of 45° then the area available to resist the load, at the flange to web junction is:

$$w(N + 2k) \tag{6.30}$$

for the interior load and

$$w(N + k) \tag{6.31}$$

for the reaction, where k is the distance from the outside of the flange to the toe of the fillet at the flange to web junction. It has been found that the biaxial stress condition in the vicinity to the flange-to-web junction increases the apparent yield stress of the material by approximately 25%. Thus the factored compressive resistance of the crippling area can be calculated from

139

Clause 15.8 of CSA Standard S16.1-1974 as:

$$B_r = 1.25 \, \phi F_y \, w(N + 2k) \; \text{\textit{ / factored compressive (6.32)}}$$

— factored compressive resistance of the crippled area.

for an interior load point and:

$$B_r = 1.25 \, \phi \, w(N + k) \, F_y \qquad\qquad (6.33)$$

for an exterior reaction.

In Equations 6.32 and 6.33 a value of ϕ = 0.90 is employed. The design of the beam bearing plate will be discussed in Chapter 10.

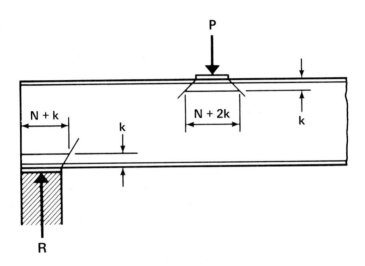

Figure 6.13
Concentrated Loads and Reactions

If the factored compressive resistance is exceeded, the length of the bearing plate may be increased or a pair of bearing stiffeners might be provided to help carry the load. The detailed design of bearing stiffeners will be covered in Chapter 9.

In the case of extremely slender webs, failure may be accompanied by a buckling motion of the web. To guard against this possibility Clause 15.5.1 of CSA Standard S16.1-1974 requires that the unframed ends of girders having h/w ratios greater than $420/\sqrt{F_y}$ must be provided with pairs of bearing stiffeners.

Example 6.8

Given

The end of a W18x50 member of G40.21 50W steel (F_y = 50 ksi) is supported on a bearing plate 8 inches long. The reaction is 140 kips. Are bearing stiffeners required?

Solution

The required dimensions for the W18x50 section are listed in Appendix A:

k = 1.063 in.
w = 0.358 in.

The factored compressive resistance at the flange to web fillet is given by Equation 6.33:

$$B_r = 1.25 \ F_y \ \phi \ w(N + k)$$

$$= 1.25 \times 44 \times 0.90 \times 0.358 \ (8.0 + 1.06)$$

$$= 160 \ \text{kips}$$

Since the factored resistance is greater than the reaction produced by the factored loads, the member support is satisfactory for bearing. For this member the web slenderness is well below $420/\sqrt{F_y}$ and thus bearing stiffeners are not required to satisfy Clause 15.5.1 of CSA Standard S16.1-1974.

6.13 Special Topics in Beam Design

In this chapter the basic problems associated with beam design have been discussed. Throughout, it has been assumed that the loading and restraint conditions on the member are such that the cross-section is bent about its major (x—x) axis.

Many problems arise in design in which the cross-section is bent biaxially, that is, components of bending moments are produced about both principal axes. Such a condition arises, for example, if the member is used as a purlin on a sloping roof. A general discussion of these problems is included in References 6.1 and 6.10, and a detailed design example is included in Reference 6.18, which includes a discussion of the influence of sag rods on the purlin bending moments.

A second class of problems not covered in this chapter includes those in which the applied loads produce a torque about the longitudinal axis of the member. In this situation, the torque is usually accompanied by bending about one or both principal axes of the cross-section. This type of problem might arise in the design of lintels, eave struts, crane girders and in many other situations. The material contained in References 6.1, 6.10 and 6.18 should be consulted for additional information.

In almost every phase of design the digital computer is used to facilitate the process. The Canadian Institute of Steel Construction together with the Canadian Steel Industries Construction Council has developed a program called Rapid Evaluation of Steel Structures (RESST) to assist in the selection of the most economical floor system for particular situations. Further information on this program may be obtained from the CISC.

6.14 Beams in Plastically Designed Structures

In a structure designed to resist moments and forces calculated on the basis of a plastic analysis, the beams are required to deliver a moment capacity equal to M_p. In addition, however, portions of the beams must be able to act as plastic hinges that is, must be able to resist a moment of M_p while undergoing considerable inelastic rotation. The required behaviour of a plastic hinge region is illustrated by the curve for Class 1 sections in Figure 6.6.

The additional inelastic rotation requirement means that the flange plate will be subjected to larger average strains than will the flange of a Class 2 section. The limiting flange and web slenderness ratios are correspondingly reduced to those appropriate for a Class 1 section. As given in Equations 6.8 and 6.14 respectively, the limits are:

$$\frac{b_o}{t} \leqslant 54/\sqrt{F_y}$$

and:

$$\frac{h}{w} \leqslant 420/\sqrt{F_y}$$

Members in plastically designed structures must also be braced laterally so that the full M_p value can be delivered by the beam and also to ensure that the member can deform inelastically (at plastic hinge locations) as shown by curve B of Figure 6.9.

There is a distinct difference between the behaviour of a beam subjected to a uniform bending moment (Figure 6.9) and that subjected to a moment gradient (Figure 6.6). In the uniform moment case yielding extends over a considerable length of the member as the beam moment approaches M_p, and weakens the beam significantly with respect to lateral buckling.[6.4] To achieve the desired behaviour, the distance from a plastic hinge (which must be braced laterally) to the adjacent braced point, L_{cr}, is limited in Clause 13.7 of CSA Standard S16.1-1974, to:

$$L_{cr} = 210 \, r_y/\sqrt{F_y} \tag{6.34}$$

If there is only a slight moment gradient on the member segment between the two laterally braced points, Equation 6.34 is applicable, for example if $M/M_p > 0.5$. In this context, M/M_p is the ratio of the smaller to the larger bending moment on the member segment, positive if the segment is bent in single curvature.

In the moment gradient case, for $M/M_p \leqslant 0.5$, the situation is not as severe.[6.5] In this case, to achieve the desired behaviour, Clause 13.7 of CSA Standard S16.1-1974 limits the critical length to:

$$L_{cr} = 375 \, r_y/\sqrt{F_y} \tag{6.35}$$

In regions removed from potential plastic hinge locations these provisions do not apply; in fact the bracing spacing would be the same as that specified for the same member in a structure designed on the basis of an elastic analysis.[6.5]

References

6.1 "Structural Steel Design", 2nd Edition, Edited by L. Tall, Ronald Press Company, New York, 1974.

6.2 Canadian Standards Association, CSA Standard S16-1974, "Steel Structures for Buildings-Limit States Design", Canadian Standards Association, Rexdale, Ontario, 1974.

6.3 Redwood, R. G., "Design of Beams with Web Openings", Canadian Steel Industries Construction Council, Toronto, Ontario, 1973.

6.4 Timoshenko, S. P. and Gere, J. M., "Mechanics of Materials", Van Nostrand Reinhold Company, New York, 1972.

6.5 WRC-ASCE Joint Committee, "Plastic Design in Steel, A Guide and Commentary", 2nd Edition, American Society of Civil Engineers, New York, 1971.

6.6 Galambos, T. V., "Structural Members and Frames", Prentice-Hall, Inc., Englewood Cliffs, New Jersey, 1968.

6.7 Bresler, B., Lin, T. Y. and Scalzi, J. B., "Design of Steel Structures, 2nd Edition," John Wiley and Sons, Inc., New York, 1968.

6.8 Lukey, A. F. and Adams, P. F., "Rotation Capacity of Beams Under Moment Gradient", Journal of the Structural Division, American Society of Civil Engineers, Volume 95, ST6, June, 1969.

6.9 CSA Standard S136-1974, "Cold Formed Steel Structural Members", Canadian Standards Association, Rexdale, Ontario, 1974.

6.10 McGuire, W., "Steel Structures", Prentice-Hall, Inc., Englewood Cliffs, N.J., 1968.

6.11 Holtz, N. and Kulak, G. L., "Web Slenderness Limits for Compact Beams", Dept. of Civil Engineering, University of Alberta, Report No. 43, March 1973.

6.12 Holtz, N. and Kulak, G. L., "Web Slenderness Limits for Non-Compact Beams", Dept. of Civil Engineering, University of Alberta, Report No. 51, August, 1975.

6.13 Galambos, T. V. and Ravindra, M. K., "Load and Resistance Factor Design Criteria for Steel Beams", Research Report No. 27, Civil and Environmental Engineering Department, Washington University, St. Louis, Missouri, 1974.

6.14 "Limit States Design Steel Manual", Canadian Institute of Steel Construction, Toronto, Ontario, 1977.

6.15 Brockenbrough, R. L., "Criteria for Heat Curving Steel Beams and Girders", Journal of the Structural Division, American Society of Civil Engineers, Vol. 96, ST10, October, 1970.

6.16 "Handbook of Steel Construction", 2nd Edition, Canadian Institute of Steel Construction, Toronto, Ontario, 1976.

6.17 Nethercot, D. A. and Trahair, N. S., "Inelastic Lateral Buckling of Determinate Beams", Research Report No. R64, University of Sheffield, Sheffield, England, 1975.

6.18 Lothers, J. E., "Design of Structural Steel", 3rd Edition, Prentice-Hall, Inc., Englewood Cliffs, New Jersey, 1972.

CHAPTER 7

BEAM-COLUMNS

7.1 Introduction

Beam-columns are those members in a structure that are subjected to significant axial loads and bending moments. Generally in a building structure beam-columns are vertical elements and are subjected to loads and moments as a result of the action of adjacent members. A typical situation is shown in Figure 7.1(a) where a portion of the framing for an office building is shown; the members are joined using moment-resistant connections. If the spans and loadings are not symmetrical, the beam loading will induce bending moments at the column ends and the beam shears plus the loads from the column segment above will subject the member to an axial force. The resulting free body diagram is shown in Figure 7.1(b).

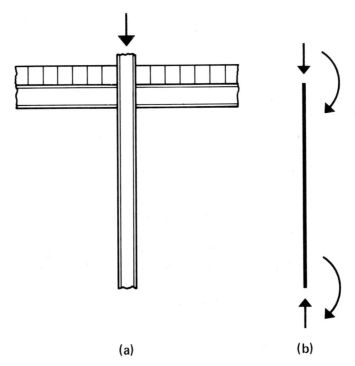

(a)   (b)

Figure 7.1
Beam-Column Loading Condition

The design of a beam-column is based on the ultimate member strength.[7.1] Depending on the member proportions the ultimate strength may be limited by overall stability of the member or by the bending strength of a particular cross-section, usually at a load or reaction point.[7.2] For this reason both failure possibilities must be checked for any given member. In addition, as for beams and columns, the possibility of premature plate buckling must be eliminated by satisfying the pertinent width-to-thickness limitations.[7.1]

7.2 Cross-Sectional Strength

A small element of length cut from the member shown in Figure 7.1, is shown to a larger scale in Figure 7.2(a). The element is subjected to an axial force, C, applied at the centroid and to a bending moment, M, applied about the strong axis of the section. For small values of bending moments, the strain distribution is shown in Figure 7.2(b), along with the corresponding stress distribution. In this situation the neutral axis is shifted (from the centroid) so that the net compressive force produced by the internal stresses will be sufficient to balance the applied force, C. It is assumed that at this stage the total strains, including the residual strains, are low enough so that yielding does not occur.

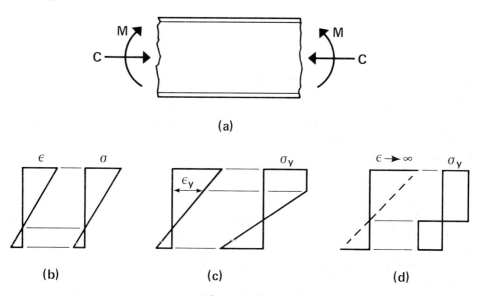

Figure 7.2
Stress and Strain Distributions

As the bending moment is increased parts of the section will yield, as shown in Figure 7.2(c). The strains due to the applied moments and forces are shown in this figure along with the corresponding stresses. The neutral axis has moved up slightly from the position shown in Figure 7.2(b) since the stress distribution is no longer linear. The residual strain distribution (not shown) will modify the progression of yielding slightly but will not affect the results.[7.1]

As bending continues the strain distribution is assumed to remain linear, as shown in Figure 7.2(d); in the final stages the strains would approach infinite values and yielding would penetrate completely across the section as shown by the stress distribution in Figure 7.2(d). Although the stress distribution shown is not attainable (the stresses in the vicinity of the neutral axis cannot actually reach the yield value) the resisting moment computed on the basis of this stress distribution gives an excellent estimate of the ultimate capacity of the cross-section.[7.1]

The ultimate moment capacity, reduced to account for the presence of an axial force, is denoted by M_{pc}. In situations where the axial force, C, is less than approximately 0.15 C_y (C_y denotes the yield load $A\sigma_y$), M_{pc} is equal to the full plastic moment capacity, M_p. For higher values of the axial force, M_{pc} is given for I-shaped members by:[7.1]

$$M_{pc} = 1.18 \, M_p \, (1 - C/C_y) \tag{7.1}$$

In order to avoid a premature local failure, the maximum moment should be less than the value M_{pc} given by Equation 7.1. CSA Standard S16.1 expresses this equation in Clause 13.8.2, in a slightly different form:[7.3]

$$\frac{C_f}{C_r} + \frac{0.85 \, M_f}{M_r} \leqslant 1.0 \tag{7.2}$$

where $C_r = \phi C_y$ and $M_r = \phi M_p$. The terms C_f and M_f denote the axial force and the maximum bending moment, respectively, caused by the factored loads. The performance factor, ϕ, in Equation 7.2 is taken as 0.90 to agree approximately with the limiting cases of an axially loaded column, (as M_f approaches zero) and a beam (as C_f approaches zero). For sections other than I shapes bent about their strong axes, relationships similar to the above must be developed following the principles depicted in Figure 7.2.

The relationship expressed by Equation 7.2 implies that complete yielding will occur throughout the cross-section.* Thus Equation 7.2 applies only to those sections falling within Class 1 or 2, as defined in Clause 11.2 of CSA Standard S16.1-1974, since the plates must be sufficiently stocky that premature local buckling does not occur. Where this cannot be guaranteed, the bending moment on the section must be restricted to a lesser value. For example, in the case of a Class 3 section, it is assumed that the capacity of the section will be attained once the bending moment reaches a value sufficient to cause yielding. This is expressed in Clause 13.8.3 of CSA Standard S16.1-1974 as:

$$\frac{C_f}{C_r} + \frac{M_f}{M_r} \leqslant 1.0 \tag{7.3}$$

*Note that Equation 7.2 is not completely compatible with Equation 4.2 for a column of zero length, as M_f approaches zero, but the difference is negligible.

where the terms are as defined for Equation 7.2 except that $M_r = \phi M_y$. In the case of a Class 4 section, the capacity must be further restricted and in Equation 7.3 M_r is taken as the product of the performance factor and the moment required to cause local buckling of the section. The plate width-to-thickness ratios required to ensure that the above capacities can be achieved will be summarized in the following section.

Example 7.1

Given

The W10x49 member of G40.21 44W steel (F_y = 44 ksi) is subjected to the axial force and bending moments shown in Figure 7.3(a). The bending moments and force are those corresponding to the application of the factored loads to the structure. Is the member adequate with regard to local bending strength?

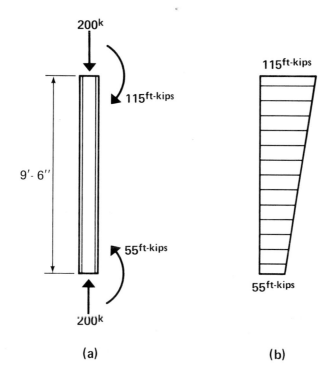

(a)   (b)

Figure 7.3
Loading Condition — Example 7.1

Solution

The W10x49 is a Class 2 section in G40.21 44W steel (the plate requirements will be discussed in the following section) and thus the member will be satisfactory providing it complies with Equation 7.2, the strength interaction equation.

147

The required cross-section properties for the W10x49 are listed in Appendix A:

$$A = 14.4 \text{ in}^2$$
$$Z_x = 60.3 \text{ in}^3$$

The bending moment diagram is shown in Figure 7.3(b). The critical location for local bending is at the upper end of the column where the bending moment is a maximum. At this location the axial load is $C_f = 200$ kips and the bending moment is $M_f = 115$ ft. kips.

The factored compressive resistance is:

$$C_r = \phi A F_y = 0.90 \times 14.4 \times 44 = 570 \text{ kips}$$

and the factored moment resistance is given by Equation 6.7:

$$M_r = \phi Z_x F_y = 0.90 \times 60.3 \times 44 = 2390 \text{ inch kips}$$

The strength interaction equation, Equation 7.2, then becomes:

$$\frac{C_f}{C_r} + 0.85 \frac{M_f}{M_r} \leqslant 1.0$$

$$\frac{200}{570} + 0.85 \times \frac{115 \times 12}{2390} \leqslant 1.0$$

$$0.84 \leqslant 1.0$$

The W10x49 is satisfactory.

7.3 Plate Slenderness Limitations for Beam-Columns

The use of Equations 7.2 and 7.3 for design implies that the component plates of the cross-section are sufficiently stocky so that the section can resist a moment equal to the reduced plastic moment capacity, M_{pc}, in the case of Class 1 or 2 sections, or the yield or critical moment for Class 3 or 4 sections. The requirements for the compression flange in these situations are the same as those for a beam. Thus the discussion of Section 6.4 is also relevant for the beam-column and the same limits on flange width-to-thickness ratios are used. These limits are summarized in Table 7.1.

For the web plate the situation is not as simple. If the axial force in the beam-column is relatively small, the neutral axis will be close to the mid-depth of the cross-section. Where the axial force is zero the limitation on the clear web depth-to-thickness ratio is the same as that for girders, as discussed in Chapter 6. For the various sections, these limitations are summarized in Table 7.1.

TABLE 7.1
Width-Thickness Ratios: Compression Elements

Description of Element	Section Classification		
	Class 1 Plastic Design	Class 2 Compact	Class 3 Non-Compact
Flanges of I sections.	$\dfrac{b_o}{t} \le \dfrac{54}{\sqrt{F_y}}$ Eqn. 6.8	$\dfrac{b_o}{t} \le \dfrac{64}{\sqrt{F_y}}$ Eqn. 6.9	$\dfrac{b_o}{t} \le \dfrac{100}{\sqrt{F_y}}$ Eqn. 6.11
Webs in members subjected to flexural compression	$\dfrac{h}{w} \le \dfrac{420}{\sqrt{F_y}}$ Eqn. 6.14	$\dfrac{h}{w} \le \dfrac{520}{\sqrt{F_y}}$ Eqn. 6.15	$\dfrac{h}{w} \le \dfrac{690}{\sqrt{F_y}}$ Eqn. 6.16
Webs in members subjected to axial compression	$\dfrac{h}{w} \le \dfrac{255}{\sqrt{F_y}}$	$\dfrac{h}{w} \le \dfrac{255}{\sqrt{F_y}}$	$\dfrac{h}{w} \le \dfrac{255}{\sqrt{F_y}}$
Webs in members subjected to combined flexural and axial compression	$\dfrac{h}{w} \le \dfrac{420}{\sqrt{F_y}}\left(1 - 1.40\,\dfrac{C_f}{C_y}\right)†$ Eqn. 7.4	when $\dfrac{C_f}{C_y} \le 0.15$, $\dfrac{h}{w} \le \dfrac{520}{\sqrt{F_y}}\left(1 - 1.28\,\dfrac{C_f}{C_y}\right)†$ when $\dfrac{C_f}{C_y} > 0.15$, $\dfrac{h}{w} \le \dfrac{450}{\sqrt{F_y}}\left(1 - 0.43\,\dfrac{C_f}{C_y}\right)†$	when $\dfrac{C_f}{C_y} \le 0.15$, $\dfrac{h}{w} \le \dfrac{690}{\sqrt{F_y}}\left(1 - 2.60\,\dfrac{C_f}{C_y}\right)†$ when $\dfrac{C_f}{C_y} > 0.15$, $\dfrac{h}{w} \le \dfrac{450}{\sqrt{F_y}}\left(1 - 0.43\,\dfrac{C_f}{C_y}\right)†$

† $\dfrac{h}{w}$ need not be less than $\dfrac{255}{\sqrt{F_y}}$. (See Chapter 4)

In situations where the axial force is large, the neutral axis will be in the tension flange and the entire web plate will be subjected to compression.[7.1] Thus, for members subjected to relatively large axial forces, the limiting web clear depth-to-thickness ratio is the same as that for an axially loaded column (See Chapter 4) and is shown in Table 7.1.

For Class 1 sections the limit of $255/\sqrt{F_y}$ is appropriate for C_f/C_y ratios of 0.28 and greater while for Class 2 and 3 sections this limit is not reached except under conditions of pure axial load.

In situations where the axial force is not zero but is relatively small, the neutral axis will lie between the centroid and the tension flange. If the axial force is small enough (for a Class 1 section) so that the ratio of C_f/C_y is less than 0.28, the neutral axis will be in the web[7.1] and the limitation on the clear web depth-to-thickness is given in Clause 11.2 of CSA Standard S16.1-1974 as:

$$\frac{h}{w} \leqslant \frac{420}{\sqrt{F_y}}[1 - 1.40 \frac{C_f}{C_y}] \tag{7.4}$$

The use of Equation 7.4 ensures that the limit on the web slenderness ratio becomes more restrictive as C_f/C_y increases, a reflection of the increasing proportion of the plate depth which is subjected to compressive stress.

The validity of Equation 7.4 was established on the basis of experimental work and in the past this relationship has been applied also to Class 2 and 3 sections. More recently experimental work has been completed which led to the formulation of more liberal requirements for these sections.[7.4, 7.5] These requirements are contained in Clause 11.2 of CSA Standard S16.1-1974. For a Class 2 section if $C_f/C_y < 0.15$:[7.4]

$$\frac{h}{w} \leqslant \frac{520}{\sqrt{F_y}}(1 - 1.28 \frac{C_f}{C_y}) \tag{7.5a}$$

and if $C_f/C_y > 0.15$:

$$\frac{h}{w} \leqslant \frac{450}{\sqrt{F_y}}(1 - 0.43 \frac{C_f}{C_y}) \tag{7.5b}$$

Similarly, for a Class 3 section if $C_f/C_y \leqslant 0.15$:[7.5]

$$\frac{h}{w} \leqslant \frac{690}{\sqrt{F_y}}(1 - 2.60 \frac{C_f}{C_y}) \tag{7.6a}$$

and if $C_f/C_y > 0.15$:

$$\frac{h}{w} \leqslant \frac{450}{\sqrt{F_y}}(1 - 0.43 \frac{C_f}{C_y}) \tag{7.6b}$$

150

The provisions for Class 1, 2 and 3 sections are included in Table 7.1 and are depicted graphically in Figure 7.4. For Class 4 or slender sections limits on web slenderness are not specified directly; rather the terms M_r and C_r in Equation 7.3 depend directly on the web depth-to-thickness ratio. The implications of this are discussed in Chapters 4 and 9.[7.6]

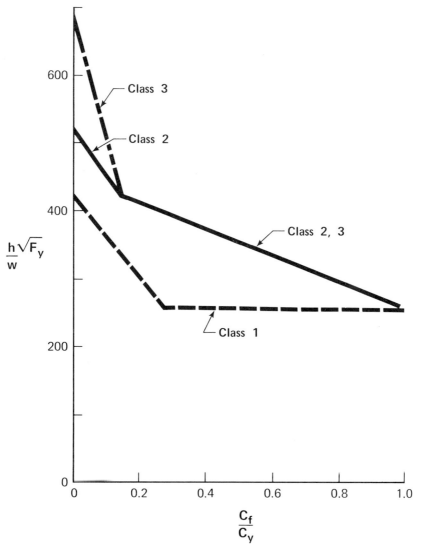

Figure 7.4
Web Slenderness Limits

Example 7.2

Given

Check the W10x49 section of G40.12 44W steel (F_y = 44 ksi) used in Example 7.1 to ensure that the member meets the requirements for a Class 2 section.

Solution

The cross-section dimensions and properties for the W10x49 section are listed in Appendix A:

$$d = 10.00 \text{ in.} \qquad\qquad t = 0.558 \text{ in.}$$
$$b = 10.00 \text{ in.} \qquad\qquad w = 0.340 \text{ in.}$$
$$A = 14.4 \text{ in.}^2 \qquad\qquad r_x = 4.35 \text{ in.}$$

The flange slenderness is computed as:

$$\frac{b_o}{t} = \frac{b}{2t} = \frac{10.00}{2 \times 0.558} = 8.96$$

The allowable flange slenderness ratio is given by Equation 6.9 as:

$$\frac{64}{\sqrt{F_y}} = \frac{64}{\sqrt{44}} = 9.65$$

Since the actual flange slenderness is less than the specified limit, the flange plate meets the requirements for a Class 2 section. Before the web plate can be checked the ratio C_f/C_y must be calculated as a measure of the significance of the axial load term.

$$C_f = 200 \text{ kips}$$

$$C_y = F_y \times A = 44 \times 14.4 = 634 \text{ kips}$$

$$C_f/C_y = 200/634 = 0.32$$

Since $C_f/C_y = 0.32$ exceeds 0.15 it is probable that the neutral axis falls within the tension flange and Equation 7.5(b) will be used to compute the limiting web slenderness.

The approximate web slenderness ratio (using "t" instead of "k" as explained in Chapter 6) is tabulated in Reference 7.7 and is calculated below:

$$\frac{h}{w} = \frac{d - 2t}{w} = \frac{10.00 - (2 \times 0.558)}{0.340} = 26.1$$

The allowable web slenderness ratio is calculated from Equation 7.5(b):

$$\frac{h}{w} \leqslant \frac{450}{\sqrt{F_y}}(1 - 0.43 \frac{C_f}{C_y})$$

$$\leqslant \frac{450}{\sqrt{44}}(1 - 0.43 \times \frac{200}{634})$$

$$\leqslant 58.6$$

Since the actual web slenderness ratio is less than the allowable the web plate is satisfactory and the section meets the requirements for a compact or Class 2 section.

7.4 Moment-Curvature-Thrust Relationship

In many situations the attainment of the reduced plastic moment capacity at the critical section marks the ultimate strength of the member. For example a beam-column of length L subjected to an axial load C and a single end moment M_O is shown in Figure 7.5. The member has pinned ends and it is assumed that translation does not occur.

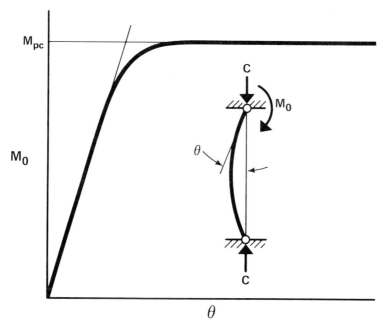

Figure 7.5
Moment-Rotation Relationship

The behaviour of the member is illustrated by Figure 7.5, which plots the applied end moment, M_O, against the corresponding rotation, θ. The $M_O - \theta$ relationship is determined by assuming that the axial load remains constant as the end moment is increased, up to the maximum capacity of the member. For low values of M_O, the member behaves elastically; as the moment is increased, the outside fibres will yield. The strain distribution at this stage is shown in Figure 7.2(c) together with the corresponding stress distribution. When the bending moment at the critical location reaches M_{pc}, the maximum capacity of the member will be attained. For the member shown this will occur when the end moment, M_O, is equal to M_{pc}, since the maximum moment occurs at the member end.[7.1] The maximum capacity of this type of member is given by Equation 7.2.

153

In other situations the member does not fail by exceeding the strength of the cross-section but rather fails because of overall instability.[7.2] To predict the capacity of a beam-column which fails in this manner it is first necessary to develop relationships between the moment and curvature (for a particular axial force or thrust), the M-κ-C relationship.[7.1] The loading condition for a small length of the member is shown in Figure 7.6(a). It is assumed that the strain distribution is that shown in Figure 7.6(b) and is similar to that considered previously in Figure 7.2. The strain distribution is characterized by the curvature, κ, and the strain at the centroid, ϵ_0.

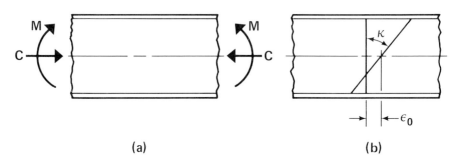

(a)   (b)

Figure 7.6
Strain Distribution

For a given strain distribution, the stress in each fibre can be obtained from the stress-strain relationship of Figure 2.3. The axial thrust, C, is computed as:

$$C = \int_A \sigma \, dA \qquad\qquad (7.7)$$

and the internal bending moment, M, is:

$$M = \int_A \sigma \, y \, dA \qquad\qquad (7.8)$$

By repeating this process for various strain distributions, curves such as those shown in Figure 7.7 can be generated. These curves plot M/M_p against κ/κ_p for various values of C/C_y, where $\kappa_p = M_p/EI$.

For a particular value of C/C_y the initial portion of the relationship is linear and reflects the fact that in the elastic range $\kappa = M/EI$. As yielding is initiated the relationship becomes non-linear and finally the curve is asymptotic to a value of M corresponding to M_{pc}, the reduced plastic moment capacity. The full lines in Figure 7.7 show the relationships obtained neglecting the presence of residual strains in the cross-section while the curves shown by the dashed lines include this effect. The residual strains produce earlier yielding in some portions of the cross-section and thus increase the curvatures. However, the ultimate capacity of the section is unchanged.[7.1]

154

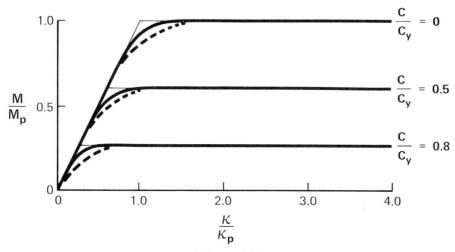

Figure 7.7
Moment-Curvature-Thrust Relationships

The relationships shown in Figure 7.7 are relatively insensitive to the cross-section (for W type shapes) and may be used to obtain the curvature corresponding to a particular internal force and bending moment. The slope of the M-κ relationship is a measure of the stiffness of the cross-section. Thus the curved (inelastic) portions represent regions where the stiffness of the member (resistance to an increase in moment) has decreased. For high values of C/C_y, this stiffness reduction will occur under the application of axial load alone, since the section will be partially yielded due to the high compressive residual strains at the flange tips. Note for example, the M-κ relationship in Figure 7.7 for $C/C_y = 0.8$, considering the presence of residual strains.

7.5 Overall Member Strength

The member shown in Figure 7.8(a) is subjected to an axial load, C, and to equal and opposite end moments, M_0. The primary and secondary bending moment diagrams for the member are shown in Figures 7.8(b) and (c) respectively. Because the member is subjected to a symmetrical loading condition, the maximum deflection, and therefore the maximum secondary moment, occurs at mid-height. Each element along the member length is then subjected to an axial thrust, C, and to a bending moment, M, which is the total of the primary and secondary bending moments at the location considered. Under the action of these forces the element will develop curvatures in accordance with the relationship shown in Figure 7.7 for the particular C/C_y ratio of the member.

The end rotation corresponding to a given end moment value may be determined by summing the curvatures along half the length of the member. In this manner moment-rotation (M-θ) relationships may be developed, similar to the one shown schematically in Figure 7.9.[7.8] The M-θ relationship describes the response of a particular member to increasing end moments while the axial force is held constant.

155

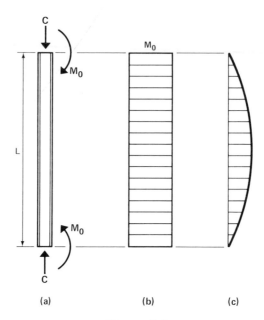

(a)   (b)   (c)

Figure 7.8
Primary and Secondary Bending Moments

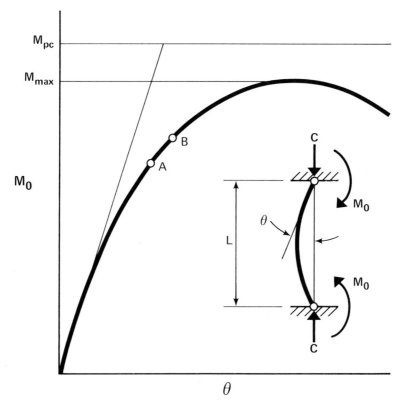

Figure 7.9
Moment-Rotation Relationship

When the end moments are first applied, the member behaves elastically; under increasing moments, the strains at various locations in the member reach the yield level and the corresponding curvatures increase at a more rapid rate in accordance with the relationships of Figure 7.7. The deflections also increase rapidly since the deflection is a function of the magnitude and distribution of the curvatures along the member length. The rapid increases in deflections are accompanied by corresponding increases in the secondary moments.

Figure 7.10 shows a free body diagram of the lower half of the member at two different stages of loading, shown as 'A' and 'B' on the M-θ curve of Figure 7.9. For equilibrium at stage 'A' the moment at mid-height, M_A, is equal to:

$$M_A = M_{oA} + C\Delta_A \tag{7.9}$$

A similar relationship holds for stage 'B'. The increase in end moment between stages 'A' and 'B' is thus given by:

$$(M_{oB} - M_{oA}) = (M_B - M_A) - C(\Delta_B - \Delta_A) \tag{7.10}$$

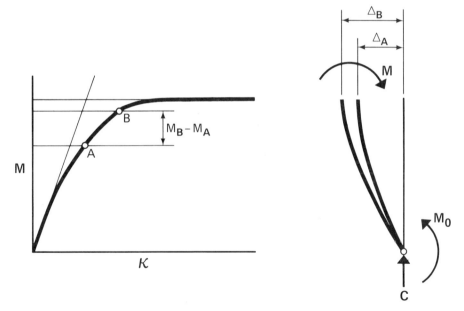

Figure 7.10
Stability of Beam-Column

The change in resisting moment $(M_B - M_A)$ must always be positive but as the extent of the yielding spreads at the mid-height of the member, the rate of increase will diminish. The resisting moment will increase according to the M-κ relationship of Figure 7.7. This is shown schematically at the left hand side of Figure 7.10. The second term in Equation 7.10, $C(\Delta_B - \Delta_A)$, will increase rapidly since the curvatures, and therefore the deflections, are

157

increasing rapidly in the inelastic range. Since the axial load remains constant it is possible for the right hand side of Equation 7.10 to become zero and then negative before the ultimate strength (M_{pc}) of the cross-section is reached at the mid-height of the member. At corresponding stages, the end moment must reach a maximum and then reduce, to maintain equilibrium.

The attainment of the maximum member strength in this situation is not related to the ultimate capacity of the cross-section but rather depends on the overall stiffness of the member, its length, the axial load and the loading and support conditions. After the member has reached its ultimate capacity, M_{MAX}, in Figure 7.9, unloading is accompanied by inelastic instability.[7.9]

Because of the many factors involved in the failure, the ultimate strength of a beam-column cannot be determined directly. Instead the complete moment-rotation relationship must be predicted and the peak value (M_{MAX} in Figure 7.9) is then the ultimate strength.[7.8] The initial portion of the moment-rotation relationship can be predicted by solving the appropriate differential equation since the moment and curvature are related through the flexural rigidity, EI, of the member.

As the end moments are increased, however, yielding occurs in the central portion of the member and the moment-curvature relationship changes in accordance with Figure 7.7. At this stage a numerical procedure is used to determine the shape of the moment-rotation relationship.[7.8] The deflected shape of the member is first assumed and the primary and secondary bending moments are computed at several locations along the member length. Using the moment-curvature relationships of Figure 7.7, the corresponding curvatures are determined and these are integrated to determine the end rotation of the member and the deflected shape. The process is repeated until the final deflected shape agrees with that assumed initially.

The above procedure is repeated for increasing values of the end moment, up to the ultimate strength. For different members, having particular end moment conditions and slenderness ratios, the maximum end moment capacities, expressed as M/M_p are plotted versus the axial load ratios, C/C_y, in Figure 7.11. The ultimate strengths are shown as the solid curves in this figure.

The determination of the ultimate strength for a particular member is a tedious process and not suited to design office use. For design purposes a so-called stability interaction equation has been fitted to the results shown by the dashed curves in Figure 7.11.[7.10] The stability interaction equation is used to predict the ultimate strength of a member as governed by overall instability and is given in Clause 13.8 of CSA Standard S16.1-1974 as:[7.3]

$$\frac{C_f}{C_r} + \frac{\omega\, M_f}{M_r\left(1 - \dfrac{C_f}{C_e}\right)} \leqslant 1.0 \tag{7.11}$$

where:

M_f = maximum end moment on the member produced by the factored loads.

C_f = axial load on the member produced by the factored loads.

C_r = the factored compressive resistance developed by the member if subjected to an axial load. For Class 1, 2 and 3 sections the factored compressive resistance is based on Equation 4.2 and reflects the overall behaviour of the member. For Class 4 sections the factored compressive resistance is computed on the basis of the local buckling strength of the plate elements (See Section 4.1).

C_e = $\dfrac{286,000A}{(KL/r_x)^2}$, the elastic buckling strength of the member where KL/r_x represents the slenderness ratio in the plane of bending. The effective length factor, K, is defined in Chapter 5.

ω = equivalent moment factor; $\omega = 1.0$ for equal end moments as in Figure 7.9. See also Section 7.7 and 7.10.

M_r = The factored moment resistance developed by the member if subjected to loads causing bending moments without significant axial force. If the member is completely braced laterally the factored moment resistance is based on Equation 6.7 for Class 1 and 2 sections and Equation 6.12 for Class 3 sections. For laterally braced Class 4 sections the factored moment resistance is a direct function of the local buckling capacity as discussed in Section 6.4.

The curves of Figure 7.11 and the above discussion imply that the member under consideration is braced to prevent premature failure by lateral-torsional buckling. If sufficient bracing is not provided to prevent this type of action then the factored moment resistance, M_r, in Equation 7.11 is reduced as discussed in Section 6.10. In addition, the factored compressive resistance, C_r, would be based on the larger effective slenderness ratio, that is K_xL/r_x or K_yL/r_y.

If the primary bending moment is not uniform over the member length, the strength of the column will be greater than that predicted above.[7.9] To account for this strength increase, an equivalent moment factor, ω is used to reduce the computed bending moment. This will be discussed further in Section 7.7.

The term $1/[1 - \dfrac{C_f}{C_e}]$ in Equation 7.11 is an amplification factor and attempts to account for the secondary moments produced by the axial load acting on the deformed member. The actual support conditions at the member ends are considered by adjusting the effective length of the member. This effective length enters into Equation 7.11 in the terms C_r and C_e and for the

159

conditions described above, the calculation of this factor is based on the assumption that sway is prevented. The implications of this assumption will be discussed further in Sections 7.10 and 7.11 and will be illustrated in Chapter 11.

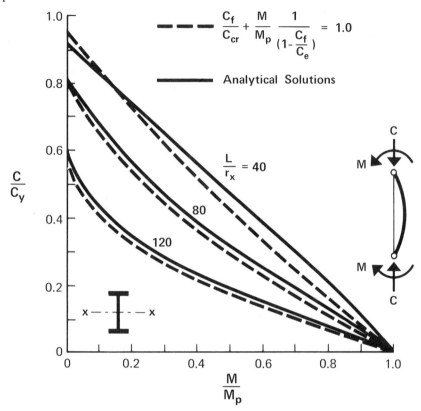

Figure 7.11
Ultimate Strength Interaction Relationships

7.6 Summary of Design Provisions

A beam-column subjected to an axial force and to end moments may fail in one of three ways. The flange or web plate may buckle locally causing a reduction in strength of the member. Except for Class 4 sections, the provisions of CSA Standard S16.1 were designed to postpone local buckling until after the overall member capacity has been reached. These provisions were discussed in Section 7.3 and illustrated by Example 7.2.

If the plate width-to-thickness limits contained in CSA Standard S16.1 are met then overall member failure will be accompanied either by inelastic instability or by the attainment of the cross-sectional capacity at a load or reaction point. For a particular member both these possibilities must be checked. If the cross-section meets the requirements of Equation 7.2 or 7.3 then the member has adequate local strength. This equation is checked at the location along the member length having the largest primary bending moment.

160

If the member also meets the requirements of Equation 7.11 it is adequate with regard to failure of the complete member by inelastic instability. This equation is applied to the member as a whole using the maximum (primary) moment along the member length. In any particular member it is unlikely that the provisions of both Equations 7.2 or 7.3 and 7.11 will be satisfied exactly. It is necessary only that the left-hand sides of both equations be less than unity.

The use of Equation 7.2 has been illustrated in Example 7.1. The two examples following are used to illustrate the provisions of Equation 7.11. The complete assessment of a particular member would include checking either Equation 7.2 or 7.3 and Equation 7.11.

Example 7.3

Given

A W10x49 member of G40.21 44W steel (F_y = 44 ksi) is subjected to an axial force of 200 kips and end moments of 115 ft. kips (strong axis bending). The moments and forces are those caused by the factored loading condition. The member is 12'-0" long and is pinned at both ends. The moments are applied so as to bend the member in symmetrical single curvature as shown in Figure 7.12. Is the member adequate to resist the moments and force shown? (The member is assumed to be braced so that lateral torsional buckling cannot occur.)

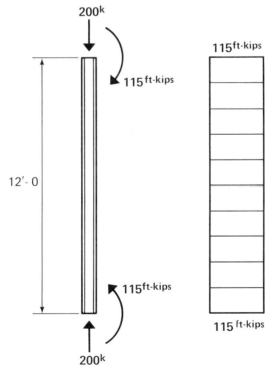

Figure 7.12
Loading Condition — Example 7.3

161

The local member strength at the support point has been checked in Example 7.1 and found to be adequate. In Example 7.2 the same section was shown to meet the requirements for a Class 2 section under a similar loading condition. The cross-section has also been checked as an axially loaded column in Example 4.3. This example will check the member capacity only with respect to inelastic instability.

Solution

The required cross-section properties for the W10x49 section are listed in Appendix A:

$$A = 14.4 \text{ in.}^2 \qquad Z_x = 60.3 \text{ in.}^3 \qquad r_x = 4.35 \text{ in.}$$

The axial force and maximum (primary) bending moment caused by the factored loads are:

$C_f = 200$ kips

$M_f = 115$ ft. kips $= 115 \times 12 = 1380$ inch kips

$M_r = \phi Z_x F_y = 0.90 \times 60.3 \times 44 = 2390$ inch kips

Since the member is assumed to be completely braced against lateral torsional buckling, the factored compressive resistance and the elastic buckling strength depend only on the strong axis slenderness ratio:

$$\frac{KL}{r_x} = \frac{1.0 \times 144}{4.35} = 33$$

In this calculation K is taken as unity since both ends of the member are assumed to be pinned. The non-dimensional slenderness factor is calculated from Equation 4.15 as:

$$\lambda = \frac{KL}{r} \sqrt{\frac{F_y}{\pi^2 E}} = 33 \sqrt{\frac{44}{\pi^2 \times 29000}} = 0.41$$

Since $0 \leqslant \lambda \leqslant 1.0$ the member falls within the limit of applicability of Equation 4.16(a) and with the performance factor $\phi = 0.90$ the factored compressive resistance is:

$C_r = \phi A F_y (1.035 - 0.202 \lambda - 0.222 \lambda^2)$

$\qquad = 0.90 \times 14.4 \times 44 (1.035 - 0.202 \times 0.41 - 0.222 \times 0.41^2)$

$\qquad = 524$ kips

The elastic buckling strength of the member is:

$$C_e = \frac{286000 \, A}{\left(\frac{KL}{r}\right)^2} = \frac{286000 \times 14.4}{(33)^2} = 3780 \text{ kips}$$

The equivalent moment factor $\omega = 1.0$ since the end moments are equal and produce single curvature bending. All the terms required for Equation 7.11 have now been computed and the equation is:

$$\frac{C_f}{C_r} + \frac{\omega \, M_f}{M_r(1 - C_f/C_e)} \leqslant 1.0$$

$$\frac{200}{524} + \frac{1.0 \times 1380}{2390 \left(1 - \dfrac{200}{3780}\right)} \leqslant 1.0$$

$$0.99 \leqslant 1.0$$

Since the left hand side of the stability interaction equation is less than unity the member is adequate with regard to failure by overall instability. In Example 7.1 the same member was shown to be adequate with regard to the attainment of the ultimate moment capacity at the member ends. Thus the W10x49 is satisfactory for this structural situation.

The CISC Manual[7.11] includes tabulated values of C_e/A and the amplification factor $[1/(1 - C_f/C_e)]$ on pages 4-23 and 4-24. These tables may be used to somewhat reduce the computational effort. In addition, the quantities relating to beam and column action, discussed in Chapters 4 and 6, can also be applied to the design of beam-columns.

In Example 7.3 it was assumed that the member was braced to prevent bending about the weak axis of the section. If lateral bracing were provided only at the member ends the moment capacity might be limited by premature lateral torsional buckling. To account for this possibility in design, the value of M_r used in Equation 7.11 would be reduced in accordance with the procedures described in Chapter 6 for laterally unbraced beams. In addition, the value of C_r in Equation 7.11 would be computed on the basis of the larger slenderness ratio.[7.10]

Example 7.4

Given

The W10x49 member of G40.21 44W steel (F_y = 44 ksi) considered in Example 7.3 is again to be checked under the loads and moments shown in Figure 7.12. In this example, however, it is assumed that lateral bracing is provided only at the ends of the member.

Solution

A check to ensure that the member was adequate with regard to the attainment of the cross-sectional capacity was performed in Example 7.1 and the fact that the member is now braced only at the member ends does not change the quantities involved. The member was found to be adequate with regard to local strength. The cross-section properties for the W10x49 section are listed in Appendix A:

163

$A = 14.4$ in.^{2} $r_x = 4.35$ in. $J = 1.38$ in.^{4}

$Z_x = 60.3$ in.^{3} $r_y = 2.54$ in. $I_y = 93.0$ in.^{4}

$$\frac{I_y (d-t)^2}{4} = 2070 \text{ in.}^6 = C_w$$

The axial force and maximum moment caused by the factored loads are the same as those calculated in Example 7.3, that is:

$C_f = 200$ kips

$M_f = 115$ ft. kips $= 115 \times 12 = 1380$ inch kips

Since the member may fail by bending about either principal axis the factored compressive resistance depends on the larger slenderness ratio:

$$\frac{KL}{r_x} = \frac{1.0 \times 144}{4.35} = 33$$

$$\frac{KL}{r_y} = \frac{1.0 \times 144}{2.54} = 57 \qquad\qquad \text{(Governs)}$$

For G40.21 44W steel ($F_y = 44$ ksi) the governing slenderness factor is calculated from Equation 4.15 as:

$$\lambda = \frac{KL}{r} \sqrt{\frac{F_y}{\pi^2 E}} = 57 \sqrt{\frac{44}{\pi^2 \times 29000}} = 0.71$$

Since $0 \leqslant \lambda \leqslant 1.0$ the factored compressive resistance is based on Equation 4.16(a):

$C_r = 445$ kips

The elastic buckling strength is based on the strong axis slenderness ratio as for Example 7.3:

$$C_e = \frac{286000 \, A}{\left(\dfrac{KL}{r_x}\right)^2} = \frac{286000 \times 14.4}{(33)^2} = 3780 \text{ kips}$$

and the equivalent moment factor $\omega = 1.0$.

The computation of the factored moment resistance for a laterally unbraced beam was illustrated in detail in Chapter 6. Only the results are shown below. Using Equation 6.26(a):

L = 144 inches

$$M_u = \frac{\pi}{\omega L} \sqrt{E\, I_y\, G\, J + \left(\frac{\pi E}{L}\right)^2 I_y \frac{I_y\, (d-t)^2}{4}}$$

$$= \frac{\pi}{1.0 \times 144} \sqrt{29000 \times 93.0 \times 11200 \times 1.38 + \left(\frac{\pi \times 29000}{144}\right)^2 \times 93.0 \times 2070}$$

$$= 7520 \text{ inch kips}$$

(Note M_u = 6560 inch kips by Equation 6.26(b)).

For the W10x49 section:

$$M_p = Z_x F_y = 60.3 \times 44 = 2650 \text{ inch kips}$$

The resisting moment therefore must be reduced below M_u (see Chapter 6) and is given by Equation 6.27:

$$M_r = 1.15\,\phi\, M_p\, (1 - \frac{0.28\, M_p}{M_u})$$

$$= 1.15 \times 0.90 \times 2650\, (1 - \frac{0.28 \times 2650}{7520})$$

$$= 2470 \text{ inch kips}$$

Since M_r, as computed by Equation 6.27, is greater than the capacity computed on the basis of local buckling (M_r = 2390 inch kips. See Example 7.3) the resisting moment for the member is calculated using Equation 6.7:

$$M_r = \phi Z_x F_y = \phi M_p = 2390 \text{ inch kips}$$

The stability interaction equation, Equation 7.11, is then checked using the above quantities and:

$$\frac{C_f}{C_r} + \frac{\omega\, M_f}{M_r\, (1 - \frac{C_f}{C_e})} \leqslant 1.0$$

$$\frac{200}{445} + \frac{1.0 \times 1380}{2390\, (1 - \frac{200}{3780})} \leqslant 1.0$$

$$0.45 + 0.61 \leqslant 1.0$$

$$1.06 \not< 1.0$$

In this example the stability interaction equation sums to 1.06, an indication that the member is not adequate to resist the axial force and applied moments in the laterally unsupported condition (although in some instances 6% underdesign might be regarded as acceptable). It is worth emphasizing that the value of C_e, and thus the amplication factor, is based on KL/r_x (not the larger KL/r_y) as a reflection of the fact that the secondary moments depend on the deflections in the plane of the applied moments.

7.7 Non-Uniform Bending Moments

As discussed briefly in Section 6.10, if the primary bending moment is not uniform over the length of the member the strength is increased above that for the equivalent uniform moment condition. When the member is subjected to a non-uniform moment condition the zones of yielding are restricted to relatively small areas, usually at one end of the member. Thus the reduction in stiffness associated with inelastic action develops at the end of the member rather than in the central portion, a less severe condition for the development of secondary moments. To reflect this increase in strength in the stability interaction equation Clause 13.8.4 of CSA Standard S16.1-1974 requires that the factored bending moment, M_f, is multiplied by:

$$\omega = 0.6 + 0.4 \frac{M_{f1}}{M_{f2}} \tag{7.12a}$$

but

$$\omega \not< 0.4 \tag{7.12b}$$

where M_{f2} and M_{f1} are the larger and smaller moments respectively acting at the ends of the member. M_{f1} and M_{f2} are both positive if the member is deformed into single curvature and M_{f1} is negative if the member is in double curvature. Values of ω are listed on page 4-22 of the CISC Manual.[7.11]

Example 7.5

Given

The W10x49 member of G40.21 44W steel, (F_y = 44 ksi) used for Example 7.3 is subjected to an axial force of 200 kips and to a bending moment, applied at the top of the member, of 115 ft. kips. The member is shown in Figure 7.13 with the corresponding primary bending moment diagram. Is the member adequate to resist the moments and force shown?

The local member strength has been checked in Example 7.1 and is satisfactory under this new loading condition. This example will be concerned with the adequacy of the member as governed by overall instability and will use the quantities computed in Example 7.3. The member is again assumed to be braced laterally to prevent premature lateral torsional buckling.

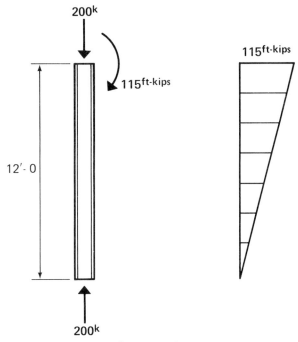

Figure 7.13
Loading Condition — Example 7.5

Solution

The applied force and end moment are the same as those of Example 7.3. In this example, the maximum end moment occurs at the upper end of the member.

C_f = 200 kips

M_f = 115 ft. kips = 115 x 12 = 1380 inch kips

The resistances are also the same as those computed in Example 7.3.

M_r = 2390 inch kips

C_r = 524 kips

C_e = 3780 kips

In Example 7.3, the equivalent moment factor was unity as the member was subjected to equal end moments. In this example, however, the equivalent moment factor is calculated from Equation 7.12.

M_{f1} = 0
M_{f2} = 115 ft. kips

$$\omega = 0.6 + 0.4 \text{ x } \frac{0}{115} = 0.6$$

Since ω = 0.6 is greater than 0.4, use ω = 0.6

The stability interaction equation, Equation 7.11, is checked for the above quantities.

$$\frac{C_f}{C_r} + \frac{\omega \, M_f}{M_r \, (1 - \dfrac{C_f}{C_e})} \leqslant 1.0$$

$$\frac{200}{524} + \frac{0.6 \times 1380}{2390 \, (1 - \dfrac{200}{3780})} \leqslant 1.0$$

$$0.38 + 0.37 \leqslant 1.0$$

$$0.75 \leqslant 1.0$$

The W10x49 is more than adequate to resist the applied moment and force, indicating the less severe loading condition caused by the non-uniform end moment condition. The requirements of Equation 7.2 would also have to be checked to ensure that the member is satisfactory.

Bracing and connection details affect beam-column strength.
(Photo courtesy Heavy Construction News)

7.8 Effective Length as Applied to Beam-Column Design

In the examples of this chapter, the members have been assumed to be pin-ended. In this condition the overall strength of the member is independent of the stiffness of the adjacent members and is a function only of the stiffness of the member itself as well as the loading condition. In an actual structure, however, the stiffnesses of members framing into either end of the beam column influence the bending moment distribution and the deformation pattern, and thus the ultimate strength, of the member.[7.10]

This influence is accounted for in the stability interaction equation by basing the calculation of the terms C_r and C_e on the effective slenderness ratio of the member. In this way the additional stiffness provided to the beam-column by the restraining beams is considered in assessing the strength of the member.[7.2]

7.9 Design Process

In the design process the member size is first estimated then checked against the two interaction equations. In the following example it will be assumed that the girder sizes have been selected previously and that the column under consideration is to be the second storey of a three storey lift.

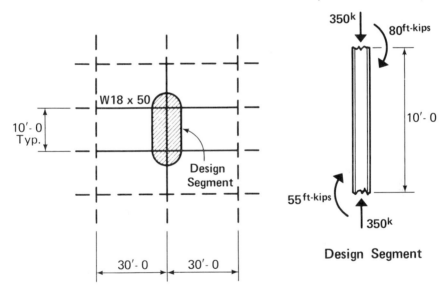

Figure 7.14
Loading Condition — Example 7.6

Example 7.6

Given

A column is to be designed for the structural arrangement shown in Figure 7.14. The girder-to-column connections are designed to resist moment. The members are of G40.21 44W steel (F_y = 44 ksi) and are braced to

169

prevent premature failure by lateral buckling. The sway forces in the structure are to be resisted by a vertical truss system. Select the column.

Solution

As an initial trial, the W10x49 section will be selected. The cross-section properties are listed in Appendix A:

$$A = 14.4 \text{ in.}^2 \qquad\qquad I_x = 273 \text{ in.}^4$$

$$r_x = 4.35 \text{ in.} \qquad\qquad Z_x = 60.3 \text{ in.}^3$$

The girders have been selected previously as W18x50 sections. From Appendix A:

$$I_x = 802 \text{ in.}^4$$

The factored axial force and bending moment are shown in Figure 7.14, with the larger bending moment at the top of the member.

$$C_f = 350 \text{ kips}$$

$$M_f = 80 \text{ ft. kips} = 80 \times 12 = 960 \text{ inch kips}$$

The W10x49 meets the requirements of a Class 2 section (see Table 7.1) and the factored compressive resistance (to be used in the strength interaction equation) is equal to the factored yield load:

$$C_r = \phi A \, F_y = 0.90 \times 14.4 \times 44 = 570 \text{ kips}$$

and the factored moment resistance is calculated from Equation 6.7 as:

$$M_r = \phi \, Z_x \, F_y = 0.90 \times 60.3 \times 44 = 2390 \text{ inch kips}$$

At this stage of the design, the strength interaction equation, Equation 7.2, is checked to ensure that the cross section has adequate strength:

$$\frac{C_f}{C_r} + \frac{0.85 \, M_f}{M_r} \leqslant 1.0$$

$$\frac{350}{570} + \frac{0.85 \times 960}{2390} \leqslant 1.0$$

$$0.96 < 1.0$$

The W10x49 is adequate for local strength.

The terms C_r and C_e in the stability interaction equation depend on the effective slenderness ratio, which in turn is a function of the relative column to girder stiffnesses at either end (see Chapter 5).

170

$$G_U = G_L = \frac{\Sigma I_c / L_c}{\Sigma I_g / L_g}$$

$$= \frac{\dfrac{273}{10 \times 12} + \dfrac{273}{10 \times 12}}{\dfrac{802}{30 \times 12} + \dfrac{802}{30 \times 12}} = 1.02$$

The effective length factor is now selected from the Nomograph, Figure 5.6.

K = 0.77

$$\frac{KL}{r_X} = \frac{0.77 \times 10 \times 12}{4.35} = 21$$

For G40.21 44W steel, the slenderness factor is calculated from Equation 4.15:

$$\lambda = \frac{KL}{r} \sqrt{\frac{F_y}{\pi^2 E}}$$

$$= 21 \sqrt{\frac{44}{\pi^2 \times 29000}} = 0.26$$

Since $0 \leqslant \lambda = 1.0$ the member falls within the limits of applicability of Equation 4.16(a) and:

$$C_r = \phi A F_y (1.035 - 0.202\,\lambda - 0.222\,\lambda^2)$$

$$= 0.90 \times 14.4 \times 44\,(1.035 - 0.202 \times 0.26 - 0.222 \times 0.26^2)$$

$$= 552 \text{ kips}$$

The elastic buckling strength of the member is:

$$C_e = \frac{286000\,A}{\left(\dfrac{KL}{r}\right)^2} = \frac{286000 \times 14.4}{(21)^2} = 9340 \text{ kips}$$

The end moments are not equal and the equivalent moment factor is calculated from Equation 7.12:

$$\omega = 0.6 + 0.4\,\frac{M_{f1}}{M_{f2}}$$

$$= 0.6 + 0.4\,(-\frac{55}{80}) = 0.33$$

But ω can not be less than 0.4

Note that the member is deformed into a double curvature shape so that in the above calculation the ratio M_{f1}/M_{f2} is negative.

171

Using the above quantities the stability interaction equation, Equation 7.11, may now be checked.

$$\frac{C_f}{C_r} + \frac{\omega \, M_f}{M_r \left(1 - \dfrac{C_f}{C_e}\right)} \leqslant 1.0$$

$$\frac{350}{552} + \frac{0.4 \times 960}{2390 \left(1 - \dfrac{350}{9340}\right)} \leqslant 1.0$$

$$0.80 \leqslant 1.0$$

The W10x49 section is adequate for this situation. Although the stability interaction equation sums to 0.80, the strength interaction equation sums to 0.96. Thus the section chosen has little excess capacity and a lighter trial section would probably not be adequate.

7.10 Compensation for Sway Effects

In the previous sections the behaviour of beam-columns was described and procedures were developed for the design of such members. Throughout the discussion, the column was assumed not to translate under the application of forces and moments. In fact, all structures do translate during the loading process and the vertical forces acting on the displaced structure induce bending moments and forces which must be considered in the design of the members.[7.2] These moments and forces are termed sway or P-delta effects and are not normally computed in the analysis used to determine the distribution of bending moments throughout the structure. In many structures the sway effects are resisted by stiff vertical shear walls or a truss system; in these cases the columns may be designed according to the procedures discussed previously.[7.2]

Where the sway effects must be resisted by the frame action of the building, however, a portion of the strength of the column must be reserved for this purpose. One way that this can be achieved for moment resistant frames is by computing the effective length factor on the basis of the sway-permitted case (see Chapter 5) and adjusting the equivalent moment factor so that:[7.12]

$$\omega = 0.85 \tag{7.13}$$

The adjusted values of K and ω are used in the stability interaction equation as shown in Figure 7.15. The solid curves are for the single column shown in the inset to the figure. The results plotted correspond to the attainment of the ultimate load capacity. The moment at the column top, M_c, is non-dimensionalized as M_c/M_p and plotted against the axial load ratio, C/C_y. The primary bending moment ($M_c = Vh$) is shown as the lower solid curve while the total bending moment which includes the sway effects ($M_c = Vh + C\Delta$) is shown as the upper solid curve. The difference in moments between the two curves is then a measure of the sway effect.

172

The stability interaction equation with K based on the sway permitted condition and ω given by Equation 7.13 is plotted as the dashed curve in Figure 7.15. In this situation the interaction equation ensures that only a portion of the member strength will be used to resist the computed forces and bending moments.[7.2] The remaining reserve strength is available to resist the (uncalculated) sway moments.[7.12]

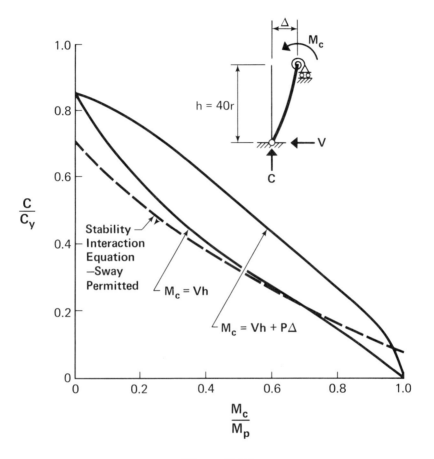

Figure 7.15
Interaction Relationships — Sway Permitted

If the column design is based on an effective length and equivalent moment factor appropriate to the sway-prevented condition then the reserve strength is no longer provided. The implication here is that the secondary or sway effects must be computed and resisted by another portion of the structure, usually a vertical truss or shear wall system.[7.2] Alternatively, if the sway-prevented condition is to be used for the design of the columns in a structure, the sway effects can be computed directly and the additional bending moments included in the design values.[7.2] This second approach will be discussed in Section 7.11 and both possibilities will be illustrated in Chapter 11.

173

Example 7.7

Given

A W10x49 member of G40.21 44W steel (F_y = 44 ksi) is subjected to an axial force of 350 kips and end moments of 80 ft. kips and 55 ft. kips as shown in Figure 7.14. The moment and force are those caused by the factored loads. The member is prevented from lateral buckling. The sway effects were not included in the analysis used to determine the distribution of bending moments throughout the structure nor will a vertical truss system be used in the structure. Is the W10x49 adequate in this situation?

Solution

The cross-sectional properties for the W10x49 section are listed in Appendix A:

$$A = 14.4 \text{ in.}^2 \qquad\qquad I_x = 273 \text{ in.}^4$$

$$r_x = 4.35 \text{ in.} \qquad\qquad Z_x = 60.3 \text{ in.}^3$$

The girders have been selected previously as W18x50 sections. From Appendix A:

$$I_x = 802 \text{ in.}^4$$

The factored axial force and applied moment are the same as those used for Example 7.6 with the maximum end moment at the upper end of the member.

$$C_f = 350 \text{ kips}$$

$$M_f = 80 \text{ ft. kips} = 80 \times 12 = 960 \text{ inch kips}$$

Following the discussion of Example 7.6, the additional quantities required for the strength interaction equation are the factored yield load:

$$C_r = \phi A F_y = 570 \text{ kips}$$

and the factored moment resistance (factored plastic moment capacity) is calculated from Equation 6.7:

$$M_r = \phi Z_x F_y = 2390 \text{ inch kips}$$

The strength interaction equation, Equation 7.2, is then checked:

$$\frac{C_f}{C_r} + \frac{0.85 M_f}{M_r} \leqslant 1.0$$

$$\frac{350}{570} + \frac{0.85 \times 960}{2390} \leqslant 1.0$$

$$0.96 < 1.0$$

174

The W10x49 is adequate for local strength; this condition is unchanged from Example 7.6.

The terms C_r and C_e, used in the stability interaction equation, depend on the effective slenderness ratio, which in turn is a function of the relative stiffnesses at the column ends.

$$G_U = G_L = \frac{\Sigma \, I_c/L_c}{\Sigma \, I_g/L_g}$$

$$= \frac{\dfrac{273}{10 \text{ x } 12} + \dfrac{273}{10 \text{ x } 12}}{\dfrac{802}{30 \text{ x } 12} + \dfrac{802}{30 \text{ x } 12}} = 1.02$$

Since the sway forces must now be resisted by the flexural action of the beams and columns, the effective length factor is selected from the sway-permitted nomograph, Figure 5.13.

$$K = 1.31$$

$$\frac{KL}{r_X} = \frac{1.31 \text{ x } 10 \text{ x } 12}{4.35} = 36$$

For G40.21 44W steel, the slenderness factor is given by Equation 4.15:

$$\lambda = \frac{KL}{r} \sqrt{\frac{F_y}{\pi^2 E}}$$

$$= 36 \sqrt{\frac{44}{\pi^2 \text{ x } 29000}} = 0.45$$

Since $0 \leqslant \lambda \leqslant 1.0$ the member falls within the limits of applicability of Equation 4.16(a) and

$$C_r - \phi A F_y \, (1.035 - 0.202 \, \lambda \quad 0.222 \, \lambda^2)$$

$$= 0.90 \text{ x } 14.4 \text{ x } 44 \, (1.035 - 0.202 \text{ x } 0.45 - 0.222 \text{ x } 0.45^2)$$

$$= 513 \text{ kips}$$

The elastic buckling strength of the member is:

$$C_e = \frac{286000 \, A}{\left(\dfrac{KL}{r}\right)^2} = \frac{286000 \text{ x } 14.4}{(36)^2} = 3180 \text{ kips}$$

For the sway-permitted condition the equivalent moment factor is given by Equation 7.13:

$$\omega = 0.85$$

Using these quantities the stability interaction equation, Equation 7.11, may be checked:

$$\frac{C_f}{C_r} + \frac{\omega \, M_f}{M_r \left(1 - \dfrac{C_f}{C_e}\right)} \leqslant 1.0$$

$$\frac{350}{513} + \frac{0.85 \times 960}{2390 \left(1 - \dfrac{350}{3180}\right)} \leqslant 1.0$$

$$1.07 \nleqslant 1.0$$

The W10x49 section used in this situation is not adequate. By comparison with Example 7.6 the implied allowance (change from 0.80 to 1.07 in stability interaction equation) for the sway effects in this example is approximately 25% of the member capacity. It is this requirement for extra reserve strength which makes the W10x49 unsuitable in this situation. It should be noted that this method of dealing with sway effects does not make allowances for the extra moments induced in the girders of a structure.

7.11 Direct Compensation for Sway Effects

In Section 7.10 the traditional design procedure for beam columns was described. This procedure accounts, in an indirect manner, for the sway effects, but its use is restricted to moment resistant frames.[7.3] In addition, in the traditional procedure, the structure must be classified as sway prevented or sway permitted in the initial stage of design. One effect of this is that structures resisting sway effects partly by a bracing system and partly by frame action cannot be recognized. Nor can the traditional design approach properly accommodate structures in which stability for a series of interconnected frames is provided by a single frame.

In this section a direct technique will be developed, called the P∆ technique, which can be used to directly assess the sway effects. In essence, the technique consists simply of calculating the extra moments (or forces in a braced structure) induced in the structure by the vertical loads acting through the lateral displacements of the structure. Once these extra moments have been calculated and included in the design values, no need exists to "oversize" the columns in anticipation of resisting the uncalculated P∆ moments. In fact, the structure is "sway prevented" as far as the column design is concerned, since the full capacity of the column section may now be used to resist the design moments. Thus both the effective length factor and the equivalent moment factor may be based on the sway prevented model.[7.2, 7.13, 7.14]

Another way of looking at this technique is to consider the curves shown in Figure 7.16. The solid curves represent the maximum moment capacities for the simple unbraced column shown in the inset to the figure. The traditional design procedure (K based on the sway permitted model and ω = 0.85) results in the lower dashed line, representing the results of the stability interaction equation, which permits the designer to use only a portion of the strength of the column; the remainder is held in reserve to resist the moment caused by the sway effect. However, since in the PΔ method these additional moments are included in the design values the full capacity of the section may be used to resist the total moments. To accomplish this the effective length factor is computed on the sway prevented model and ω is given by Equation 7.12.

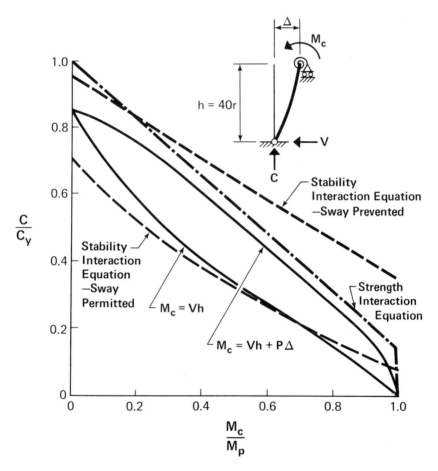

Figure 7.16
Interaction Relationships — Sway Permitted and Sway Prevented

The results of this procedure are reflected in the upper dashed line in Figure 7.16, which shows the stability interaction equation based on the sway prevented condition. The broken line in the figure represents the strength interaction equation. The envelope formed by these two lines reasonably predicts the full strength of the member.

Example 7.8

Given

A W10x49 member of G40.21 44W steel (F_y = 44 ksi) is subjected to an axial force of 350 kips and to end moments of 90 ft. kips and 60 ft. kips as shown in Figure 7.17. The member is prevented from lateral buckling. The sway effects (additional end moments) have been computed from an analysis of the structure and have been included in the above values. This accounts for the differences in end moments from those used in Example 7.6. Is the member adequate to resist the moments and force shown?

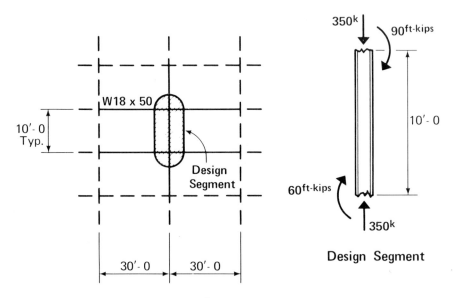

Figure 7.17
Loading Condition — Example 7.8

Solution

The W10x49 is a Class 2 section in G40.21 44W steel (the plate requirements were checked in Example 7.2) and thus the member will have adequate local strength provided it complies with Equation 7.2, the strength interaction equation.

The required cross-section properties for the W10x49 are listed in Appendix A:

$$A = 14.4 \text{ in.}^2 \qquad\qquad r_x = 4.35 \text{ in.}$$

$$Z_x = 60.3 \text{ in.}^3 \qquad\qquad I_x = 273 \text{ in.}^4$$

The bending moments are shown in Figure 7.17(b). The critical location for local bending is at the upper end of the column. At this location the axial load is C_f = 350 kips and the bending moment is M_f = 90 ft. kips.

178

The factored compressive resistance is:

$C_r = \phi A \, F_y = 0.90 \times 14.4 \times 44 = 570$ kips

and the factored moment resistance is calculated using Equation 6.7:

$M_r = \phi Z_x \, F_y = 0.90 \times 60.3 \times 44 = 2390$ inch kips

The strength interaction equation, Equation 7.2, then becomes:

$$\frac{C_f}{C_r} + 0.85 \frac{M_f}{M_r} \leqslant 1.0$$

$$\frac{350}{570} + \frac{0.85 \times 90 \times 12}{2390} \leqslant 1.0$$

$1.0 \leqslant 1.0$

The W10x49 is satisfactory with regard to local strength. The increased end moment caused by the $P\Delta$ effect, has increased the summation for the strength interaction equation above the value obtained in Example 7.7.

The overall capacity of the member must now be checked against the requirements of the stability interaction equation. The resistances have been computed previously in Example 7.6 as:

$M_r = 2390$ inch kips

$C_r = 552$ kips

$C_e = 9340$ kips

Note that the values of C_r and C_e have been calculated on the basis of the "sway prevented" effective lengths ($K = 0.77$, $\lambda = 0.26$) since the sway moments have been computed and added into the design values. This is in contrast to the procedures used in Example 7.7, which based the calculations on the "sway-permitted" effective length.

In keeping with the above, the equivalent moment factor is calculated using Equation 7.12:

$$\omega = 0.6 + 0.4 \frac{M_{f1}}{M_{f2}}$$

$$= 0.6 + 0.4 \left(\frac{-60}{90}\right) = 0.33$$

But ω can not be less than 0.4

Using the above quantities the stability interaction equation, Equation 7.11, may now be checked:

179

$$\frac{C_f}{C_r} + \frac{\omega \, M_f}{M_r \left(1 - \dfrac{C_f}{C_e}\right)} \leqslant 1.0$$

$$\frac{350}{552} + \frac{0.4 \times 90 \times 12}{2390 \left(1 - \dfrac{350}{9340}\right)} \leqslant 1.0$$

$$0.82 \leqslant 1.0$$

The W10x49 section is adequate for this situation by the procedures of the PΔ technique. By comparison with the results of Examples 7.6 and 7.7 it can be seen that the direct influence of the sway effects is to increase the end moments by approximately 10%. Thus the indirect allowance for the PΔ effect (approximately 25%, see Example 7.7) is conservative. Generally speaking the use of the PΔ technique will result in smaller column sections than will the use of the traditional design procedure. The PΔ technique is illustrated further in Chapter 11.

7.12 Summary

Members subjected to an axial force and to bending moments may reach their ultimate capacities either through attaining the ultimate strength of the cross-section or through inelastic instability. Empirical interaction equations are used in design to provide a consistent strength against failure by either mode.

The strength interaction equation checks the local moment capacity of the cross-section at a load or reaction point while the stability interaction equation attempts to assess the overall capacity of the member. In this latter equation, the stiffness of the member, the loading condition and the boundary conditions at the member ends are all considered.

In every structure, secondary (or sway) moments will be developed by the vertical loads acting on the laterally displaced structure. In many cases these sway effects are resisted by the frame action of the columns and girders. The interaction equations may be adjusted so that only a portion of the member capacity is used to resist the primary moments. The remaining capacity is assumed to be sufficient to resist the sway effects. Alternatively for this type of structure, and always for other types, the sway effects may be computed and included in the design moments. In this case the interaction equations are based on the sway prevented conditions.

The design of beam-columns is a time consuming task. Due to the many different factors which must be considered design aids in chart or table form are not generally effective. The Canadian Institute of Steel Construction, together with the Canadian Steel Industries Construction Council, has developed a computer program to assist in the design of such members. Details of the program, "CISC-CSICC Column Selection Program 3" are available from the Canadian Institute of Steel Construction.

180

Beam-column design is important for office buildings like CIL House, Montreal.

References

7.1 WRC-ASCE Joint Committee, "Plastic Design in Steel, A Guide and Commentary", 2nd Edition, American Society of Civil Engineers, New York, 1971.

7.2 Adams, P. F., "The Design of Steel Beam Columns", Canadian Steel Industries Construction Council, Willowdale, Ontario, 1974.

7.3 Canadian Standards Association, "CSA Standard S16.1-1974, Steel Structure for Buildings—Limit States Design", Canadian Standards Association, Rexdale, Ontario, 1974.

7.4 Perlynn, M. J., and Kulak, G. L., "Web Slenderness Limits for Compact Beam-Columns", Department of Civil Engineering, University of Alberta, Report No. 50, September 1974.

7.5 Nash, D. S., and Kulak, G. L., "Web Slenderness Limits for Non-Compact Beam-Columns", Department of Civil Engineering, University of Alberta, Report No. 53, March 1976.

7.6 McGuire, W., "Steel Structures", Prentice-Hall Inc., Englewood Cliffs, N.J., 1968.

7.7 "Handbook of Steel Construction", 2nd Edition, Canadian Institute of Steel Construction, Toronto, Ontario, 1976.

7.8 Galambos, T. V. and Ketter, R. L., "Columns Under Combined Bending and Thrust", Journal of the Engineering Mechanics Division, American Society of Civil Engineers, Vol. 85, EM2, April 1959.

7.9 Galambos, T. V., "Structural Members and Frames", Prentice-Hall, Inc., Englewood Cliffs, N.J., 1968.

7.10 Structural Stability Research Council, "Guide to Stability Design Criteria for Metal Structures", 3rd Edition, B. G. Johnston, Editor, John Wiley & Sons, New York, 1976.

7.11 "Limit States Design Steel Manual", Canadian Institute of Steel Construction, Toronto, Ontario, 1977.

7.12 Yura, J. A. and Galambos, T. V., "The Ultimate Strength of Single Storey Frames", Journal of the Structural Division, American Society of Civil Engineers, Vol. 91, ST5, October 1965.

7.13 Wood, B. R., Beaulieu, D. and Adams, P. F., "Column Design by P-Delta Method", Journal of the Structural Division, American Society of Civil Engineers, Vol. 102, ST2, February 1976.

7.14 Wood, B. R., Beaulieu, D. and Adams, P. F., "Further Aspects of Design by P-Delta Method", Journal of the Structural Division, American Society of Civil Engineers, Vol. 102, ST3, March 1976.

CHAPTER 8

COMPOSITE DESIGN

8.1 Introduction

A frequent type of construction in both buildings and bridges uses concrete slabs supported by steel beams. The slabs serve to transfer the floor or deck loads to the steel beams. These beams must carry the entire loading, including the dead load of the slab, by themselves. Since the beams and slabs deflect together and as the concrete slabs are normally adjacent to the compression side of the beam cross-section, it was logical to expect that some effort would be made to see if these two elements could be made to act together—a composite cross-section. In the usual situation, this can be accomplished by a mechanical connection between the slab and the steel beam. The resulting system can prove to be both structurally and economically advantageous.

Assuming that adequate interconnection between the slab and the beam can be provided, some of the resulting advantages of the composite cross-section are immediately apparent. The slab will be in compression, a condition particularly suitable for concrete. As the load is now carried by both the steel and the concrete, the size of the steel beam required will be less than that for the non-composite case. This means a reduction in steel weight, a direct cost saving, and usually a reduction of the overall depth of the beam and slab. This latter reduction may not be important in a low-rise building but it can provide significant savings in a multi-storey building, or in a highway overpass. Composite beams will be stiffer than non-composite beams of the same size and they will have better overload capacity. The principal disadvantage of the system is the additional cost of providing the connection between the slab and the beam. Except for short or lightly loaded spans, the saving provided by the reduction in beam size should be greater than the cost of the necessary connectors.

The principal force that must be transferred if the slab and beam are to act as a unit is the horizontal shear at the interface of these elements. This can be accomplished by attaching connectors to the top flange of the steel beam. These connectors will be imbedded in the concrete as the slab is poured and will bear against the hardened concrete when loads are applied. Figure 8.1(a) shows short lengths of channel attached by welding along the toe and heel. Three, four, or five-inch deep channels are commonly used. Adequate cover must be maintained between the top of the channel and the slab surface.

Figure 8.1(b) shows the attachment of welded studs to the beam flange. These are proprietary products, the principal feature being that a welding "gun" is used to simultaneously hold the stud in position and make a weld at its contact with the beam. Studs range in diameter from 1/2 inch to 7/8 inch and normally are about 3 inches long. Installation is rapid and can be done either in the shop or in the field. Studs are probably the most commonly used type of shear connector at the present time.

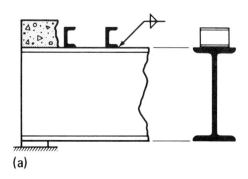

(a)

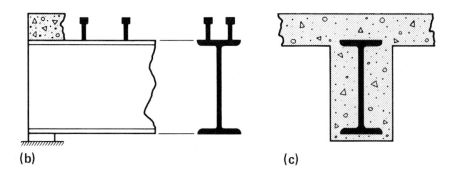

(b)   (c)

Figure 8.1
Methods of Attaining Composite Action

A different way of attaining composite action is shown in Figure 8.1(c). Here the steel beam is completely encased in concrete and the load transfer would be by bond between these elements. Although this arrangement does take care of the fireproofing of the steel that is required in many situations, the added dead load of the concrete around the beam is substantial. This system is not often used in modern building construction and will not be discussed here.

8.2 Effective Area of Concrete

In making strength calculations, the area of slab that may be considered tributary to each beam must be established. Theoretically, this will be a function of the span length, the shape of the moment diagram, and Poisson's ratio for the material. Based on these considerations and the results of tests, rules have evolved which provide a sufficiently accurate assessment. The requirements for buildings as given in CSA S16.1 (Clause 17.3.2) may be summarized as:

(a) For slabs extending on both sides of the steel beam the effective slab width is the least of

    i   One-fourth of the beam span
    ii   Sixteen times the slab thickness plus the flange width of the steel section
    iii Centre-to-centre distance of steel beams.

(b) For slabs extending only on one side of the steel beam the effective projection of the slab beyond the edge of the steel beam is the least of

    i   One-tenth of the beam span
    ii   Six times the slab thickness
    iii One-half the clear distance to the adjacent steel beam.

8.3 Influence of Construction Method

Until recently, the design of composite sections has been differentiated by the method of construction.[8.1] If the steel beams are shored (supported at close intervals) during the pouring of the slab and if the shores remain in place until the concrete has attained a reasonable amount of its 28-day strength (usually 75%), then the composite section is available to carry all loads upon removal of the shores. This apparently simple situation is complicated by the fact that the hardened concrete will tend to creep under the sustained action of long-term loads, however. The stresses due to these loads (usually, the dead loads) are thereby increased over their nominal value.

In the more common method of construction, the forms carrying the wet concrete are supported directly by the steel beam. The steel section alone must carry the loads imposed at this time. After the concrete has fully hardened, the composite cross-section is available to carry all subsequently imposed loads.

Despite the differences in these two methods, tests have shown that the ultimate load that can be carried by a given cross-section is independent of the method of construction.[8.2, 8.3] CSA Standard S16.1 assumes therefore that the total load is to be applied to the composite section, regardless of the method of construction. (The adequacy of the steel section under the dead load of the wet concrete plus formwork must be checked). In order to guard against yielding of the bottom flange of an unshored steel beam under the specified loads, a condition that would influence deflections, it is stipulated in Clause 17.6 of the Standard that the stresses in the tension flange of the steel section are not to exceed 0.90 F_y prior to hardening of the concrete. The loads to be considered are those applied both prior to hardening of the concrete and those applied after. Since this is a service requirement, the loads to be considered are the specified loads. In the form of an equation this can be expressed as:

$$\frac{M_1}{S_s} + \frac{M_2}{S_t} \leqslant 0.90\, F_y \tag{8.1}$$

where M_1 =   moment caused by the specified loads which act on the member prior to attainment of 75% of the required concrete strength.

         M_2 =   moment caused by the specified loads which act on the member subsequent to attainment of 75% of the required concrete strength.

         S_s =   elastic section modulus, referred to the bottom flange, of the steel section alone.

         S_t =   elastic section modulus, referred to the bottom flange, of the composite steel-concrete section.

In order to calculate the section modulus of the composite section (S_t), the designer must deal with the combination of the two different structural materials. This is accomplished by transforming the area of the concrete slab into an equivalent area of steel in the ratio of the modulii of elasticity of the two materials. This modular ratio ($n = E_s/E_c$) is usually prescribed in the applicable building code. It is customary to apply the reduction to the slab width rather than to its thickness or to some proportion of each.

Composite girders, used in a bridge.
(Photo courtesy Heavy Construction News)

8.4 Strength Calculations

The strength of a beam made of only one material must be evaluated on the basis of its shear and flexural capacities. In addition, a check is usually made of the deflection of the member acting under specified loads. All of these requirements apply equally to the composite beam and, in addition, the designer must ensure that the two parts act as a single unit.

In the case of steel beams, it was assumed that the beam web carried all of the vertical shear force. The same approach is appropriate for composite beams and, as outlined in Section 6.8, the shear resistance can therefore be expressed as:

$$V_r = \phi\, A_w\, F_s \tag{8.2}$$

where A_w = shear area (d x w for rolled steel shapes)

F_s = 0.66 F_y (except for deep members; see Section 9.4).

The flexural capacity of a composite beam is evaluated on the basis that the concrete does not resist tension. Two cases must be considered, one in which the neutral axis falls within the concrete slab and one in which it falls within the steel section. Which of the two possibilities is applicable must be determined by trial.

Neutral Axis in the Slab — The stress conditions for a cross-section in which the neutral axis lies in the slab are shown in Figure 8.2. In accordance with the ultimate strength evaluation of concrete,[8.4] the ultimate compressive stress in the concrete is taken as 0.85 F'_c, where F'_c is the 28-day compressive strength. The corresponding compressive force is

$$C'_r = \phi_c \times 0.85\; F'_c \times b \times a$$

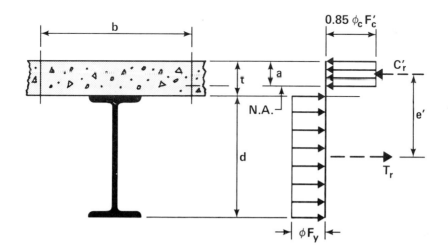

Figure 8.2
Composite Cross-Section — Neutral Axis in Slab

187

The dimensions b and a are shown in Figure 8.2. The performance factor for concrete, ϕ_c, is to be taken as 0.67.[8.3] Calling the cross-sectional area of the steel A_s, an equilibrium equation for horizontal forces can be written as:

$$0.85 \, \phi_c \, F'_c \, b \, a = \phi \, A_s \, F_y$$

Solving for the unknown quantity a;

$$a = \frac{\phi \, A_s \, F_y}{0.85 \, \phi_c \, F'_c \, b} \qquad (8.3)$$

If the calculated value of a is not equal to or less than the slab thickness (t), then the assumption that the neutral axis lies in the slab is not valid and the other alternative must be examined. If the neutral axis does lie in the slab, the ultimate moment resistance can now be evaluated as (S16.1 Clause 17.4.3(a));

$$M_{rc} = \phi \, A_s \, F_y \, e' \qquad (8.4)$$

Equation 8.4 is obtained by summing moments about the location of the resultant compressive force in the slab. The lever arm between the compressive and tensile forces (e') is shown in Figure 8.2. It can be calculated using the known value of a (Equation 8.3) and the cross-sectional dimensions t and d (Figure 8.2).

The shear connectors must transfer the total force at the interface of the concrete slab and the steel section. This is given by either the total compressive force, C'_r, or the total tensile force, T_r. Since they are equal, either can be used. For the situation shown in Figure 8.2, it is convenient to calculate the tensile force as representing the horizontal shear force to be transferred, V_h.

$$V_h = A_s \, F_y \qquad (8.5)$$

Note that Equation 8.5 does not include the performance factor ϕ since it would be unconservative here to use less than the maximum force that could be attained.

The proportioning and spacing of the shear connectors necessary to meet the requirements of the necessary shear transfer (Equation 8.5) will be discussed in Section 8.5.

Example 8.1

Given

Determine the flexural capacity of the cross-section shown in Figure 8.3. The effective slab width has been established as 85 in., the 28-day strength of the concrete is 3000 psi, and the steel is G40.21 44W.

188

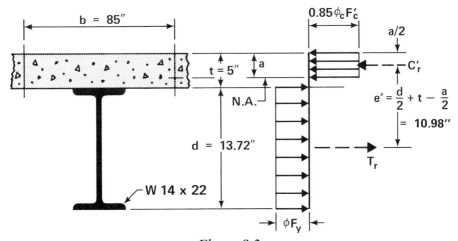

Figure 8.3
Composite Cross-Section — Example 8.1

Solution

From Appendix A, the cross-sectional area of a W14x22 is 6.49 in.² and its depth is 13.72 in. Assume that the neutral axis lies in the slab. Using Equation 8.3;

$$a = \frac{0.90 \times 6.49 \text{ in.}^2 \times 44 \text{ ksi}}{0.85 \times 0.67 \times 3 \text{ ksi} \times 85 \text{ in.}} = 1.77 \text{ in.}$$

Since this is less than the slab thickness of 5 in., the neutral axis does lie in the slab. As shown in Figure 8.3, the distance between the centroids of the two forces can now be determined. Using Equation 8.4, the flexural resistance of the cross-section is

$$M_{rc} = 0.90 \times 6.49 \text{ in.}^2 \times 44 \text{ ksi} \times 10.98 \text{ in.} = 2820 \text{ in.-kips}$$

Neutral Axis in the Steel Section — If the neutral axis lies in the steel section, the full depth of the concrete slab is in compression and the steel section is fully yielded in compression above the neutral axis and fully yielded in tension below the neutral axis. This condition is shown in Figure 8.4.

The location of the neutral axis can again be obtained by considering equilibrium of the horizontal forces. For this case,

$$T = C_r + C_r'   \hspace{3cm} (8.6)$$

where T =   the tensile force in the steel section below the neutral axis

C_r =   the compressive force in the steel section above the neutral axis

C_r' =   the compressive force in the concrete.

189

Another expression for the tensile force can be written:

$$T = \phi \, A_s \, F_y - C_r \tag{8.7}$$

Equations 8.6 and 8.7 can be used to solve for the value of the compressive force in the steel;

$$C_r = \frac{\phi \, A_s \, F_y - C_r'}{2} \tag{8.8}$$

Substituting for C_r' the value of $0.85 \, \phi_c \, F_c' \, bt$;

$$C_r = \frac{\phi \, A_s \, F_y - 0.85 \, \phi_c \, F_c' \, bt}{2} \tag{8.9}$$

Taking moments of forces about the centroid of the tensile force and using the moment arms shown in Figure 8.4, the flexural resistance of the cross-section is given by (S16.1 Clause 17.4.3);

$$M_{rc} = C_r \, e + C_r' \, e' \tag{8.10}$$

Whenever the neutral axis lies in the steel section, it is implicit that the steel section must accommodate plastic strains in both tension and compression. The section chosen should, therefore, be a Class 1 or Class 2 section in order that it is capable of developing its plastic moment capacity.

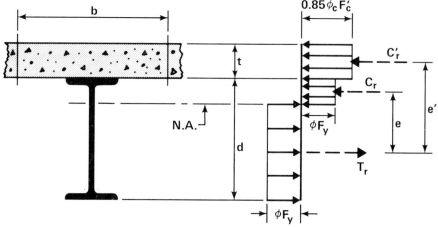

Figure 8.4
Composite Cross-Section — Neutral Axis in Steel Section

As was the situation when the neutral axis lay in the slab, the shear connectors must transfer the total force at the slab-steel section interface. When the neutral axis falls in the steel section, this is conveniently described using the compressive force above the interface, C_r'. Again, it is conservative to not include the performance factor. The requirement is therefore (S16.1 Clause 17.4.5);

$$V_h = 0.85 \, b \, t \, F_c' \tag{8.11}$$

Example 8.2

Given

Determine the flexural capacity of the cross-section shown in Figure 8.5. The effective slab width has been established as 72 in., the 28-day compressive strength of the concrete is 3000 psi, and the steel is G40.21 44W.

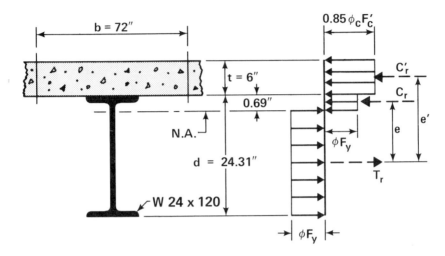

Figure 8.5
Composite Cross-Section — Example 8.2

Solution

From Table 7-3 in Appendix A, it is found that the W24x120 is a Group 2 section for which the yield point is 44 ksi. The cross-sectional properties needed are, from Appendix A:

$$A = 35.4 \text{ in.}^2, \quad d = 24.31 \text{ in.} \quad b = 12.09 \text{ in.}, \quad t = 0.93 \text{ in.}$$

Assume that the neutral axis is in the slab. Using Equation 8.3:

$$a = \frac{0.90 \times 35.4 \text{ in.}^2 \times 44 \text{ ksi}}{0.85 \times 0.67 \times 3 \text{ ksi} \times 72 \text{ in.}} = 11.4 \text{ in.}$$

Since this is greater than the slab thickness (6 in.), the neutral axis is not in the slab and the assumption was incorrect.

Since it is now established that the slab is entirely in compression, the resultant compressive force in the concrete can be calculated:

$$C_r' = 0.85 \times 0.67 \times 72 \text{ in.} \times 6 \text{ in.} \times 3 \text{ ksi} = 738 \text{ kips}$$

The compressive force in the steel (Equation 8.9) is therefore

$$C_r = \frac{0.90 \times 35.4 \text{ in.}^2 \times 44 \text{ ksi} - 738^k}{2} = 332 \text{ kips}$$

191

Assuming that the flange (or only a portion) of the W24x120 will be sufficient to carry this force, the depth of flange necessary is

$$d_f = \frac{332 \text{ kips}}{0.9 \text{ x } 44 \text{ ksi x } 12.09 \text{ in.}} = 0.69 \text{ in.}$$

Since this is less than the total flange thickness (0.93 in.), the assumption was correct. The centroid of the area below the neutral axis can be obtained by summing area moments about the bottom of the section as;

$$\bar{y} = \frac{35.4 \text{ in.}^2 \text{ x } 12.15 \text{ in.} - 0.69 \text{ in. x } 12.09 \text{ in. x } 23.96 \text{ in.}}{35.4 \text{ in.}^2 - 0.69 \text{ in. x } 12.09 \text{ in.}} = 8.51 \text{ in.}$$

and now, $e = 24.31 - 0.69/2 - 8.51 = 15.46$ in.

$$e' = 24.31 + 3 - 8.51 = 18.80 \text{ in.}$$

Finally, the resisting moment is

$$M_{rc} = (332 \text{ x } 15.46) + (738 \text{ x } 18.80) = 19000 \text{ in. kips}$$

A check will show that this section meets the local buckling requirements for a Class 2 section.

8.5 Shear Connectors

The strength of the shear connectors necessary to transmit the forces at the slab-steel section interface can be established from tests, for most commonly encountered situations, values based on test results are given in the Standard. For an end-welded stud with a height to diameter ratio of at least four, Clause 17.3.6(a) of the Standard specifies a factored shear resistance (q_r) as the lesser of:

$$q_r = 0.5 \, A_{sc} \sqrt{F'_c \, E_c} \tag{8.12}$$

or, $q_r = 65 \, A_{sc}$ (8.13)

In these equations, the results will be expressed in kips per stud with A_{sc} the cross-sectional area (in.^{2}) per stud, E_c the modulus of elasticity of concrete (ksi), and F'_c the 28-day compressive strength of the concrete (ksi).

The expression given in Equation 8.12 is based mainly on test results[8.5] and is valid for studs fully embedded in solid slabs of normal or lightweight concrete. It represents the stud capacity as achieved when the concrete adjacent to the stud fails by crushing. The same tests showed that if the stud itself failed, failure occurred only after considerable bending of the stud. Equation 8.13 is, therefore, an expression for the tensile capacity of the stud. It assumes that the stud steel has a minimum tensile strength of 65 ksi. If it is known that the steel of which the studs are made has a lower minimum tensile strength, Equation 8.13 should be adjusted accordingly.

The Standard also gives an expression for the strength of the less frequently used channel shear connector.

192

The required number of shear connectors, as established using the force to be transferred (Equation 8.5 to 8.11) and the prescribed resistance per connector (Equation 8.12 or 8.13), can be uniformly distributed between the point of maximum moment and an adjacent zero moment location. When concentrated loads are present, certain other restrictions are placed on the number of shear connectors (CSA S16.1 Clause 17.4.8).

Example 8.3

Given

The beam and column layout of a typical interior bay of an office building is shown in Figure 8.6. The beam B1 is to be designed as a composite steel-concrete member using G40.21 44W and concrete with a 28-day compressive strength of 3000 psi and a modulus of elasticity of 3.1×10^3 ksi. The section will not be shored during construction. Use a dead load factor (α_D) of 1.25 and a live load factor (α_L) of 1.50, as appropriate.

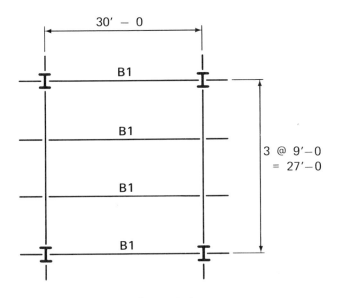

Figure 8.6
Beam and Girder Layout — Example 8.3

Solution

The superimposed specified loads are

Dead load:	5 in. concrete slab, forms	63 psf
	tile flooring	1
	hung ceiling, lights, etc.	2
	movable steel partitions	4
	Total	70 psf
Live Load (National Building Code)		50 psf

193

A trial section must be chosen and the capacity checked with respect to (a) strength of the steel section with regard to loads applied before the concrete hardens (b) strength of the composite section in flexure (c) shear capacity of the section (d) behaviour of the section under specified loads (e) proportioning of the shear connectors. Assuming simple support conditions and adequate lateral support, a suitable non-composite beam would be a W16x36. The composite section will be lighter and a W14x22 will be tried. This is a Class 2 section with F_y = 44 ksi for G40.21 44W steel. The cross-sectional properties that will be required are (from Appendix A):

A = 6.49 in.^{2} dw = 3.16 in.^{2} d = 13.72 in. b = 5.00 in.

S = 28.9 in.^{3} Z = 33.1 in.^{3} I = 198 in.^{4} r_t = 1.27 in.

d/A_f = 8.19 in.$^{-1}$

Design steel section to carry loads prior to hardening of concrete. Provide lateral bracing to the compression flange at L/5 = 72 in.

Load — slab + forms = 63 psf x load factor

$$= 63 \times 1.25 = 79 \text{ psf}$$

or, per foot of beam,

$$9 \text{ ft. x } 79 \text{ psf} = 711 \text{ lb./ft.}$$

plus estimated beam dead load

$$= 22 \text{ lb./ft. x } 1.25 = 28 \text{ lb./ft.}$$

Total factored load = 739 lb./ft.

$$M_f = \frac{0.739 \times 30^2}{8} = 83.1 \text{ ft. kips}$$

For the W14x22,

$$M_p = ZF_y = 33.1 \text{ in.}^3 \text{ x } 44 \text{ ksi x } \frac{1}{12} \text{ ft./in.} = 121 \text{ ft. kips}$$

$$M_u = S\sqrt{\sigma_1{}^2 + \sigma_2{}^2} \qquad \qquad \text{(Clause 13.6 of S16.1)}$$

$$\sigma_1 = \frac{20\,000}{Ld/A_f} = \frac{20\,000}{72 \times 8.19} = 33.9 \text{ ksi}$$

$$\sigma_2 = \frac{250\,000}{(L/r_t)^2} = \frac{250\,000}{(72/1.27)^2} = 77.8 \text{ ksi}$$

$$M_u = 28.9 \text{ in.}^3 \text{ x } 84.9 \text{ ksi x } \frac{1}{12} \text{ ft./in.} = 204 \text{ ft. kips}$$

Since $M_u > \dfrac{2}{3} M_p$,

$$M_r = 1.15\phi\, M_p\, (1 - \frac{0.28\, M_p}{M_u})$$

$$= 1.15 \times 0.90 \times 121\, (1 - \frac{0.28 \times 121}{204}) = 104 \text{ ft. kips}$$

or, $M_r = \phi\, M_p = 0.90 \times 121 = 109$ ft. kips.

Thus, the resistance of the section under these conditions is 104 ft. kips while the factored moment is 83.1 ft. kips. The W14x22 is satisfactory with respect to non-composite action.

Establish the capacity of the composite section—

Loads: Dead load factored

70 psf x 1.25 = 88 psf

Live load factored

50 psf x 1.5 = 75 psf

Total = 163 psf

or, per foot beam,

9 ft. x 163 psf = 1467 lb./ft.

plus factored beam dead load 27 lb./ft.

Total = 1494 lb./ft. = 1.49 kips/ft.

$$M_f = \frac{1.49 \times 30^2}{8} = 168 \text{ ft. kips}$$

Effective slab width of composite section—

i   1/4 x 30 ft. = 7.5 ft. = 90 in.

ii   (16 x 5 in.) + 5 in. = 85 in.   (Governs)

iii 9 ft. = 108 in.

This is the section used for Example 8.1. The calculations there gave

M_{rc} = 2820 in. kips = 235 ft. kips

The W14x22 is satisfactory when acting compositely with the concrete slab in resisting the total factored moment.

The capacity of the section in resisting the maximum vertical shear is (Equation 8.2)

$V_r = 0.90 \times 3.16 \text{ in.}^2 \times .66 \times 44 \text{ ksi} = 82.6 \text{ kips}$

The maximum factored shear is

$$V_f = 1.49 \text{ kips/ft. x } 30 \text{ ft. x } 1/2 = 22.4 \text{ kips} \qquad \text{(Satisfactory)}$$

Behaviour of the section under specified loads—Assume that the neutral axis for elastic conditions will lie in the steel and the slab will therefore be fully effective. Taking moments about the base of the steel beam,

Steel section: $A = 6.49 \text{ in.}^2$, $y = \dfrac{d}{2} = 6.86 \text{ in.}$, $Ay = 44.5 \text{ in.}^3$

Slab: $A = \dfrac{85}{9} \text{ x } 5.0 = 47.2 \text{ in.}^2$, $y = (13.72 + 2.50) = 16.22 \text{ in.}$, $Ay = 766 \text{ in.}^3$

(The modular ratio has been taken as 9).

$\Sigma A = 53.7 \text{ in.}^2 \qquad \Sigma Ay = 810 \text{ in.}^3$

$$\bar{y} = \frac{\Sigma Ay}{\Sigma A} = \frac{810}{53.7} = 15.08 \text{ in. } (> d = 13.72 \text{ in.})$$

Since the neutral axis does not fall below the slab, the assumption that the concrete is fully effective was incorrect. The location of a neutral axis which falls in the slab must be determined by trial. Assume here that the neutral axis is located 1.60 in. above the steel beam. Again taking moments about the base of the steel beam,

Steel section: $A = 6.49 \text{ in.}^2$, $y = 6.86 \text{ in.}$, $Ay = 44.5 \text{ in.}^3$

Slab: $A = \dfrac{85}{9} \text{x } 3.4 = 32.1 \text{ in.}^2$, $y = (13.72 + 1.60 + 1.70) = 17.02 \text{ in.}$, $Ay = 546 \text{ in.}^3$

$\Sigma A = 38.6 \qquad \Sigma Ay = 590$

$$\bar{y} = \frac{\Sigma Ay}{\Sigma A} = \frac{590}{38.6} = 15.28 \text{ in.}$$

or, 1.56 in. above the steel beam.

This will be taken as close enough agreement. Consider the location of the neutral axis to be 15.28 in. above the base of the steel beam. Calculating the moment of inertia,

Steel section: About own centre of gravity—	198 in.⁴
$+ 6.49 \text{ x } \left(\dfrac{13.72}{2} + 1.60\right)^2 =$	464
Slab: $\dfrac{1}{12} \text{x } \dfrac{85}{9} \text{ x } 3.40^3 =$	31
$\dfrac{85}{9} \text{ x } 3.40 \text{ x } 1.70^2$	93
	786 in.⁴

196

The section modulus, referred to the bottom flange, of the composite section is

$$S_t = \frac{786 \text{ in.}^4}{(13.72 + 1.60) \text{ in.}} = 51.3 \text{ in.}^3$$

The specified load acting prior to hardening of the concrete is:

slab + forms   63 psf

or, per foot beam,

9 ft. x 63 psf = 567 lb./ft.

plus estimated beam dead load 22 lb./ft.

Total = 589 lb./ft.

From which, $M_1 = \dfrac{0.589 \times 30^2}{8} = 66.3 \text{ ft. kips}$

The specified load acting subsequent to hardening of the concrete:

tile, ceiling, partitions, live load = 57 psf

or, per foot beam,

9 ft. x 57 psf = 513 lb./ft.

From which, $M_2 = \dfrac{0.513 \times 30^2}{8} = 57.7 \text{ ft. kips}$

Now, checking Equation 8.1,

$$\frac{M_1}{S_s} + \frac{M_2}{S_t} = \frac{66.3 \times 12}{28.9} + \frac{57.7 \times 12}{51.3} = 41.0 \text{ ksi}$$

The limit is 0.90 F_y or 39.6 ksi for 44 ksi yield steel. This section is underdesigned by about 1%. This will be considered satisfactory.

Shear Connectors—Try 1/2 in. diameter studs x 2-1/2 in. long. These will have adequate cover in the 5 in. slab and the ratio h/d is greater than 4. The cross-sectional area per stud is 0.20 in.^{2}. Checking Equation 8.12,

$q_r = 0.5 \times 0.20 \text{ in.}^2 \times \sqrt{3 \text{ ksi} \times 3.1 \times 10^3 \text{ ksi}} = 9.6 \text{ kips}$ (Governs)

Or, from Equation 8.13,

$q_r = 65 \text{ ksi} \times 0.20 \text{ in.}^2 = 13 \text{ kips}$

The load to be transferred (Equation 8.5) is

$V_n = 6.49 \text{ in.}^2 \times 44 \text{ ksi} = 286 \text{ kips}$

Number of connectors required between midspan and ends;

$$N = \frac{286}{9.6} = 30$$

(or 60 connectors in the total length of the beam).

Since the span is approximately 30 ft. (subject to the actual details of the beam-to-girder connection), the studs could be installed in pairs spaced every 12 in. The last pair of studs would be 6 in. from the intersection of the beam and girder.

The W14x22 that was used here is probably the lightest section that would be satisfactory. It represents a saving of 14 lb. per ft. over the least-weight non-composite section. If a reduction in depth were considered important, a 10 in. or 12 in. deep section could be investigated. The result would be a heavier section than the one used in the example.

Attachment of a coverplate on the bottom flange of the steel beam could be used to bring the neutral axis down below the level of the slab. This provides better utilization of the concrete and the resulting steel section. The steel weight would likely be less than the 22 lb. per foot obtained in the example but there would be an additional cost in attaching the coverplate. Economically, it would probably not be advantageous in a lightly loaded span such as this one.

The design of composite beams can be aided considerably by the use of the "Composite Beam-Trial Selection Tables" contained in Part 5 of the CISC Manual. Here, the necessary cross-sectional properties are tabulated for a wide range of steel shapes in combination with a 5 in. concrete slab. The tables are limited by the fact that they are restricted to the use of a 5 in. concrete slab with a 28-day specified strength of 3000 psi. In addition, the effective slab widths listed are derived from CSA S16.1 Clause 17.3.2 parts (b) and (c) but not (a). The latter is a restriction based on span length and it cannot conveniently be included in the tables.

8.6 Behaviour Under Negative Moment

Under the action of a negative bending moment the concrete slab in a composite section will be subjected to tension and is therefore considered ineffective. However, the steel reinforcement in the slab which runs parallel to the beam and which is within the effective slab width can be considered to carry a share of the negative moment, providing certain conditions are met. These are that shear connectors be provided in this region and that the reinforcement have adequate embedment in a zone of positive moment.[8.6] Theoretically, shear connectors should not be necessary in this region as the concrete is assumed to be cracked and ineffective. However, the short portions of uncracked concrete that inevitably will be present, if anchored to the steel beam, will serve to transfer load more gradually into the reinforcement than if the embedment length of the bars alone were expected to transfer load. This is illustrated in Figure 8.7.

198

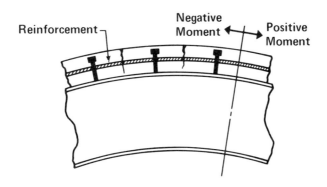

Figure 8.7
Behaviour Under Negative Moment

If the conditions described above are met, an ultimate strength analysis can be applied to the cross-section. Assuming that the neutral axis will fall somewhere in the steel beam, the ultimate capacity can be calculated by considering the reinforcing bars acting in tension, a portion of the steel beam also acting in tension, and the remainder of the steel beam acting in compression. It should be noted that in the usual situation more of the beam cross-section will be in compression than in a non-composite steel beam. The buckling tendency is therefore increased (both local and lateral buckling) and the rotation capacity is also likely to be reduced.

In parallel with the ultimate strength considerations used to proportion the shear connectors in a positive moment region, a similar approach is taken here. A conservative estimate of the number required is obtained by considering that there must be sufficient shear connectors to produce yielding in the longitudinal slab reinforcement. In CSA S16.1, this requirement is expressed as (Clause 17.4.7);

$$V_h = A_r F_{yr} \qquad (8.14)$$

where A_r =   area of longitudinal reinforcement contained within the effective slab width

           F_{yr} =   minimum specified yield strength of the longitudinal reinforcing steel.

The number of shear connectors required between any maximum negative moment and an adjacent zero moment location can now be determined.

8.7 Deflections

The calculation of the deflection of a composite beam under the specified loads is complicated by the fact that, under long-term loads, the concrete will tend to creep. Deflections are therefore greater than those predicted using conventional analysis. The Standard suggests that, unless test results or a more exact analysis are available the calculated deflection produced by long-term loads be increased by 15 percent to account for the influence of creep. The deflection of a composite beam can then be calculated as the sum of:

1. Deflection due to loads applied before composite action is attained (steel beam alone is effective).

2. Deflection due to short-term loads applied to the composite section.

3. Deflection due to long-term loads applied to the composite section with the 15% upward adjustment applied to this deflection.

Finally, the designer should be alert to recognize situations in which the effect of shear upon the deflections is significant. As pointed out earlier, only the web of the steel section is considered effective in resisting shear. This capacity is generally reduced below that which would have been provided for a non-composite beam. If loads are high or spans are short, the contribution of shear to the total deflection may be important.

Example 8.4

Given

Calculate the deflection of the composite beam designed in Example 8.3.

Solution

All deflections will be calculated on the basis that the beam acts as a simple span. The completed beam, particularly after composite action has been obtained, will be stiffer than this assumption would indicate.

Non-composite beam: the steel beam acts alone to carry the slab load, formwork, plus its own dead weight. This is

$$63 \text{ psf x 9 ft.} \qquad = 567 \text{ lb./ft.}$$

$$\text{plus beam dead load} \quad = \underline{22 \text{ lb./ft.}}$$

$$\text{Total} \qquad \qquad 589 \text{ lb./ft.}$$

Therefore,

$$\Delta_1 = \frac{5}{384} \frac{wL^4}{EI} = \frac{5}{384} \times \frac{0.589 \text{ x } (30 \text{ x } 12)^4}{30 \text{ x } 10^3 \text{ x } 198} \times \frac{1}{12} = 1.83 \text{ in.}$$

Composite beam, short-term loads: it will be assumed that half the specified live load acts on a long-term basis and half on a short-term basis. Since the total live load was 50 psf, the short-term load per foot of the beam is

$$9 \text{ ft. x 25 psf} = 225 \text{ lb./ft.}$$

The corresponding deflection, using the moment of inertia of the composite section calculated in Example 8.3, is

$$\Delta_2 = \frac{5}{384} \times \frac{0.225 \text{ x } (30 \text{ x } 12)^4}{30 \text{ x } 10^3 \text{ x } 786} \times \frac{1}{12} = 0.17 \text{ in.}$$

200

Composite beam, long-term loads: The assumed long-term load has been established as 25 psf. To this must be added the weight of the tile, hung ceiling, lights, and partitions as listed in Example 8.3. These add up to 7 psf so that the long-term load per foot of beam is

$(25 + 7)$ psf x 9 ft. = 288 lb./ft.

The deflection due to this load acting on the composite section, and including the 15 percent allowance for long-term load effect, is

$$\Delta_3 = 1.15 \text{ x } \frac{5}{384} \text{ x } \frac{0.288 \text{ x } (30 \text{ x } 12)^4}{30 \text{ x } 10^3 \text{ x } 786} \text{ x } \frac{1}{12} = 0.26 \text{ in.}$$

The total deflection is therefore $1.83 + 0.17 + 0.26 = 2.26$ in. At least the major part of this would have to be accounted for in the construction of the beam. This could be handled by

1. Cambering of the steel beam.

2. Control of the slab thickness.

3. Shoring of the steel beam at the time of placing of the concrete.

If the latter control were used, the deflections on the non-composite section could be substantially reduced. At the same time, the amount of long-term load would be increased and the calculation of deflection for this effect adjusted accordingly.

8.8 Miscellaneous Considerations

Extra Slab Steel—Only rarely will the assumption of a simply-supported condition be met exactly for beams. The details of the end supports almost always provide a certain amount of restraint. The presence of the concrete slab in the composite section will accentuate this tendency. For example, the concrete slab in Figure 8.6 will probably be cast continuously over the girders. This will then be a region of unintentional negative moment and the concrete will tend to develop undesirable cracks at the top surface. Extra reinforcing should be placed near the top of the slab in such locations so that this cracking will be minimized.

It is also observed that longitudinal cracking may occur in the slab directly over the steel section. This results from the longitudinal shear forces acting at the slab-steel section interface. It can be controlled by providing additional reinforcement placed in the lower portion of the slab and transverse to the length of the beam. Clause 17.3.3 of the Standard should be consulted for details.

Partial Composite Action—Complete composite action is not always needed and it may be economically desirable to provide fewer than the number of shear connectors required for complete interaction.[8.7] The Standard indicates that the situation is acceptable as long as the designer provides at least one-half of the theoretical number of shear connectors required for full composite action (Clause 17.4.4). Starting from the basis that the horizontal shear force transferred (V_h) will be equal to the total capacity of the shear connectors actually provided ($\phi_c Q_r$) between points of maximum and zero moment, the flexural capacity of the cross-section can again be calculated using Equation 8.10. The compressive force C_r is defined by Equation 8.8 with

$$C'_r = \phi_c Q_r \tag{8.15}$$

$$\text{and} \quad a = \frac{C'_r}{0.85\ \phi\ F'_c\ b} \tag{8.16}$$

Composite Beams Employing Sheet Steel Forms—One of the most important recent developments in the design of economically framed steel buildings has been the development of design rules which enable slabs cast on sheet steel forms to be considered as acting compositely with the steel beam.[8.8] These sheet steel forms may be flat but usually contain at least small corrugations, as shown in Figure 8.8, to increase the bending strength. The form supports the weight of the wet concrete between beams and provides a working platform during construction. Stud shear connectors are used in this situation. The CSA S16.1 Standard places limits on the thickness of the sheet steel so that the studs can be successfully welded through to the beam (Clause 17.3.5.3).

An equally common form is that shown in Figure 8.9. In effect, the corrugations have been increased and they are now termed ribs. The sheet steel "form" is usually now referred to as a "deck". The greater bending stiffness of the deck means that a larger beam spacing can be permitted for a given sheet metal thickness. As shown in Figure 8.9, voids are formed by the ribs. Often these can be advantageously used as telephone and power conduits.

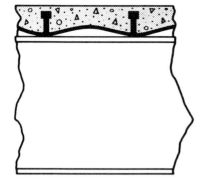

Figure 8.8
Composite Beam Using
Sheet Steel Forms

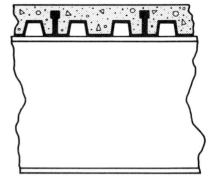

Figure 8.9
Composite Beam Using
Cellular Steel Decking

The method of design of composite sections made using sheet steel forms or metal decking proceeds as outlined for the more general case. The CSA S16.1 Standard places limits on the sheet steel thickness and the height and spacing of the corrugations or ribs. Within the limits of these requirements, the effective depth of the slab is taken as the distance from the top of the highest corrugation to the top of the slab. Stud connector capacities are also given in the Standard for the case when sheet steel forms are used (Clause 17.3.6). The CISC Manual provides extensive tables for determination of the properties of composite beams which use metal decking.

References

8.1 Viest, I. M., Fountain, R. S., and Singleton, R. C., "Composite Construction in Steel and Concrete", McGraw-Hill, New York, 1958.

8.2 "Tentative Recommendations for the Design and Construction of Composite Beams and Girders and Buildings", Progress Report of the Joint ASCE-ACI Committee on Composite Construction, Journal of the Structural Division, ASCE, Vol. 85, No. ST12, December, 1960.

8.3 Slutter, R. G., and Driscoll, G. C. Jr., "Ultimate Strength of Composite Members", Conference on Composite Design in Steel and Concrete for Bridges and Buildings Proceedings, ASCE, Pittsburgh, 1962.

8.4 Canadian Standards Association, "Concrete Materials and Methods of Construction", CSA A23.1-1973, Rexdale, Ontario.

8.5 Ollgaard, J. G., Slutter, R. G., and Fisher, J. W., "Shear Strength of Stud Connectors in Lightweight and Normal-Weight Concrete", AISC Engineering Journal, April, 1971.

8.6 Davison, J. H., and Longworth, J., "Composite Beams in Negative Bending", Structural Engineering Report No. 7, Department of Civil Engineering, University of Alberta, May, 1969.

8.7 Slutter, R. G., and Driscoll, G. C. Jr., "Flexural Strength of Steel-Concrete Composite Beams", Journal of the Structural Division, ASCE, Vol. 91, No. ST2, April, 1965.

8.8 Fisher, J. W., "Design of Composite Beams with Formed Metal Deck", Engineering Journal, AISC, Vol. 7, No. 3, July, 1970.

CHAPTER 9

PLATE GIRDERS

9.1 Introduction

The fundamental concepts which were developed in Chapter 6 to describe the behaviour of beams are equally applicable to plate girders. A plate girder is generally defined as a built-up flexural member having a slender web. It is particularly the presence of the slender web that requires further attention when designing a plate girder.

Plate girders are used extensively in modern bridges.

Members which carry loads acting perpendicular to their longitudinal axis are generally most efficient when the largest proportion of the cross-section is placed at the extremities, that is, in the flanges. As spans and/or loads increase, the distance between flanges should be increased for economical placement of material within the cross-section. When the range of rolled shapes has been exceeded, the designer turns to the built-up shapes that will be discussed in this Chapter. These, in turn, give way to trusses as the economical depth of the plate girders is exceeded. Plate girders have generally found their greatest application in spanning distances in the order of 80 to 150 feet. Modern fabrication methods have increased the upper limit considerably, however, and in bridges plate girders exceeding 400 feet are not uncommon.

In the past, the most economical built-up sections were generally those with webs so thin that they had to be stiffened at intervals. Current fabrication costs, however, indicate that relatively thicker webs, unstiffened, may be more economical. A cost evaluation will be necessary in order to decide which type to use. In the case of the stiffened web, the stiffening elements will most often be placed transversely to the length of the girder but longitudinal stiffeners may also be used. Highway bridges often use transverse stiffeners on one side of a plate girder web and a longitudinal stiffener on the other. Such an arrangement is shown in Figure 9.1.

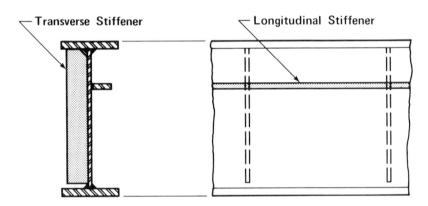

Figure 9.1
Plate Girder with Longitudinal and Transverse Stiffeners

Present-day fabrication of plate girders will almost always be done by welding, although field splices are usually made with high-strength bolts. As well as providing economic advantages, the welded girder is less cluttered and is more pleasing in appearance than one made using bolts or rivets. It is also relatively easy in welded construction to make cross-sectional or material property changes with length as the strength requirements vary. Both of these techniques are used extensively in plate girder design.

The discussion of the design requirements for plate girders will proceed in accordance with the requirements set forth in CSA Standard S16.1-1974, Steel Structures for Buildings—Limit States Design. The standard governing highway bridge design (CSA S6-1966) follows the underlying principles developed here but differs in detail. Attention will be focused on I-shaped girders although other configurations are often used. In particular, box girders are frequently used in highway bridges.

9.2 Preliminary Proportioning

The selection of the most economical girder depends on a number of variables but it will be principally a function of the weight of steel used and the amount of fabrication. A preliminary estimate of an economical girder depth can be made on the basis of the optimum depth for resisting moment. Adapting a suggestion made for working stress design;[9.1]

$$h \simeq 5.4 \left(\frac{M_f}{F_y} \right)^{1/3}$$
(9.1)

where   h = optimum web depth, inches

   M_f = maximum factored moment, inch kips

   F = yield stress, ksi

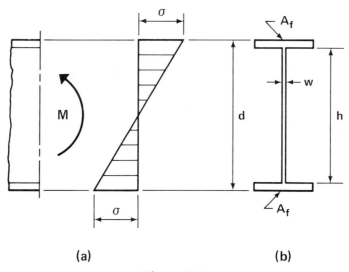

(a)   (b)

Figure 9.2
Plate Girder Notation

Whether Equation 9.1 is used at the starting point or whether some architectural, clearance, deflection, or other criterion is used, the choice of a girder depth means that an approximate flange size can be chosen. If it is assumed that the flange material will be able to reach yield, that the contribution of the web to bending resistance can be neglected, and that lateral-torsional buckling will not govern the design, then a preliminary flange size can be obtained from

$$A_f = \frac{M_f}{F_y h}$$
(9.2)

(Equation 9.2 also assumes that the flange areas are concentrated at the top and bottom of the web. For plate girders, the differences between the overall

207

depth d, the web height h, and the distance between the flange centroids are not large.)

As was explained in Chapter 6, the designer must examine whether the section is a Class 1, 2, 3, or 4 cross-section and evaluate conditions of lateral support for the compression flange. Because of the slender web, it will be seen that plate girder cross-sections will almost always fall in the Class 3 category. Also, it will generally be advantageous to provide lateral support at intervals close enough that lateral-torsional buckling will not govern the design. Equation 9.2 therefore, gives a reasonable starting point for choosing a preliminary flange size.

The flange selected should meet the plate slenderness requirements (b/t) outlined in Chapter 6.

Once a trial web depth has been established, an assumption that the web carries all the shear (as in rolled shapes) will enable the web thickness, w, to be established from the expression

$$A_w = \frac{V_f}{\phi F_s} = w\,h \tag{9.3}$$

As will be discussed in Section 9.4, the ultimate shear strength, F_s, is a function of web slenderness and of whether or not transverse stiffeners are present. If stiffeners are used, F_s also depends upon the ratio of the stiffener spacing to web depth. In either case, stiffened or unstiffened, the maximum shear strength (CSA S16.1) will be 0.66 F_y and the maximum web slenderness for statically loaded girders (corresponding to a minimum shear stress) is 12,000/F_y. Although the range of shear strength is rather large for unstiffened girders, there is less variation for stiffened girders. For example, the shear strength will be between 29.0 ksi and 16.9 ksi for stiffened girders of 44 ksi yield steel in which the stiffener spacing is equal to the girder depth. As a first approximation, a value of F_s for use in Equation 9.3 can be obtained by considering the upper limit of web slenderness, that is, h/w ⩽ 12,000/F_y, and an assumed stiffener spacing in the range of one to two times the girder depth. The CISC Manual tabulates the product ϕF_s for various steel grades as a function of web slenderness and stiffener spacing. Other considerations, such as the minimum thickness of web required for corrosion protection, must also be included when establishing preliminary proportions for the web. All these aspects are illustrated in the Design Example, Section 9.8.

9.3 Design of Cross-Section for Bending

Having chosen preliminary dimensions for the web and flanges, the section must then be checked to see whether the flexural capacity of the cross-section is equal to or greater than the factored moment. Since failure can be either by buckling or by yielding, both of these possibilities must be examined.

Web Buckling under Pure Flexure—The application of a bending moment to the cross-section will, according to conventional beam theory, give a distribution of stress under working loads such as shown in Figure 9.2(a). The thin web is relatively unstable, however, and will also have an initial out-of-flatness. Consequently, it is to be expected that at higher loads the web will not resist the stresses indicated but will throw off some of its load onto the stiffer flange.[9.2] Thus, the web will be less effective than expected and the flange will receive a higher stress than that calculated using ordinary beam theory. Tests have verified this intuitive concept and qualitative results are shown in Figure 9.3.

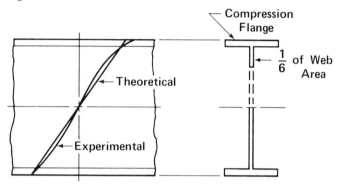

Figure 9.3
Theoretical and Experimental Distribution of Bending Stress

The effect of the "soft" web upon the load-carrying capacity of the flange is treated by simply considering a portion of the web on the compression side to be ineffective. In accordance with the development of the resistance of the compression flange of a beam (Section 6.10), the cross-section effective in resisting lateral or lateral-torsional buckling is taken as the flange plus one-sixth of the web area adjacent to the flange.

In treating the problem of the increased stress in the flange as a result of unloading of the web, it is assumed that the maximum moment that can be carried is that corresponding to the yield moment, M_y. The thin web will not permit the attainment of the theoretical plastic moment of the section. A linear reduction to this maximum attainable value is then applied. It is a function of the web slenderness, the relative proportions of the flange and web, and the buckling load of the web (including the restraint provided to the web by the flanges). The requirement specified by CSA S16.1 is (Clause 15.3)

$$M_r' = M_r \left[1.0 - 0.0005 \frac{A_w}{A_f} \left(\frac{h}{w} - \frac{690}{\sqrt{M_r/\phi S}} \right) \right] \qquad (9.4)$$

where M_r' = reduced factored moment resistance

   M_r = basic factored moment resistance (not to exceed ϕM_y)

   h = web depth, in.

w = web thickness, in.

A_w = web area, in.^{2}

A_f = compression flange area, in.^{2}

In most cases, the reduction in moment resistance will not be large and there will be no reduction for web slenderness values less than $690/\sqrt{M_r/\phi S'}$. For a girder made of steel with 44 ksi yield and for a Class 3 cross-section, this corresponds to a web slenderness (h/w) of 104, for example.

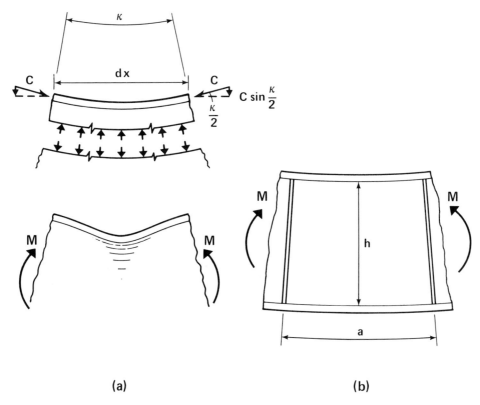

(a)   (b)

Figure 9.4
Vertical Buckling of Web

Vertical Buckling of Web—As the curvature which accompanies bending occurs, a vertical force is transmitted from the flanges into the web. Conditions on the compression side of the girder are illustrated in Figure 9.4. A similar situation exists on the tension side but as no possibility of buckling will be present there, only the condition shown needs to be examined. The applied force is

$$F = C \sin\frac{\kappa}{2} \simeq A_f \sigma_f \frac{\kappa}{2}$$

where the stress and area terms are those related to the compression flange.

210

Using $\dfrac{\kappa}{2} = \dfrac{\epsilon_f dx}{h/2}$, we obtain

$$F = 2A_f\, \sigma_f\, \epsilon_f\, \frac{dx}{h}$$

The resisting force of the web will be the web area (w dx) times the Euler buckling stress of this element. The buckling equations for plates take the same general form as those developed in Chapter 4 for long columns. In terms of load, the expression was

$$P_{cr} = \frac{\pi^2\, EI}{(KL)^2}$$

or, in terms of stress

$$\sigma_{cr} = \frac{\pi^2\, E}{\left(\dfrac{KL}{r}\right)^2}$$

The term K was a factor introduced in Chapter 5 to permit the equations to be applied to columns with various end conditions. The equation for critical stress can be rewritten as

$$\sigma_{cr} = k\, \frac{\pi^2\, E}{\left(\dfrac{L}{r}\right)^2}$$

where $k = (1/K)^2$

If a thin plate of thickness w and a height h which is large compared to its width b is subjected to a compressive force (Figure 9.5), the buckling stress is given by

$$\sigma_{cr} = k\, \frac{\pi^2\, E}{(1-\nu^2)\,(b/r)^2}$$

The inclusion of Poisson's ratio, ν, takes into account that, unlike column buckling, two-way action is occurring here. The radius of gyration is $r = w/\sqrt{12}$. Upon substitution, this gives

$$\sigma_{cr} = k\, \frac{\pi^2\, E}{12(1-\nu^2)\left(\dfrac{b}{w}\right)^2}$$

The value of k is determined by the longitudinal boundary conditions and the ratio a/h. If the dimensions are such that $a \geqslant h$, as would be expected in the constant moment region pictured in Figure 9.4(b), the expression becomes

$$\sigma_{cr} = k \frac{\pi^2 E}{12(1-\nu^2)\left(\dfrac{h}{w}\right)^2} \tag{9.5}$$

For this case, k can conservatively be taken as unity.

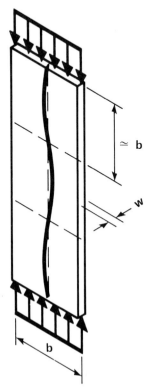

Figure 9.5
Plate Buckling

The resisting force of the web subjected to the compressive load pictured in Figure 9.4 will be equal to the web area (w dx) times the buckling stress given by Equation 9.5. Equating the applied and resisting forces,

$$2A_f \sigma_f \epsilon_f \frac{dx}{h} = \left(\frac{\pi^2 E}{12(1-\nu^2)\left(\dfrac{h}{w}\right)^2}\right) w\, dx$$

or,

$$\frac{h}{w} = \sqrt{\frac{\pi^2 E}{12(1-\nu^2)} \frac{A_w}{A_f} \frac{1}{2\,\sigma_f \epsilon_f}} \quad , \text{ where } A_w = wh$$

In order to provide a design requirement, this expression will be put in terms of an inequality and two assumptions will be made:

212

(1) Residual Stresses are distributed linearly, as shown in Figure 4.5(a). Thus, $\epsilon_f = (\sigma_y + \sigma_r)/E$.

_(2) The limit of web area to compression flange area will be taken as 0.5. This will generally give conservative results for plate girders but some welded wide flange shapes with relatively high web slenderness have web to flange area ratios of almost unity[9.3]

It is also noted that the stress in the compression flange, σ_f, should reach σ_y before buckling occurs. Making these substitutions and using a value of 0.3 for Poisson's ratio;

$$\frac{h}{w} \leqslant \frac{0.48\ E}{\sqrt{\sigma_y(\sigma_y + \sigma_r)}}, \tag{9.6}$$

Considering the residual stress to be approximately one-third of the yield stress, using the notation F_y and using $E = 29 \times 10^3$ ksi, Equation 9.6 becomes

$$\frac{h}{w} \leqslant \frac{12,000}{F_y} \tag{9.7}$$

where F_y is expressed in units of ksi. This is the requirement given by the Standard in Clause 13.4.3 as the maximum permissible web slenderness.

9.4 Design of Cross-Section for Shear

While bending can be present unaccompanied by shear, a transversely loaded beam will always have shear combined with moment. In regions where shear predominates, it can be considered to act alone, however.[9.4] The resulting behaviour will be that discussed in this section. Regions in which both shear and moment are present in significant amounts will have to be examined for the resulting interaction. This will be treated in Section 9.6.

Unstiffened Girder Webs—One limit of usefulness of an unstiffened girder web acting primarily under shear is given by the stress corresponding to the buckling condition. The general expression for this case takes a form similar to Equation 9.5. (As shown in Figure 9.6, pure shear on an element is equivalent to tension and compression on adjacent faces at 45°.) Using the notation of Figure 9.5,

$$\tau_{cr} = k\ \frac{\pi^2 E}{12(1-\nu^2)\left(\dfrac{b}{w}\right)^2} \tag{9.8}$$

For $a/b \geqslant 1.0$ and simply supported edges, it is found that

$$k = 5.34 + \frac{4.0}{(a/b)^2}$$

213

and for fixed edges

$$k = 8.98 + \frac{5.6}{(a/b)^2}$$

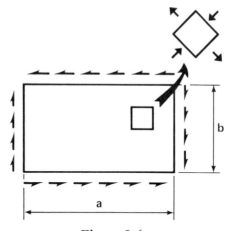

Figure 9.6
Web Subject to Pure Shear

Considering an unstiffened web to have an aspect ratio (a/b) of infinity and assuming simply supported edges, a girder "h" deep will have

$$\tau_{cr} = \frac{140,000}{\left(\dfrac{h}{w}\right)^2} \tag{9.9}$$

This is the requirement given in Clause 13.4.1(d) of the Standard (where the symbol F_s is used instead of τ_{cr}) for a/h = ∞, that is, for unstiffened webs.

The other limit for this case of the unstiffened web will be that corresponding to the load which will cause shear yielding. As indicated in Chapter 6, this will occur at a stress approximately equal to $F_y/\sqrt{3}$. Considering the beneficial effects of strain-hardening, the Standard permits a somewhat higher value and specifies the ultimate shear stress as

$$F_s = 0.66 \, F_y \tag{9.10}$$

The ultimate shear stresses for unstiffened girder webs as given by Equations 9.9 and 9.10 are shown in Figure 9.7. Principally because of the presence of residual stresses, it is to be expected that one curve cannot be directly run into the other. A transition curve between the two limiting cases, chosen mainly on the basis of test results, is shown on the figure. It is given by (CSA S16.1 Clause 13.4.1),

$$F_s = \frac{254\sqrt{F_y}}{\dfrac{h}{w}} \tag{9.11}$$

With the ultimate shear stress now established as that given by Equation 9.9, 9.10, or 9.11, the capacity of the section can be calculated as:

$$V_r = \phi \, A_w \, F_s \tag{9.12}$$

where A_w is the shear area. This would customarily be taken as the product of the total depth of the section times the web thickness for rolled shapes (dw) and the product of the web depth times the web thickness for built-up sections (hw).

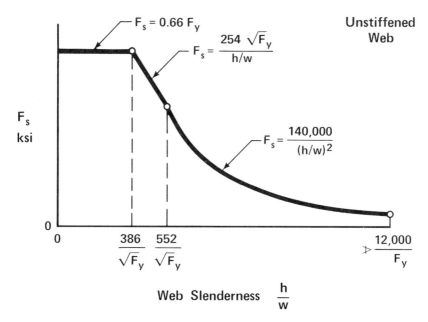

Figure 9.7
Web Shear Strength — Unstiffened Web

Stiffened Girder Webs—The upper limit of the strength of a girder web stiffened by vertical supports will be the same as that of the unstiffened girder, that is, the strength corresponding to shear yielding. Thus, one expression for ultimate shear stress in stiffened girders is the same as that given by Equation 9.10.

Buckling of the stiffened web may precede yielding, however, just as was the case in unstiffened girders. It is found here that significant additional amounts of shear past the theoretical buckling load can be carried.[9.5] Figure 9.8(a) shows a portion of a stiffened plate girder and Figure 9.8(b) shows the shear forces acting on an element in the panel. Another orientation of the element (Figure 9.8(c)) shows the compressive force that develops in the one direction and the tensile force in the other. It is this tensile component, analogous to the force in the diagonal members of a Pratt truss, that enables the girder web to carry additional shear past the point of theoretical buckling. It is referred to as tension field action and it is assumed that the corresponding contribution to the shear capacity (V_t) will be additive to the

215

shear capacity as supplied by normal beam action (V_b). The latter is simply that capacity attained at the point of theoretical web buckling –

$$V_b = \sigma_{cr} \, h \, w \tag{9.13}$$

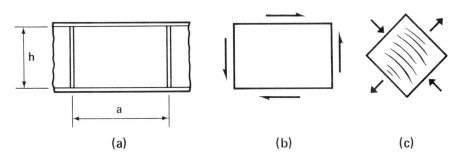

(a)   **(b)**   **(c)**

Figure 9.8
Stiffened Plate Girder Web

A necessary requirement for the additional contribution provided by the tension field action is the presence of the vertical stiffeners. They are necessary in order that the vertical components of the inclined web forces have a reaction point.

The tension field will develop only through a strip of the web, as shown in Figure 9.9(a). Using the notation shown in that figure, the vertical component of the force developed by the tension field can be described as

$$V_t = \sigma_t \, w \, (h \, \cos\theta - a \, \sin\theta) \, \sin\theta \tag{9.14}$$

It is reasonable to expect that the direction of the tension field will assume the most efficient orientation. Differentiating Equation 9.14 and setting it equal to zero gives the optimum angle as

$$\theta = \tan^{-1}\left(\sqrt{1 + (a/h)^2} - a/h\right) \tag{9.15}$$

Another expression for the shear due to the tension field action can be obtained by applying the equations of equilibrium to the free-body diagram shown in Figure 9.9(b). Using this and the result obtained in Equation 9.15 gives

$$V_t = \sigma_t \, w \, h \, \frac{1}{2\sqrt{1 + (a/h)^2}} \tag{9.16}$$

The total shear force that can be carried can now be written as

$$V_u = V_b + V_t = \sigma_{cr} \, h \, w + \sigma_t \, \frac{h \, w}{2} \, \frac{1}{\sqrt{1 + (a/h)^2}} \tag{9.17}$$

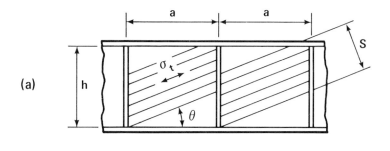

(a)

(b)

Figure 9.9
Web Tension Field

The criterion of failure will again be established as the yield condition. For any element subjected to pure shear, pure tension, or any combination, this can be approximated by a linear relationship. It also will be assumed, with only small error, that the result will be applied for $\theta = 45°$, rather than the actual angle of inclination of the tension field. The yield condition, as described, is;

$$\frac{\sigma_t}{\sigma_y} = 1 - \frac{\tau_{cr}}{\tau_y} \tag{9.18}$$

Now, Equation 9.17 can be written:

$$V_u = \sigma_{cr} \, h \, w + \frac{\sigma_y \, h \, w}{2\sqrt{1 + (a/h)^2}} - \frac{\tau_{cr} \, \sigma_y}{\tau_y} \frac{h \, w}{2} \sqrt{1 + (a/h)^2} \tag{9.19}$$

The value of τ_{cr} is given by Equation 9.8. Using the notation associated with plate girders (Figure 9.8), this can be rewritten as

$$\tau_{cr} = k_v \frac{\pi^2 E}{12(1-\nu^2)\left(\dfrac{h}{w}\right)^2} \tag{9.20}$$

where $k_v = 5.34 + \dfrac{4.0}{(a/h)^2}$ when $a/h > 1$

$\qquad k_v = 4.0 + \dfrac{5.34}{(a/h)^2}$ when $a/h < 1$

217

Similarly, σ_{cr} can be obtained from Equation 9.5. As before, the shear yield stress is taken as $\sigma_y/\sqrt{3}$, $E = 29 \times 10^3$ ksi, and $\nu = 0.30$. Using these values and dividing by the web area (h x w), an expression for the ultimate shear stress in ksi can be obtained from Equations 9.5, 9.19 and 9.20 as

$$F_s = \frac{26,200\,k_v}{(h/w)^2} + \frac{0.50\,F_y}{\sqrt{1 + (a/h)^2}} - \frac{22,690\,k_v}{\sqrt{1 + (a/h)^2}} \tag{9.21}$$

Equation 9.21 is a more fundamental form of CSA S16.1 Clause 13.4.1(d). Like any other problem associated with elastic buckling, a limit on the applicability of Equation 9.21 must be established. Based on test results, it is observed that the proportional limit in shear is about 0.80 times the shear yield value. Equation 9.21 can be set equal to this value (or its equivalent in terms of F_y) and substitutions made for E and ν in order to establish the limit of applicability of the equation. In addition, the contribution of the tension field (the second and third terms on the right-hand side of the equation) will be neglected in establishing the limit. It is considered that in the inelastic region, the shear capacity of the web is not significantly augmented by the presence of the tension field. The limit for which Equation 9.21 is valid is thereby established as;

$$\frac{h}{w} \geqslant 239\sqrt{\frac{k_v}{F_y}} \tag{9.22}$$

The upper limit of Equation 9.21 will be taken as $12000/F_y$, as developed in Section 9.3. These limits, and Equation 9.21 are shown in Figure 9.10.

The upper limit of the applicability of Equation 9.10 ($F_s = 0.66\,F_y$) is taken at the same relative location as chosen for unstiffened girder webs. This is 70% of the value established by Equation 9.21, or,

$$\frac{h}{w} \leqslant 167\sqrt{\frac{k_v}{F_y}} \tag{9.23}$$

In the transition region (see Figure 9.10), two expressions for F_v, linear with respect to web slenderness, are used;

For

$$167\sqrt{\frac{k_v}{F_y}} < \frac{h}{w} \leqslant 190\sqrt{\frac{k_v}{F_y}} ,$$

$$F_s = \frac{110\sqrt{k_v F_y}}{h/w} \tag{9.24}$$

and for

$$190\sqrt{\frac{k_v}{F_y}} < \frac{h}{w} \leqslant 239\sqrt{\frac{k_v}{F_y}} \, ,$$

$$F_s = \frac{110\sqrt{k_vF_y}}{h/w} - \frac{95\sqrt{k_vF_y}}{h/w\sqrt{1 + (a/h)^2}} + \frac{0.50\,F_y}{\sqrt{1 + (a/h)^2}} \qquad (9.25)$$

All of the requirements listed above are contained in Clause 13.4.1 of CSA S16.1 where they are expressed in a slightly different format.

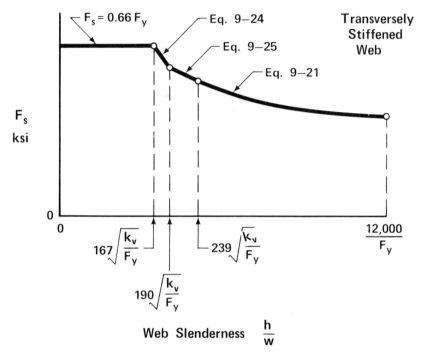

Figure 9.10
Web Shear Strength — Stiffened Web

The plots of ultimate shear stress in Figures 9.7 and 9.10 for unstiffened webs and for stiffened webs are shown to the same scale, giving an appreciation of the differences in shear-carrying capabilities of the two types of girders. As for unstiffened webs, the factored shear resistance of the stiffened girder web can now be calculated using Equation 9.12.

9.5 Stiffener Requirements

The role of transverse stiffeners in acting as posts to provide tension field action was indicated in Section 9.4. In addition, the application of concentrated loads to the girder will usually require the use of stiffeners to prevent local instability. These latter are termed bearing stiffeners.

Intermediate Transverse Stiffeners—Summation of the vertical components of the tension field action over one panel width (Figure 9.9(b)) gives the force that must be resisted by each stiffener as

$$F = \frac{\sigma_t \, h \, w}{2} \left[\frac{a}{h} - \frac{(a/h)^2}{\sqrt{1 + (a/h)^2}} \right] \tag{9.26}$$

Assuming that yielding of the stiffener will not be preceded by its buckling, Equation 9.26 can be divided by the yield point of the stiffener material (F_{ys}) and the value of σ_t given by Equation 9.18 used to provide a requirement for stiffener area (CSA S16.1 Clause 15.6.3);

$$A_s \geq \frac{a \, w}{2} \left[1 - \frac{a/h}{\sqrt{1 + (a/h)^2}} \right] \left[1 - \frac{45,000 \, k_v}{F_y \, (h/w)^2} \frac{F_y}{F_{ys}} \right] \tag{9.27}$$

The development of this equation assumes that the placement of stiffeners will be symmetrical about the web, that is, the stiffeners will be axially loaded. It is sometimes expedient to put stiffeners only on one side of the web. To account for the additional stress that will thereby result,[9.5] the CSA S16.1 Standard modifies its form of Equation 9.27 by multiplying by another factor D, where;

D = 1.0 for stiffeners furnished in pairs

D = 1.8 for stiffeners composed of angles placed on one side of the web only

D = 2.4 for stiffeners composed of plates placed on one side of the web only.

The stiffener area expressed by Equation 9.27, as modified above, is based on the requirement that full tension field action will be developed. The area may be reduced in girders, or portions of girders, where moment predominates and the full ultimate shear force will not be attained. Conservatively, the area of stiffener required (Equation 9.27) can be reduced in the ratio of V_f/V_r where

V_f = actual factored shear force in panel adjacent to stiffener

V_r = maximum factored shear resistance in panel adjacent to stiffener.

The force in the stiffener must be transferred into and out of the web from top to bottom. The exact manner in which this occurs is indeterminate. The assumption upon which the CSA requirement is based is that the force F described in Equation 9.26 must be transferred in one-third of the web depth. Rather than compute each actual stiffener force, an approximation of the maximum possible value is used to establish the shear flow (kips per inch) at each location of a transverse stiffener as

$$v = 0.00026 \, h (F_y)^{3/2} \tag{9.28}$$

Fasteners (usually, fillet welds) would be provided to meet this shear flow requirement. Customarily, they would be provided to meet the requirements of Equation 9.28 over the full depth of the stiffener.

Plate girders with transverse stiffeners were used for this bridge in Edmonton.

In addition to being able to resist the force imposed upon it by the tension field action, an intermediate transverse stiffener should have sufficient rigidity so that the web does not move out-of-plane at this location. With some theoretical justification and much evidence of practical satisfactory behaviour, the S16.1 requirement is (Clause 15.6.3);

$$I_s \geq \left(\frac{h}{50}\right)^4 \tag{9.29}$$

in which I_S = moment of inertia of stiffener (single or pair) about an axis in the plane of the web, in.[4]. Naturally, there is the concomitant requirement that the b/t ratio of the stiffener be established as for any element under compression.

The horizontal component of the tension field stress is resisted mainly by the flanges but also partly by the girder web. At the ends of the girder, the horizontal stress component in the web must either be taken out of the member or resisted internally. It is generally not convenient to provide an external reaction and experience shows that, if the force is resisted by internal action only, considerable distortion of the girder occurs in the vicinity of the free end. The usual solution is simply to establish an end panel in which tension field action is not permitted to develop.

The limit on end panel size can be obtained by consideration of the expression governing shear buckling, Equation 9.20. Using the average value of k_V of 7.34, the expression can be solved as

$$\frac{h}{w} = \frac{440}{\sqrt{\tau_{cr}}}$$

or, in terms of the factored shear force,

$$\frac{h}{w} = \frac{440}{\sqrt{V_f/\phi A_w}}$$

Because of the way in which k_V was defined with respect to the length parameters a and h, this must be interpreted as a restriction on the lesser panel dimension. Thus, the requirement may be stated (S16.1 Clause 15.6.1).

$$a \text{ or } h \text{ (whichever least)} \leqslant \frac{440\,w}{\sqrt{V_f/\phi A_w}} \qquad (9.30)$$

The choice of stiffener spacing and the factored shear resistance in the resulting panels are, of course, interdependent. The increased factored shear resistance which will result from an increased number of stiffeners must be compared to the additional cost of these stiffeners. The S16.1 Standard does place limits on maximum stiffener spacing, however. These are (Clause 15.6.2);

for $h/w \leqslant 150$; $a/h \leqslant 3$ $\hspace{3cm}$ (9.31)

and for $h/w > 150$; $a/h \leqslant \dfrac{67,500}{(h/w)^2}$ $\hspace{1.5cm}$ (9.32)

The first restriction reflects the fact that when the stiffener spacing to web depth ratio exceeds about 3, the effectiveness of the tension field is minor. The second restriction is related to ease in handling and fabrication.

The stiffener requirements as outlined in this section have been promulgated on the basis that a node point in the web be established and that the vertical reaction of the tension field force be accommodated. The required size, stiffness, and spacing of the stiffeners have been established. The only outstanding question concerns the detail of the stiffener in the vicinity of the flanges.

222

In addition to the requirements already discussed, the stiffener serves to maintain the shape of the cross-section as loads are applied and the girder distorts. Formerly, this was accomplished by fitting the stiffeners closely against both flanges and providing a light weld at the junctions. This is an expensive fabrication technique and also introduces residual stresses which will affect the fatigue life of the girder. Recent studies have shown that, since the tension flange will be self-aligning, the stiffener can safely be stopped short of this flange.[9.5] This detail is shown in Figure 9.11. To prevent a local buckle in the girder web in what will be a region of high strain, the amount of this cut-back should not exceed six times the web thickness but it should be greater than four times the web thickness in order to provide a reasonable strain gradient.

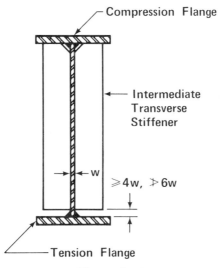

Figure 9.11
Intermediate Transverse Stiffener

The stiffener should be fitted against the underside of the compression flange, as also shown in Figure 9.11. If the stiffener is present on both sides of the web, no weld is needed between the flange and stiffener. When a stiffener is placed only on one side of the web, a nominal weld should be placed between the web and flange. A weld should be present in either case if lateral bracing is attached to the stiffener, frequently the situation. The inside corners of the stiffener should be clipped to clear the flange-to-web weld.

Bearing Stiffeners—The possibility of web crippling, that is, local failure of the web under application of a concentrated load, was discussed in Chapter 6. It was pointed out that if the bearing resistance of the web (Equation 6.32 and 6.33) was exceeded, bearing stiffeners could be introduced to help carry the load. The relatively thin web in plate girders means that bearing stiffeners are generally needed at points of concentrated load. If the girder end does not frame into another beam or into a column, they are mandatory when the web slenderness exceeds $420/\sqrt{F_y}$.

223

Bearing stiffeners are customarily designed as axially loaded columns, considering the cross-section to consist of the stiffener plus a strip of web with a width equal to 25 times the web thickness at interior stiffeners or 12 times the web thickness at end stiffeners. The effective column length is taken as 3/4 of the actual stiffener length. As well as checking the capacity of this equivalent column, the bearing capacity of the area of stiffener outside the web-flange girder weld and the capacity of the gross area of the stiffeners must be checked. The stiffeners should extend out as far as practicable toward the edge of the flange. They must meet the width-thickness ratios required to prevent local buckling. Bearing stiffeners can be stopped short of the flange opposite to the one through which the load is being delivered. The detailed design of both intermediate and bearing stiffeners is part of the Design Example of Section 9.8.

9.6 Combined Shear and Moment

The presence of significant quantities of shear and moment together can occur, for example, at the interior supports of a continuous beam. In such cases, the effect of the interaction between these two forces upon girder strength must be examined.[9.4].

The yield moment as carried by the flanges alone can be expressed as

$$M_{f1} = \sigma_y \, d \, A_f \tag{9.33a}$$

If the web is considered to contribute to the moment capacity, the yield moment can be expressed[9.6] as:

$$M_y = \sigma_y \, d \, (A_f + \frac{1}{6} A_w) \tag{9.33b}$$

Likewise, the plastic moment of the section can be put in the form

$$M_p = \sigma_y \, d \, (A_f + \frac{1}{4} A_w) \tag{9.33c}$$

As outlined in Section 9.5, the ultimate shear strength of a plate girder is considered to be independent of any contribution from the flanges. Therefore, for the region in which the flanges are assumed to provide the total moment capacity, the shear strength will not be reduced due to the presence of moment. Using the terminology of Equation 9.33, this can be written as

$$\frac{V_f}{V_u} = 1.0 \text{ for } 0 < \frac{M_f}{M_y} < \frac{M_{f1}}{M_y}$$

where V_f and M_f are the factored shear and moment.

If the shear is zero, the maximum moment that can be carried (theoretically) is the plastic moment. Thus,

$$\frac{V_f}{V_u} = 0 \text{ for } \frac{M_f}{M_y} = \frac{M_p}{M_y}$$

224

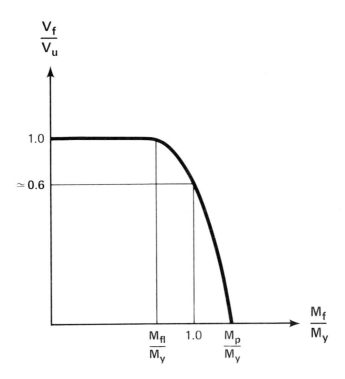

Figure 9.12
Shear-Moment Interaction

These portions of the interaction curve are shown in Figure 9.12. The only portion over which true interaction occurs then is over the range

$$0 \leqslant \frac{V_f}{V_u} \leqslant 1$$

and

$$\frac{M_{f1}}{M_y} \leqslant \frac{M_f}{M_y} \leqslant \frac{M_p}{M_y}$$

A parabolic curve, tangent at the lower end, is found to be in good agreement with the test results in this region. This takes the form

$$\left(\frac{V_f}{V_u}\right)^2 + \frac{M_f - M_{f1}}{M_p - M_{f1}} = 1 \tag{9.34}$$

It was noted earlier that girders with slender webs will not be able to attain the plastic moment. The curve is therefore cut off by the vertical line $M_f/M_r' = 1.0$ where M_r' is the moment evaluated from Equation 9.4. The re-remaining curved portion can be closely approximated by a straight line.

The end points of the straight line can be established by using the parabolic equation, Equation 9.34. The abscissa

$$\frac{M_f}{M_y} = \frac{M_{f1}}{M_y}$$

can be obtained using Equation 9.33 as

$$\frac{M_f}{M_y} = \frac{A_f}{A_f + \dfrac{A_w}{6}}$$

It is found that the ratio A_w/A_f usually ranges between about 0.5 and 2.0. A conservative result will be given here by using the higher limit and

$$\frac{M_f}{M_y} = 0.75$$

The ordinate for the abscissa $M_f/M_y = 1$ can likewise be obtained from Equation 9.34 and use of the lower limit of A_w/A_f as

$$\frac{V_f}{V_u} \simeq 0.6$$

The equation of the straight line joining these end points gives the CSA S16.1 interaction check (Clause 13.4.6);

$$0.727 \frac{M_f}{M_r} + 0.455 \frac{V_f}{V_r} \leqslant 1.0 \tag{9.35}$$

The interaction check is required only if the factored shear force at the section being considered exceeds 60% of the shear resistance of the section and if the girder proportions are such that the tension field action develops, that is, when $h/w > 190\sqrt{k_v/F_y}$.

9.7 Application of Direct Loads

Uniformly distributed loads applied to the compression flange of a plate girder or concentrated loads not supported by a bearing stiffener can cause web buckling in a mode similar to that due to the curvature resulting from bending (Section 9.3). The governing equation is again Equation 9.5. Considering the usual load situation, the tension flange may be considered to provide simple support to the web and the compression flange to provide either a fixed or simple condition. The condition of fixed support would occur when the flange is restrained from rotation as when a uniformly applied load comes in through a concrete slab.

Since the intensity of the compressive force diminishes from top to bottom of the web, the value of k in Equation 9.5 is taken as 5.5 (fixed compression flange) or as 2.0 (no flange restraint to web plate). However, since k is also a function of the width of the panel to its depth, these simplified values are expanded as shown in Equation 9.36. The quantity $\pi^2 E/12(1-\nu^2)$ in the equation is, for steel, equal to 26,200. The Standard uses a value 16,700 in order to recognize the vulnerability of light webs to instability and to allow for local overloads on the floor area. Incorporating the performance factor ϕ and the bearing area into Equation 9.5, the resulting expressions are (CSA S16.1 Clause 15.9);

$$B_r = \phi \frac{16,700}{(h/w)^2} [5.5 + \frac{4}{(a/h)^2}] A \qquad (9.36a)$$

when the flange is restrained, or, for a flange free to rotate

$$B_r = \phi \frac{16,700}{(h/w)^2} [2 + \frac{4}{(a/h)^2}] A \qquad (9.36b)$$

For distributed loads, A is taken as the product of the panel length times the web thickness. For concentrated loads or for loads distributed over partial length of a panel, A is taken as the web thickness times the lesser panel dimension, a or h.

9.8 Design Example

Given

Design the plate girder for which the span and loading are shown in Figure 9.13. The uniformly distributed load is applied through a concrete slab while the concentrated load is applied to the top flange of the girder through a 12 in. x 12 in. baseplate. Assume that sufficient lateral bracing will be supplied to the top flange such that lateral-torsional buckling need not be considered. Use G40.21 44W throughout (F_y = 44 ksi).

Solution

Use Equation 9.1 to obtain an estimated web depth—

$$h = 5.4 \left(\frac{3900 \text{ x } 12}{44}\right)^{1/3} = 55.1 \text{ in.}$$

Try h = 56 in.

Approximate flange area (Equation 9.2)—

$$A_f = \frac{3900 \text{ x } 12}{44 \text{ x } 56} = 19.0 \text{ in.}^2$$

Try 19 x 1 flange plates

Check slenderness: b/t = 9.5/1 = 9.5 (b = half flange width).
For a Class 3 section, allowable = $100/\sqrt{44}$ = 15.1   O.K.

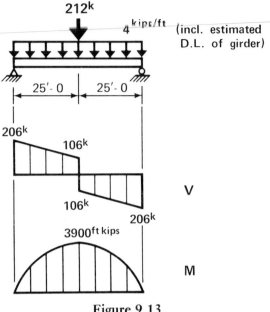

Figure 9.13
Design Example

Trial web thickness:

Maximum slenderness (Equation 9.7), $\dfrac{h}{w} \leqslant \dfrac{12000}{44} = 273$ or, for h = 56 in., minimum w = 0.21 in.

For protection against corrosion, minimum w (S16.1 Clause 6.4) = 3/16 in.

For no reduction in flange stress (Equation 9.4) $\dfrac{h}{w} = \dfrac{690}{\sqrt{44}} = 104$ or, for h = 56 in., w = 0.54 in.

Based on an assumed stiffener spacing equal to the web depth (a/h = 1) and the maximum web slenderness tabulated, from page 5-10 of the Manual, ϕF_S = 15.5 ksi. Using Equation 9.3,

$$A_w = \frac{V_f}{\phi F_s} = \frac{206}{15.5} = 13.3 \text{ in.}^2$$

or, for h = 56 in., w = 0.24 in.

Considering all of the above requirements, try w = 5/16 in. (A_w = 56 x 0.3125 = 17.5 in.^{2}, h/w = 179).

The trial section consists of a 5/16 x 56 web plate with 19 x 1 flanges. The moment of inertia of this cross-section is 35,442 in.^{4}. It has already been established that the trial flange section meets the requirement for a Class 3 section. A comparison of the actual slenderness of the web with the upper limit prescribed by the Standard (Clause 11.2) will show that the web chosen

228

here exceeds the limit. This is almost always the case for plate girders. The bending capacity of the section will therefore be governed by Equation 9.4. The basic capacity, M_r, will be calculated first:

$$M_r = \phi \, S \, F_y = 0.90 \times \frac{35\,442}{29} \times 44 \times \frac{1}{12} = 4033 \text{ ft-kips}$$

Now, using Equation 9.4,

$$M'_r = 4033 \left[1.0 - 0.0005 \times \frac{17.5}{19.0} \left(179 - \frac{690}{\sqrt{\dfrac{4033 \times 12}{0.9 \times 1222}}} \right) \right] = 3890 \text{ ft-kips}$$

This is less than 1% under the actual factored moment of 3900 ft-kips. The trial cross-section will therefore be taken as satisfactory with respect to bending.

The section just chosen and checked is needed only at the location of maximum moment. It is usual to reduce the cross-section of a welded girder at least once as the moment decreases. Assume here that the flange size will be changed once only. Try a cross-section consisting of 12 x 1 flange plates and the 5/16 x 56 web. For this section;

$$I = 24,069 \text{ in.}^4$$

$$M_r = 0.90 \times \frac{24069}{29} \times 44 \times \frac{1}{12} = 2739 \text{ ft-kips}$$

$$M'_r = 2739 \left[1.0 - 0.0005 \times \frac{17.5}{12.0} \left(179 - \frac{690}{\sqrt{\dfrac{2739 \times 12}{0.9 \times 830}}} \right) \right] = 2590 \text{ ft-kips}$$

This moment is found to occur approximately 10 ft. from centreline. Figure 9.14 shows the detail at the location where the 19 in. wide plate meets the 12 in. wide plate. The transition allows for the gradual flow of stress from one section to the other. A full penetration groove weld would be used to join the two plates.

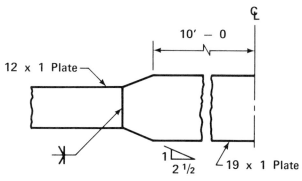

Figure 9.14
Flange Plate Transition

In order to have an unstiffened web, the actual shear would have to be less than that given by Equation 9.9, that is;

$$F_s = \frac{140,000}{179 \times 179} = 4.37 \text{ ksi}$$

The actual shear at the end of the beam is

$$f_s = \frac{206}{17.5} = 11.8 \text{ ksi} > F_s. \text{ Stiffeners are therefore needed.}$$

End panel spacing (Equation 9.30),

$$a \text{ or } h \leqslant \frac{440 \times .3125}{\sqrt{206/(0.9 \times 17.5)}} = 38.0 \text{ in.}$$

Since h = 56 in., the dimension a ≤ 38 in.

Intermediate Stiffeners:

Shear at 38 in. from end = 202 kips

$$f_s = \frac{202}{17.5} = 11.5 \text{ ksi}$$

Max. allowable stiffener spacing (Equation 9.32) is

$$a = \frac{56 \times 67,500}{179 \times 179} = 118 \text{ in.}$$

(or, a/h = 2.11)

Use a = 118 in. as a trial stiffener spacing. From Equation 9.20,

$$k_v = 5.34 + \frac{4.0}{(2.11)^2} = 6.24$$

Checking Equation 9.22,

$$\frac{h}{w} \geqslant 239 \sqrt{\frac{6.24}{44}} = 90$$

Actual h/w = 179, therefore the ultimate shear stress is given by Equation 9.21;

$$F_s = \frac{26,200 \times 6.24}{179 \times 179} + \frac{0.50 \times 44}{\sqrt{1 + 2.11^2}} - \frac{22,690 \times 6.24}{179 \times 179 \times \sqrt{1 + 2.11^2}}$$

$$= 12.6 \text{ ksi} > f_s$$

Since the actual shear is less than the ultimate shear capacity for this maximum permissible stiffener spacing, this spacing will be chosen. The exact layout will be determined when it has been established whether a bearing stiffener is needed under the concentrated load.

The effect of combined shear and moment should be examined. At centreline, V_f = 106 kips, F_s = 12.6 ksi and, using Equation 9.12,

$$V_r = 0.90 \times 17.5 \times 12.6 = 198 \text{ kips}$$

As explained in Section 9.6, interaction of shear and moment is critical only when V_f equals or exceeds 60% of V_r. Since 60% x 198 is greater than V_f, the interaction is not critical at this location.

The location of 60% V_r (119 kips) is approximately 3.25 feet from centreline. At this point, M_f = 3534 ft-kips. The resistance of the section in bending is still 3887 ft-kips. Checking the interaction relationship (Equation 9.35);

$$0.725 \times \frac{3534}{3887} + 0.455 \times \frac{119}{198} = 0.93 < 1$$

Thus, it may be concluded that shear-moment interaction is not critical in this beam.

The stability of the web under directly applied loads: since all panels are loaded at the same intensity, any panel can be examined. Considering the end panel, which is 38 in. long, and using Equation 9.36(a) since the flange can be assumed to be restrained by the concrete slab, the resistance is;

$$B_r = \frac{0.9 \times 16,700}{179 \times 179} [5.5 + \frac{4}{(2.11)^2}] \; 38 \times \frac{5}{16} = 35.6 \text{ kips}$$

The actual bearing load in this same distance is

$$P = 4 \times \frac{38}{12} = 12.7 \text{ kips.}$$

The girder is therefore satisfactory with respect to the uniformly distributed load.

Design of Bearing Stiffeners—If bearing stiffeners are not required, the factored concentrated load must be less than the capacity prescribed in Clause 15.9 or S16.1, that is;

$$B_r = 0.9 \times \frac{16,700}{179 \times 179} [5.5 + \frac{4}{(2.11)^2}] \times .3125 \times 56 = 52.5 \text{ kips}$$

Since the factored concentrated load (212 kips) is in excess of this value, a stiffener will be required under the load. Bearing stiffeners will also be required at each end of the girder since the actual web slenderness (179) exceeds the prescribed limit of $420/\sqrt{44} = 63$.

231

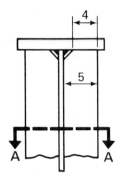 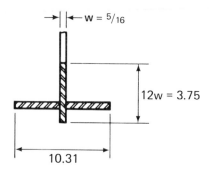

Section A—A

Figure 9.15
Bearing Stiffener

At the ends, try two 5 x 1/2 plates as shown in Figure 9.15. These extend nearly to the edge of the flange. In the calculations following, the requirements of Clause 15.5 of CSA S16.1 are used.

$$b/t = \frac{5}{0.5} = 10 < 100/\sqrt{44}$$

$$A = (5 \times 0.5 \times 2) + (3.75 \times 0.3125) = 6.17 \text{ in.}^2$$

$$I = \frac{1}{12} \times \frac{1}{2} \times (10.31)^3 = 45.7 \text{ in.}^4$$

$$r = \sqrt{45.7/6.17} = 2.72 \text{ in.}$$

$$\frac{KL}{r} = \frac{0.75 \times 56}{2.72} = 15.4$$

Using Equations 4.15 and 4.16a (Clause 13 of the Standard),

$$\lambda = 15.4 \times .0124 = 0.19$$

$$C_r = .9 \times 6.17 \times 44 (1.035 - .202 \times .19 - .222 \times .19^2) = 245 \text{ kips}$$

Since this is greater than the actual factored load at the ends (206 kips), the behaviour of the trial section as a column is satisfactory.

Bearing on contact area—assume 4 in. bearing (see Figure 9.15). The bearing resistance (Clause 13.10(a) of the Standard);

$$B_r = 1.50 \times 0.90 \times 44 \times (4 \times 2 \times 0.5) = 238 \text{ kips.} \quad \text{Satisfactory.}$$

For the bearing stiffener required at centreline, the load (212 kips) is only slightly greater than that just checked. It is also noted that the stiffener will not be required to assist in carrying the tension field action at this point. Choose two 7 x 1/2 stiffeners (b/t = 14, < 15) at this location. By comparison with the previous case, these will be satisfactory.

232

Welding of bearing stiffener—transfer load of 212 kips.

Try a 1/4 in. fillet, E70 electrode. Along the fusion face, the strength of the base metal (Equation 10.11) is

$$V_r = 0.66 \times 0.90 \times 1/4 \times 44 = 6.53 \text{ kips/in.}$$

The strength of the weld itself (Equation 10.12) is

$$V_r = 0.50 \times 0.90 \times (1/4 \times .707) \times 70 = 5.57 \text{ kips/in.} \quad \text{Governs.}$$

Total weld length required $= \dfrac{212}{5.57} = 38.0$ in.

Use an intermittent weld-

Min. length (CSA W59-1977) = 1-1/2 in. or 4 times the fillet weld size

Max. clear spacing (Clause 18.1.2 (b) of S16.1) = 12 in. or $\dfrac{125 \times 1/2}{\sqrt{44}} = 9.4$ in.

Try 1/4 in. fillet, 1-1/2 in. long at 9 in. c/c. This will provide a total of 42 in. of weld. (See Figure 9.16)

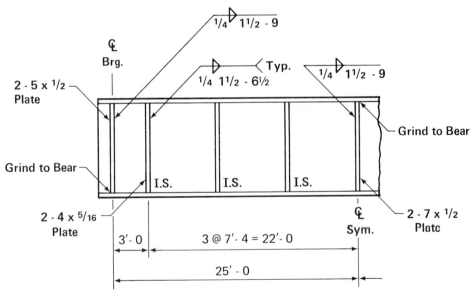

Figure 9.16
Stiffener Spacing

Design of Intermediate Stiffeners—The stiffener spacing is now chosen as shown in Figure 9.16. Three intermediate stiffeners are required each side of centreline and the actual aspect ratio is 88/56 = 1.57 and $k_v = 6.96$. Assuming that plates will be provided in pairs, the stiffener area required (Equation 9.27) is

$$A_s = \frac{88 \times .3125}{2} \left[1 - \frac{1.57}{\sqrt{1 + (1.57)^2}} \right] \left[1 - \frac{45,000 \times 6.96}{44 \times (179)^2} \right] = 1.67 \text{ in.}^2$$

Also, $I \geqslant (\frac{56}{50})^4 = 1.57$ in.^{4}

Try two 4 x 5/16 plates A = 2.50 in.^{2}

$$I = 15.0 \text{ in.}^4$$

Shear to be transferred (Equation 9.28)—

v = 0.00026 x 56 (44)$^{1.5}$ = 4.25 kips/in.

Try a 1/4 in. fillet weld.

From the calculations for the bearing stiffener welds, the strength of the weld metal will govern at 5.57 kips/in. As for those welds, try an intermittent 1/4 in. fillet weld of minimum length (1-1/2 in.). In accordance with Clause 15.6.4 of the Standard, the clear distance between welds is the lesser of

16 x web thickness = 16 x 5/16 = 5 in.   Governs.

4 x weld length = 4 x 1-1/2 = 6 in.

Try 1/4 in. fillet welds, 1-1/2 in. long, spaced at 6-1/2 in. c/c (5 in. clear between welds).

v = (5.57 x 1.5)/6.5 = 1.29 kips/in. at each web to stiffener junction. Since stiffeners have been provided in pairs, this gives four such weld locations and the total shear transfer provided is 5.16 kips/in. This exceeds the required 4.25 kips/in. and is satisfactory.

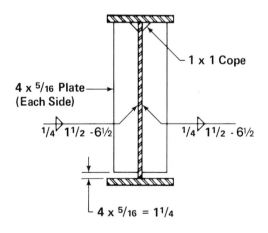

Figure 9.17
Intermediate Stiffener Details

The detail of the intermediate stiffener is shown in Figure 9.17. It should be remembered that the girder design proceeded on the basis that adequate lateral bracing for the compression flange would be provided. The calculations for location, size and connection of the lateral bracing are not included here. (Generally, it will be convenient to attach the bracing to the intermediate stiffeners. In this case, a weld between the stiffener and the compression flange of the girder would be provided to transfer the force in the bracing to the girder).

Although the design of this girder is now complete, it must be emphasized that the usual procedure would be to repeat the process for several other trial cross-sections. An examination would then be made as to which design is the most economical.

References

9.1 Bresler, B., Lin, T. Y., and Scalzi, J. B., "Design of Steel Structures", Second Edition, John Wiley and Sons, New York, 1968.

9.2 Basler, K., Yen, B. T., Mueller, J. A., and Thurlimann, B., "Web Buckling Tests on Welded Plate Girders", Bull. No. 64, Welding Research Council, New York, 1960.

9.3 Basler, K., and Thurlimann, B., "Strength of Plate Girders in Bending", Journal of the Structural Division, ASCE, Vol. 87, No. ST6, August, 1961.

9.4 Basler, K., "Strength of Plate Girders Under Combined Bending and Shear", Journal of the Structural Division, ASCE, Vol. 87, No. ST7, October, 1961.

9.5 Basler, K., "Strength of Plate Girders in Shear", Journal of the Structural Division, ASCE, Vol. 87, No. ST7, October, 1961.

9.6 Salmon, C. G., and Johnson, J. E., "Steel Structures—Design and Behaviour", Intext, Scranton, Pa., 1971.

CHAPTER 10

CONNECTIONS

10.1 Introduction

There are very few structural members for which the designer does not have to provide connections. In the most common types of framing, one member adjoins another and a connection between members is necessary to transfer the forces from one to the other. Relatively, less is known about overall connection behaviour than about the behaviour of the members being joined and design tends to be conservative at the present time. Continuing research in this area is resulting in a better understanding of connection performance, however, and, generally, more economical design of joints is evolving.

The common fastening elements for structural steel are rivets, bolts, and welds. Although widely used in the past, rivets are infrequently used today. After a brief discussion of their characteristics, emphasis will be placed on bolts and welds.

10.2 Rivets

Bar stock is used for rivets, a head being formed on one end by either hot or cold-driving in the manufacturing process. After the rivet is inserted in a hole in the connection, this end is held while a second head is formed against the gripped material. Generally the rivet is hot while this is being done.

It generally is assumed that, as a result of the driving process, the rivet fills the hole and that a joint results in which there will be no relative movement of the parts under load. In fact, the degree to which such hole-filling occurs is uncertain. Tests have shown that there is less movement (or, slip) in a comparable joint using high-strength bolts wherein a nominal 1/16 inch clearance between bolt and hole is provided.[10.1] Additionally, the properties of the rivet material are probably changed somewhat during the driving process.

Although the cost per rivet is less than that of an equal diameter high-strength bolt, it has less load-carrying capacity and requires more labour to install.

The welded and bolted towers of the Laporte suspension bridge provide a striking contrast to the riveted trusses of the famous Quebec Bridge.

10.3 Bolts

Unfinished (or, common) bolts are usually known by their ASTM designation, A307.[10.2] They are made of low-carbon steel and are generally supplied with square heads and nuts. The specified minimum tensile strength is 60 ksi. The bolts are installed by turning the nut on against the gripped parts with a spud wrench, using only the ordinary effort of a man. As such, the amount of any initial tension in the bolt can be expected to be both small and variable. This affects the load-transfer mechanism as will be described below. This type of fastener may be economical when used in light framing work and where vibration and load reversal are not a problem.

238

The more common type of bolt used in structural steel work is the high-strength bolt. These are made from heat-treated steel, either carbon steel (ASTM A325 bolts) or high-strength alloy steel (ASTM A490 bolts). The specified minimum tensile strengths are 120 ksi (up to 1 in. dia. bolts) or 105 ksi (over 1 in. to 1-1/2 in. dia.) for A325 bolts[10.3] and 150 ksi (up to 1-1/2 in. dia.) for A490 bolts.[10.4] Installation of both these and ordinary bolts is normally done in holes that are 1/16 in. greater in diameter than the fastener. Oversize or slotted holes may be used with the high-strength bolts in certain circumstances.[10.5]

Apart from the implications of the use of these high-strength steels, much of the characteristic behaviour of joints using A325 or A490 bolts results from the very high bolt preloads induced (intentionally) as a result of the installation procedure. The CSA S16.1 Standard requires that the minimum installed fastener tension be equal to 70% of the specified minimum tensile strength of the bolt. This preload is induced as the nut is turned on against the gripped material and the bolt elongates. Although two methods of attaining the desired preload are common, the calibrated wrench method and the turn-of-nut method, only the latter is now permitted by the S16.1 Standard for use in Canada. As well as being simpler, the turn-of-nut method provides better control of the preload.

In the calibrated wrench method, an air-operated wrench is adjusted to stall or cut out when the desired tension is reached. This level is established by installing a representative number of the bolts to be used in a load-measuring device. In order to minimize differences in the frictional resistance under the turned element, hardened washers under the bolt head or nut must be used in this procedure.

The turn-of-nut procedure is a method of elongation control. The parts to be connected are drawn together and the bolts brought to a "snug" condition. This is defined as the point at which an air wrench just starts to impact or as the full effort of a man using a spud wrench. (Fortunately, the exact determination of "snug" does not critically affect the final preload.) The nut is then given an additional one-half turn if the grip length of the bolt exceeds 4 bolt diameters but does not exceed 8 diameters or 8 inches. For the "short-grip" bolts (less than 4 bolt diameters in the grip), one-third turn is specified and for "long-grip" bolts (more than 8 bolt diameters in the grip), two-thirds of a turn is specified. Since the frictional resistance of the assembly is of no significance in this method, washers are not required as in the calibrated wrench method. However, to prevent galling and indentation, they are required under the turned element when A490 bolts are installed. Washers are necessary under both head and nut when A490 bolts connect material with a yield point of less than 40 ksi.

The preloads in the A325 fasteners of a relatively large joint are shown in Figure 10.1.[10.6] Using the histogram at the bottom of the figure in conjunction with the plot of bolt tension vs. bolt elongation, it can be noted that all fasteners in the joint exceeded the minimum specified preload of 40 kips and that all were loaded well into the inelastic range. Because the load-elongation response of the fasteners is relatively flat in the inelastic region, variations in the induced elongation (which includes the influence of the snug condition) produce only minor changes in the individual bolt preloads.

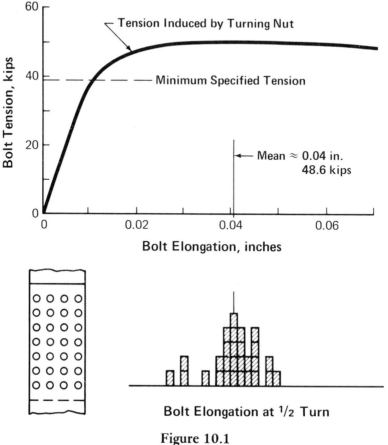

Figure 10.1
Bolt Tension vs. Bolt Elongation

A comparison of load vs. nut rotation for A325 and A490 bolts is given in Figure 10.2.[10.7] The factor of safety against twisting off can be expected to be between two and three for both types of fastener.

10.4 Welds

Welding of structural parts is accomplished by heating the parts to be joined until the joining surfaces are molten. Usually, additional material is supplied from a metal electrode which is then also involved in the heating process. Electrical power is the usual source of energy used to attain the very high temperatures required. A considerable range of electrodes is available so that an electrode may be chosen that is both compatible with the grade of steel being joined and an economical choice.[10.8] For manual welding, using "stick" electrodes, a coating on the electrode serves to supply an inert gas shield around the cooling weld, preventing oxidation and a resultant brittle weld. For submerged arc welding (an automatic welding process), a bare electrode "wire" is used in combination with a granular flux which provides the necessary "shielding" for the weld. Other processes provide the flux or shielding medium in the hollow core of the electrode. Although manual welding is used to a great extent in structural steel fabrication, automatic and semi-automatic processes account for a larger portion of structural welding.

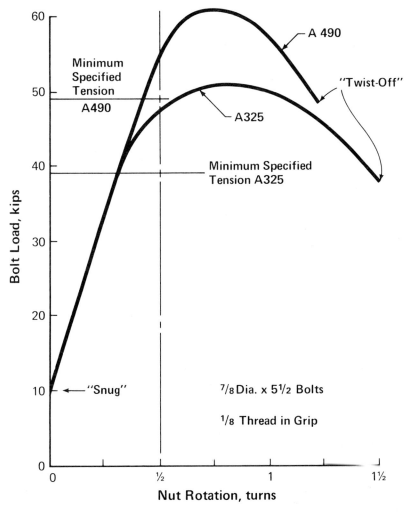

Figure 10.2
Bolt Load vs. Nut Rotation

A welded connection may be a very satisfactory structural solution since it is relatively easy to maintain full continuity of a section (such as in a beam or girder splice) or to provide full continuity at an abrupt change in cross-section (such as at a beam-to-column connection). Fabrication tolerances generally must be closer than those of bolted connections, however. Even under the most ideal conditions, inspection of the finished weld requires considerable expertise and experience and labour costs for fabrication and inspection reflect the rather high degree of skill involved in these operations.

Nevertheless, welded connections are generally more economical than bolted connections when made in the fabricator's shop, and may also, in some cases, be more economical in the field.

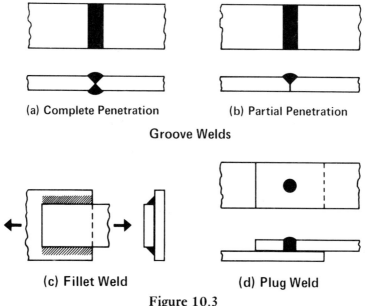

(a) Complete Penetration   (b) Partial Penetration

Groove Welds

(c) Fillet Weld   (d) Plug Weld

Figure 10.3
Common Weld Types

The main types of structural welds are shown in Figure 10.3. A groove weld may have either complete penetration (Figure 10.3(a)) or partial penetration (Figure 10.3(b)). In either case, if the deposited weld metal is made using a matching electrode grade, the deposited weld metal is as effective as the base metal itself. A full penetration groove weld therefore restores the original base metal. The partial penetration groove weld is less effective only by reason of the fact that it provides less cross-sectional material than was originally provided by the base metal. The groove is generally necessary so that the interior portion of the base metal can be properly reached. It can be shaped in a number of different ways, as well as the one shown.

A fillet weld is another commonly used weld for structural work. They are easier to make than groove welds but less effective in carrying stress. The weld may be oriented as shown in Figure 10.3(c) (a longitudinal placement of the weld), located transversely to the direction of the load, or at any angle in between these limits. As shown in Figure 10.4, both the strength and the ductility of the fillet weld are markedly dependent upon this angle of inclination.[10.9] Since specifications commonly do not recognize the strength increase shown, it will be advantageous to use the weld with the greatest ductility, the longitudinally placed fillet weld, in preference to the other orientations.

The plug (or, slot) weld shown in Figure 10.3(d) is used only infrequently in structural work.

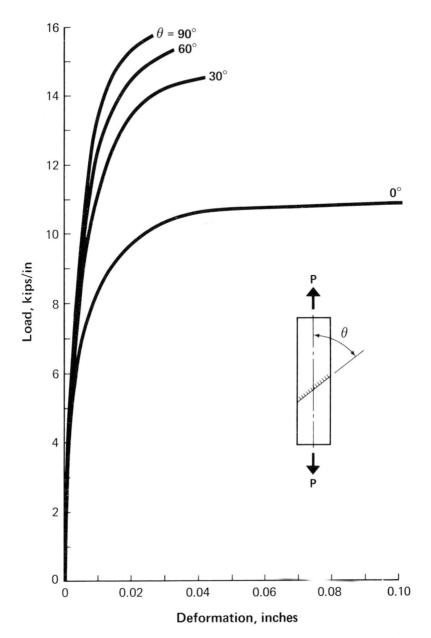

Figure 10.4
Load-Deformation Response of Fillet Welds

Because of the difficulty in trying to show a weld on an engineering drawing, it is necessary to adopt a set of symbols which will convey the necessary information concerning the size, length, spacing, etc. of the weld. Standard symbols are shown in Figure 10.5 and their use is illustrated in the design examples in this Chapter. Further information on welding symbols is available in the American Welding Society publication "Welding Symbols"—AWS A2.0.

WELDED JOINTS
Standard symbols

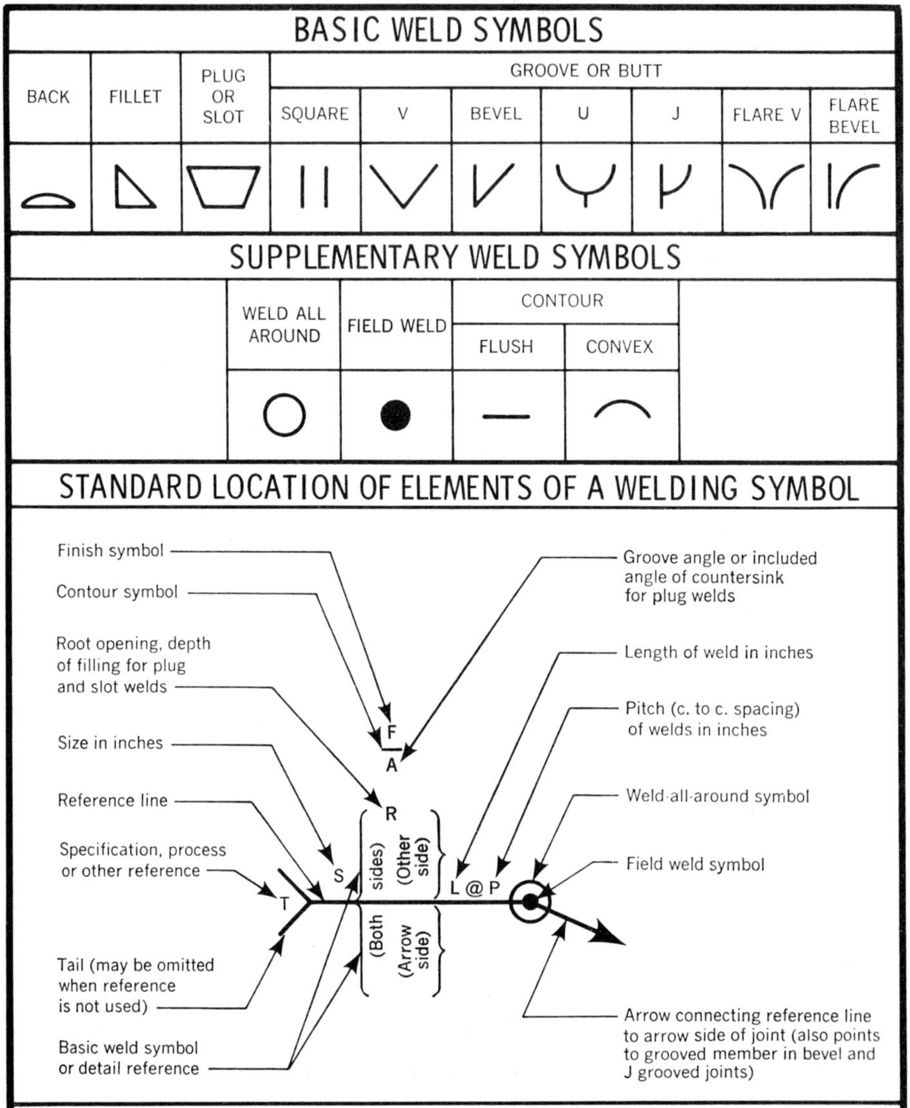

			BASIC WELD SYMBOLS							
			GROOVE OR BUTT							
BACK	FILLET	PLUG OR SLOT	SQUARE	V	BEVEL	U	J	FLARE V	FLARE BEVEL
⌒	△	⏢	‖	∨	∨	⋃	⋁	⋁	⌒

SUPPLEMENTARY WELD SYMBOLS

	WELD ALL AROUND	FIELD WELD	CONTOUR	
			FLUSH	CONVEX
	○	●	—	⌒

STANDARD LOCATION OF ELEMENTS OF A WELDING SYMBOL

Finish symbol

Contour symbol

Root opening, depth of filling for plug and slot welds

Size in inches

Reference line

Specification, process or other reference

Tail (may be omitted when reference is not used)

Basic weld symbol or detail reference

Groove angle or included angle of countersink for plug welds

Length of weld in inches

Pitch (c. to c. spacing) of welds in inches

Weld-all-around symbol

Field weld symbol

Arrow connecting reference line to arrow side of joint (also points to grooved member in bevel and J grooved joints)

F
A
R
S
T
(Both sides) (Other side)
(Arrow side)
L @ P

Note:

Size, weld symbol, length of weld and spacing must read in that order from left to right along the reference line. Neither orientation of reference line nor location of the arrow alter this rule.

The perpendicular leg of △, ∨, ⋁, ⌒ weld symbols must be at left.

Arrow and Other Side welds are of the same size unless otherwise shown.

Symbols apply between abrupt changes in direction of welding unless governed by the "all around" symbol or otherwise dimensioned.

These symbols do not explicitly provide for the case that frequently occurs in structural work, where duplicate material (such as stiffeners) occurs on the far side of a web or gusset plate. The fabricating industry has adopted this convention; that when the billing of the detail material discloses the identity of far side with near side, the welding shown for the near side shall also be duplicated on the far side.

Figure 10.5
Standard Weld Symbols

10.5 Load Transfer Mechanisms

In order to either design or to analyze a given connection, the load transfer mechanism through the fasteners must be known. The resulting forces on the fasteners can then be examined and compared with the limiting values. In addition, the strength, stability, and possibly the ductility of the connected parts must be examined in order to assure satisfactory overall behaviour of the connection.

Bolts may be subjected to shearing, tensile, or combined tensile and shearing forces, depending upon their location in the joint with respect to the external forces.

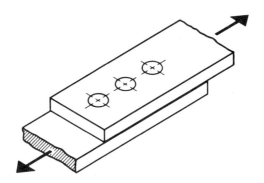

Figure 10.6(a)
Bolts in Shear: Lap Splice

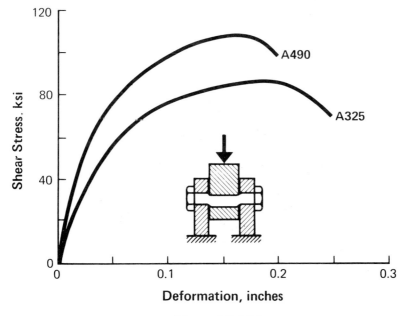

Figure 10.6(b)
Shear Response of Bolts

The bolts in a single lap connection such as shown in Figure 10.6(a) will be subjected to shearing across a single surface as the plates bear up against the fasteners. It is common practice to assume that all of the fasteners in a line share equally in carrying the load. In fact, the fasteners towards the end of the joint carry the largest portion of the load. This unequal loading of the fasteners is accentuated as the joint becomes longer.[10.10] It would not be convenient in design to use a bolt resistance that varied with joint length, however, and the S16.1 Standard simply reduces the individual bolt resistance for joints longer than 50 in.

The response of single A325 or A490 bolts to a loading producing shear on two planes is shown in Figure 10.6(b). As has been noted, the A490 bolt is a higher strength fastener than the A325 bolt. This higher strength comes at the expense of a slightly reduced ductility. It should also be noted that little, if any, of the response could be said to be elastic.

As the plates pull up against the fasteners (Figure 10.6(a)), failure can occur in one of four ways. The plate can tear through the net section, the bolt can shear at the interface of the two plates, the plate can shear out between the end fastener and the end of the plate, or the plate immediately adjacent to a bolt can pile up and/or yield as a result of the contact force between the two. The problem of net section tearing is related to the design of the member itself and this has been treated in Chapter 3. The shearing of the plate (Figure 10.7) is avoided by limiting the distance between the centreline of the bolt and the end of the plate (CSA S16.1 Clause 21). For bolts in a joint that act individually like the one shown in Figure 10.6(b), the two remaining problems are the bolt shear resistance and the plate bearing capacity. A joint in which the fasteners act as just described is termed a bearing-type connection.

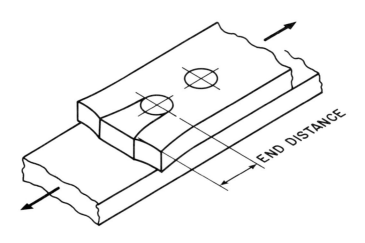

Figure 10.7
End Failure of Plate

246

The high clamping force produced by high-strength bolts provides a frictional resistance between the parts being joined. This behaviour, which occurs at an earlier stage of loading than the bearing-type behaviour just outlined, is illustrated in Figure 10.8. At some stage of loading, the frictional resistance will be overcome, the plates will slip until they bear against the fasteners and the situation is as has been described for bearing-type joints.

Clamping Force From Bolts

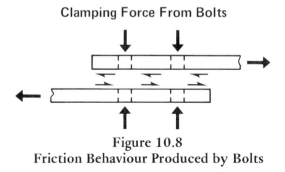

Figure 10.8
Friction Behaviour Produced by Bolts

The deformation behaviour of a typical joint is shown in Figure 10.9. The amount of the slip can theoretically be twice the hole clearance (usually, 1/16 in.) but tests show that it is usually in theorder of only one-half of the hole clearance. The designer should justify the use of friction-type connections as they will generally be less economical than a bearing-type joint. Appropriate situations would be any connection under repetitive loading (fretting might occur if the parts were allowed to slip cyclically) or structures in which slip would produce unacceptable geometrical changes (as in the case of a dish antenna, for example). In most building structures, repeated loading is not a consideration and geometry changes are unlikely as the bolts will already be in bearing at the time of installation as a natural consequence of the dead weight of the members themselves.

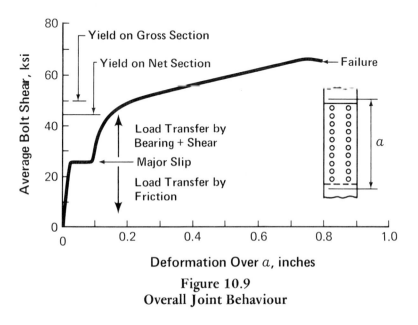

Figure 10.9
Overall Joint Behaviour

In a friction-type connection, the potential failure modes are net-section failure and slip of the plates to bring the bolts into bearing.

Direct tension loading of bolts results from conditions such as shown in Figure 10.10(a). Because the application of the external tensile load produces both an elongation of the bolt and an expansion of the precompressed plates, little, if any, change occurs in the preload of high-strength bolts. After separation of the parts, or in an assembly where the parts are not initially in contact, the external load is taken directly by the bolts. If ordinary bolts are used in a connection like this, the bolts simply act as tension members since there is no preload present.

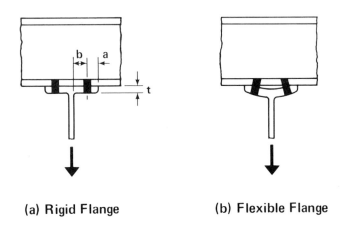

(a) Rigid Flange   **(b) Flexible Flange**

Figure 10.10
Bolts in Tension

If the parts in a tension-type connection are not relatively rigid, there is the possibility that additional forces due to prying action will exist, as shown in Figure 10.10(b). These should be taken into account in proportioning the bolts. A good estimate[10.6] of the prying force can be obtained by multiplying the nominal force per bolt by the quantity

$$Q = (\frac{3}{8} \frac{b}{a} - \frac{t^3}{20}) \tag{10.1}$$

The bolts in a connection such as the one illustrated in Figure 10.11 will be subjected to a combination of both tension and shear. An elliptical interaction expression (Clause 13.11.3 of CSA S16.1) combining the resistances for the two single effects is used in this instance.

As was indicated in Section 10.4, a groove weld simply replaces main section material. The forces in such a weld can therefore be calculated on the same basis as for the main material. The reduced cross-sectional area of partial penetration groove welds should be kept in mind when computing the forces in these elements.

248

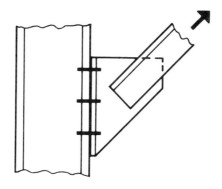

Figure 10.11
Bolts in Combined Tension and Shear

Irrespective of the actual loading, fillet welds are usually assumed to be subjected to shearing force, as they would be in the welds shown in Figure 10.3(c). For this case, and for shear loading of groove welds, the resistance of both the weld and the adjacent base metal must be examined. There are a number of rules governing minimum and maximum weld sizes, effective areas of partial penetration groove welds, and certain restrictions on details. The CSA W59 Standard should be consulted on these.[10.8]

10.6 Fastener Resistances

The resistances corresponding to the various potential failure modes are given in this section for high-strength bolts and for welds. The provisions for high-strength bolts can also be applied to common bolts (A307) except that, as discussed in Clause 10.5, only high-strength bolts are suitable for use in friction-type connections.

In providing rules for evaluating fastener resistances it is the initial premise of CSA S16.1 that the strength of a structure should be governed by the capacity of the member rather than that of the connections. Hence, the value of ϕ is to be taken as 0.67. As will be seen in the case of welds, the resistance of the connected material and of the weld metal itself must both be considered. In order to avoid confusion, the value of ϕ is taken as 0.90 for both parts but the resistances given for the weld metal incorporate a reduction to provide an additional margin of safety.

In Section 10.5, it was indicated that for bolts in bearing-type connections, the shear capacity of the bolts and the bearing capacity of the connected material immediately adjacent to the bolts remained to be evaluated. The bearing capacity of a single bolt can be represented by the resistance of the plate adjacent to the bolt, that is;

$$B_r = \sigma_b \, d \, t \qquad\qquad (10.2)$$

where σ_b is the bearing stress that can be sustained by the plate, d is the bolt diameter, and t is the plate thickness. The bearing stress will be some function of the location of the bolt with respect to the unloaded edge of the plate, e. Tests[10.6] have shown that a reasonably good representation of this is given by

$$\frac{\sigma_b}{F_u} = \frac{e}{d} \tag{10.3}$$

where F_u is the ultimate tensile strength of the plate. Substituting this expression into Equation 10.2, the bearing resistance associated with a single bolt is given by

$$B_r = e\, t\, F_u \tag{10.4}$$

Including all bolts (n) in the joint and applying the performance factor ϕ, the form given in CSA S16.1 is obtained (Clause 13.10(c)), that is,

$$B_r = \phi\, t\, n\, e\, F_u \tag{10.5}$$

The test data show that this estimate of strength is valid for ratios of e/d up to about 3, hence the inequality limit in the equation given in CSA S16.1. Beyond this limit, the failure mode changes gradually from one where the plate material shears out behind the bolt to one in which large hole and plate deformations occur. Good practice also requires that the fasteners be placed so as to satisfy the minimum end distances given in Clause 21.8 of the Standard.

It should be noted that the value of ϕ to be used in Equation 10.5 above is 0.90, not the reduced value used in other portions of connection design as described below. The rule governing bearing resistance can use the higher value since failure is never sudden or catastrophic within the rules given above.

Based on extensive testing, it has been established that the shear strength of high-strength bolts is approximately 0.60 times the tensile strength of the bolt material.[10.6] Hence, to obtain the shear resistance of a group of bolts, this quantity is multiplied by the cross-sectional area of one bolt (A_b), the number of shear planes in the joint (m), and the total number of bolts resisting the load (n) with the result (CSA S16.1 Clause 13.11.1(b));

$$V_r = 0.60\, \phi\, n\, m\, A_b\, F_u \tag{10.6}$$

Two modifications are necessary in special circumstances. If the bolt thread is intercepted by a shear plane, there is less shear area available than that given above. The ratio of the area through the thread root of a bolt to its shank area is about 0.70 for the usual structural sizes and the value of V_r given by Equation 10.6 is to be multiplied by this factor if the bolt thread is intercepted by a shear plane.

The second possible modification concerns joint length. As was noted in Section 10.5, except for the case of two bolts in line, joint strength is not linearly proportional with joint length. The average resistance per fastener decreases with the number of bolts in line. In the interest of simplicity, CSA

S16.1 breaks down joint strength into two cases. Joints less than 50 in. long require no reduction when calculating the total shear resistance of the bolts while the resistance of fasteners in joints longer than 50 in. is to be taken as 80% of the basic value. This "step" evaluation provides a reasonable approximation to the true case.

The behaviour of bolts in so-called friction-type connections, whether loaded in a shear connection or in connections where there is combined shear and tension, must be evaluated under the specified loads. As noted in Section 10.5, the requirement is that the assembly must not slip as these loads are applied.

The slip resistance of a bolted joint is given by the product of the number of faying surfaces, the coefficient of friction of the parts being joined, and the total clamping force provided by the bolts. In addition to these quantities, the Standard recognizes that the ideal situation of zero percent probability of slip is not attainable. The designer must choose the slip probability level that he thinks appropriate to the structure being considered.

Both the slip coefficient and the initial clamping force have considerable variation about their mean values. The necessary frequency distributions for these effects are known for a large number of practical cases and they have been used to evaluate the slip probability levels for various situations.[10.6]

The expression for slip resistance given in CSA S16.1 (Clause 13.12.1) is in the form:

$$V_r = 0.26 \, \mu \, m \, n \, A_b \, F_u \tag{10.7}$$

where m is the number of faying surfaces in the joint, n is the number of bolts, F_u is the ultimate tensile strength of the bolt material, and A_b the cross-sectional area per bolt corresponding to the nominal diameter.

Table 4 of the Standard gives values of μ to be used in Equation 10.7. These values combine the effects of the probable clamping force and the type of condition of the faying surfaces. They have been chosen for the 5% probability level, that is, there is a 5% chance that the joint will slip into bearing under the specified loads. For connections which are desired to be slip resistant but for which a larger probability of slip is tolerable, a table of μ-values for the 10% level is available.[10.6] The CISC Manual tabulates factored bolt resistances corresponding to both these probability levels.

The numerical modifier in Equation 10.7 (that is, 0.26) includes the necessary relationship between tensile area and nominal bolt area and the relationship between bolt tensile strength and required proof load. It also contains a component that enables the use of the equation as given along with published values of μ in the "Guide".[10.6] In this reference, they are used in conjunction with shear stress values. The CSA S16.1 Standard avoids this since bolts in a friction-type connection are, by definition, never acting in shear.

The ultimate resistance of a single high-strength bolt loaded in tension by the connected parts is equal to the product of its stress area (a value lying between the bolt shank area and the area taken through the thread roots) and the ultimate tensile strength of the bolt material. For simplicity, the equation given in Clause 13.11.2 of the Standard uses the nominal area of the bolt (A_b) and the multiplier 0.75 to provide an approximate conversion to the stress area. For a tensile connection containing "n" high-strength bolts and where F_u is the ultimate tensile strength of the bolt material, the capacity of the fasteners is therefore given by

$$T_r = 0.75 \, \phi \, n \, A_b \, F_u \tag{10.8}$$

When bolts in a bearing-type connection also have a component of tensile load in addition to the shear, they are to be proportioned according to the expression given in Clause 13.11.3 of the Standard.

$$V_f^2 + \beta \, T_f^2 \leqslant 0.56 \, \phi^2 \, \beta \, (A_b F_u)^2 \tag{10.9}$$

This is an elliptical interaction equation developed directly from test results.[10.6] The value 0.56 in the equation is the square of 0.75, the necessary conversion from nominal bolt area to stress area. The empirical parameter β depends upon bolt type and location of the shear plane with respect to the threads. The appropriate values are listed in Clause 13.11.3 of the Standard.

Bolts in a friction-type shear connection which also has a component of load parallel to the axes of the bolts are covered in Clause 13.12.2 of CSA S16.1. There are no published test results covering this situation and as a matter of judgement the following equation has been chosen:

$$\frac{V}{V_s} + 1.9 \, \frac{T}{n \, A_b \, F_u} \leqslant 1.0 \tag{10.10}$$

Taking as a base the case where there is no component of load parallel to the axes of the bolts, it is apparent that the resistance to slip will be reduced as tensile load is applied. This reduction will continue until the parts are on the verge of separation, at which time the slip resistance goes to zero. The interaction relationship given assumes linear response between the end limits of all shear and no tension, and all tension and no shear. All of the terms in Equation 10.10 follow directly from this. The quantity $1.9/(n \, A_b \, F_u)$ can be shown to be equivalent to T_r (for one bolt) as given in Equation 10.8.

In evaluating the strength of welds, the major area of consideration is that of the shear resistance of complete or partial penetration groove welds, plug and slot welds, and of fillet welds. The resistances of welds in other categories (tension or compression parallel to axis of complete or partial penetration groove welds and of fillet welds, tension or compression normal to the throat of complete groove welds, and compression normal to the throat of partial penetration groove welds) are taken as the same as those for the base metal. Tension other than parallel to the axis of partial penetration groove welds is considered to be the same as shear.

252

Groove welded beam flanges and high strength bolted beam web.

CSA S16.1 explicitly recognizes that the shear resistance of a weld must be evaluated on the basis of both the resistance of the weld itself and of the base metal adjacent to the weld.

The resistance of the base metal is given as (Clause 13.13.1);

$$V_r = 0.66 \, \phi \, A_m \, F_y \tag{10.11}$$

This is consistent with the shear resistance of a flexural member with a stocky web. The area of metal (A_m) to be used here is the area of the fusion face. The shear yield stress of steel is customarily taken to be $F_y/\sqrt{3}$, that is, $0.58 \, F_y$. The increase between this value and that given in the equation above ($0.66 \, F_y$) is attributable to the beneficial effects of strain-hardening. The value of ϕ to be used in evaluating the shear resistance of the base metal will normally be taken as 0.90.

The strength of the weld metal is given as

$$V_r = 0.50 \, \phi \, A_w \, X_u \tag{10.12}$$

The term A_w is the effective throat area of the weld and X_u is the ultimate tensile strength of the electrode (as given by the electrode classification number).

As has already been stated, both the fastening element (the weld) and the connected material are being considered in this section. Therefore in order to avoid confusion, the value of ϕ to be used in calculating the weld resistance is taken as 0.90. However, as was noted when discussing high-strength bolts, it is desirable to ensure that the fasteners will not fail before the member being connected. In that case, ϕ was modified (to 0.67). In the equation for fastener resistance given in this section, the reduction is incorporated into the modifier (0.50). As well, the modifier relates the shear strength of the weld to the electrode tensile strength as obtained by tests.

10.7 Analysis and Design of Simple Connections

A simple load transfer requirement is shown in Figure 10.12. The load may be either tensile, as indicated, or compressive. The situation could involve transfer between plates, as shown, but more often will be between gusset or splice plates and a main member. As far as the fastening elements are concerned, the principles are the same however. Attention will be focused here on the connection details and not on the complementary design aspects of the member.

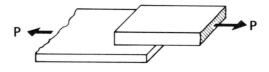

Figure 10.12
Lap Splice

Example 10.1

Given

The connection described above will be proportioned considering the fastening elements to be (a) welds, (b) high-strength bolts, friction-type connection, (c) high-strength bolts, bearing-type connection. The plate material is G40.21 44W, the factored load is 144 kips, and the specified load is 96 kips.

Solution

(a) For a welded connection using longitudinal fillet welds as shown in Figure 10.13(a), the minimum weld size is 5/16 in. (Table 4-4, CSA W59), while the maximum size permitted by CSA W59 is 1/16 in. less than the thickness of the piece against which it will be placed, 15/16 in. in this case.

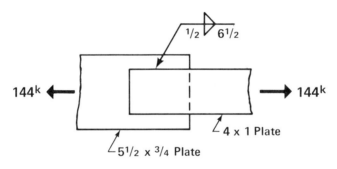

Figure 10.13(a)
Details — Welded Lap Splice

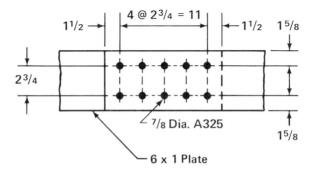

Figure 10.13(b)
Details — Bolted Lap Splice

Try a 1/2 in. fillet, E70 electrodes.

The strength of the base metal along the fusion face of the weld (i.e. next to the 1/2 in. leg of the fillet weld) is

$V_r = 0.66 \times 0.90 \times 1/2 \times 44 = 13.1$ kips/in.

The strength of the weld itself, taking the throat area as the shortest distance between the root of the weld and the surface, is

$V_r = 0.50 \times 0.90 \times (1/2 \times .707) \times 70 = 11.1$ kip/in.

The strength of the weld governs and the weld length required is therefore

$L = \dfrac{144^k}{11.1 \text{ k/in.}} = 13.0$ in.

Use 6-1/2 in. of 1/2 in. fillet weld arranged as shown in the figure. Note the information contained in the weld symbol.

(b) Try using 7/8 in. diam. A325 bolts for the bolted friction-type connection. Use the 5% slip probability level and assume that the faying surfaces are clean mill scale. For one bolt, using Clause 13.12.1 of CSA S16.1, (Equation 10.7);

$$V_s = 0.26 \times 0.59 \times 1 \text{ shear plane} \times 0.601 \text{ sq. in.} \times 120 \text{ ksi} = 11.1 \text{ kips}$$

$$\text{Number of bolts required} = \frac{96^k}{11.1 \text{ k/bolt}} = 8.65$$

Use ten 7/8 in. diam. A325 bolts in two lines.

Details (refer to Figure 10.13(b)):

    Min. bolt pitch 3 diam. = 2-5/8 in. Use 2-3/4 in.

    Min. edge distance 1-1/2 in. (Table 10, S16.1)

    Edge distance provided = 1-5/8 in. (Satisfactory)

The minimum end distance (in the line of stress), that is, the distance from the last bolt to the end of the connected part, is set by the requirements of Clause 21.8 of S16.1. Where there are more than two bolts in line, this simply refers to Table 10 of the Standard. Assuming the plate end to have been sheared, this minimum end distance for a 7/8 in. diameter bolt is given as 1-1/2 in. Although not explicitly required by the Standard, it would be good practice to also check the ultimate capacity of any connection designed as friction-type.

(c) For the bearing-type connection and again considering 7/8 in. diameter A325 bolts, for one bolt the shear resistance (Equation 10.6) is:

$$V_r = 0.60 \times 0.67 \times 1 \text{ shear plane} \times .601 \text{ sq. in.} \times 120 \text{ ksi} = 29.0 \text{ kips}$$

(assume that the threads are not intercepted by a shear plane)

The plate capacity in bearing for one bolt is (Equation 10.5);

$$B_r = 0.90 \times 1 \text{ in.} \times 1\text{-}1/2 \text{ in.} \times 65 \text{ ksi} = 87.8 \text{ kips}$$

This calculation assumes that a plate arrangement similar to that chosen for the friction-type connection would be used, that is, each plate will be 6 in. x 1 in. If plates of different thicknesses were to be used, the thickness of the thinner plate would be used in this calculation. If in double shear, the bolt bears against two plate thicknesses in one direction and one thickness in the other. The combination giving the least thickness is used in calculating the bearing resistance.

The capacity is governed by the resistance in shear and

$$\text{Number of bolts required} = \frac{144^k}{29.0 \text{ k/bolt}} = 4.97 \text{ bolts}$$

Use six 7/8 in. diam. A325 bolts in two lines. Except for the number of bolts, the details remain the same as shown in Figure 10.13(b).

Example 10.2

Given

A typical beam to column connection is illustrated in Figure 10.14. This type of arrangement is intended to transmit shear only and the beam itself would have been designed accordingly. The fastening elements could be bolts, as shown, welds, or a combination of both. In the latter case, the web framing angles would be shop-welded to either the beam or to the column and the field connection made using bolts. Consider here using 3/4 in. diameter A325 bolts in a bearing-type connection. The 2-1/4 in. dimension shown is the standard gauge for these angles. Such a small eccentricity of load can be neglected in the design of the connection. All steel is G40.21 44W and the factored reaction of the beam is 40 kips.

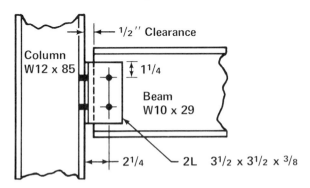

Figure 10.14
Beam-to-Column Connection

Solution

Angles to beam web:

shear resistance per bolt = 0.60 x 0.67 x 2 shear planes x .442 sq. in. x 120 ksi = 42.6 kips

The bolts bear against the beam web (5/16 in.) in one direction or the two angles (3/4 in.) in the other. Taking the governing dimension—

bearing resistance per bolt = 0.90 x 5/16 in. x 1-1/4 in. x 65 ksi = 22.8 kips

The bearing capacity governs and

$$\text{number of bolts required} = \frac{40^k}{22.8 \text{ k/bolt}} = 1.75 \text{ bolts}$$

Use two 3/4 in. diameter A325 bolts as shown in Figure 10.14.

Angles to column flange:

shear resistance per bolt = 0.60 x 0.67 x 1 shear plane x .442 sq. in. x 120 ksi = 21.3 kips bearing resistance per bolt (angle thickness is 3/4 in. and column flange thickness is (13/16 in.) = 0.90 x 13/16 in. x 1-1/4 in. x 65 ksi = 59.4 kips

The shear capacity governs and

$$\text{number of bolts required} = \frac{40 \text{ kips}}{21.3 \text{ kips/bolt}} = 1.88$$

It is considered good practice to use a minimum of two bolts in any connection. In addition, in order to maintain symmetry, use four 3/4 in. diameter A325 bolts, two in each angle leg.

In order that the connection fulfill the design assumption implied for the beam (i.e. simply supported), the detail should provide good rotational capability. In this example, this means primarily that the web framing angles should be kept as short as possible. If the beam is deep, the angles should be placed toward the top so as to provide lateral support for the compression flange. The need for considering the eccentricity of load on the fasteners should also be kept in mind. This is discussed in the next section.

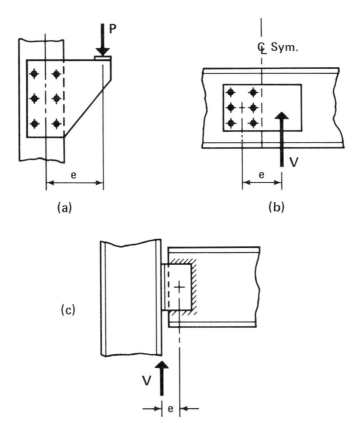

Figure 10.15
Eccentrically Loaded Connections

10.8 Eccentrically Loaded Connections

Ideally, the line of action of a force should pass through the centroid of the fastening elements. This is not always possible, however, and eccentric forces often have to be accommodated. Typical examples of this type are shown in Figure 10.15.

The traditional way of treating such connections was to assume that the fastener response to load is elastic. The fastener stresses can then be computed as the vector sum of direct shear stresses and shearing stresses due to torsion.

Figures 10.4 and 10.6 show very clearly that neither high-strength bolts nor fillet welds have any appreciable portion over which their response to load could be idealized as elastic. In addition, it is also apparent that the direction of the force on an element of weld is of significance. As a result of an appreciation of these factors, work has been carried out on the ultimate strength of eccentrically loaded connections.

The procedure that is used starts by assuming some location for the instantaneous centre of rotation of the fastener group. At the time the ultimate load is reached, the fastener furthest from the instantaneous centre will just reach its failure load and deformation. These values have been established by tests on representative numbers of bolts and short lengths of fillet weld. The deformations of the other fasteners are assumed to be proportional to their distance from the instantaneous centre and their corresponding loads can be obtained from curves like those in Figures 10.4 and 10.6(b). (It should be noted that a length of weld is broken up into a series of elemental lengths, each of which is then treated like an individual fastener.) A check of the equations of equilibrium will reveal whether or not the trial location of the instantaneous centre of rotation was the correct one. If these equations are not satisfied, a new location of the instantaneous centre is chosen and the process is repeated.

The solution described above is obviously not suitable for direct design purposes. Mathematical expressions are available, however, which describe the results to a reasonable degree of accuracy.[10.11] The general form relates the ultimate load to the moment of inertia of the fastener group through two other coefficients as

$$K = \alpha I^\beta \qquad (10.13)$$

For bolted connections, the ultimate load is obtained by multiplying the value of K given by Equation 10.13 by the double or single shear area of the fastener, as appropriate. The moment of inertia is to be expressed in units of bolts $-$ in.^{2}. For one fastener line, the I to be used is I_x. For two lines, use $I_p = I_x + I_y$. The coefficients α and β for one line of fasteners are

$$\alpha = 0.752 + \frac{55.9}{e} + \frac{369}{e^2} - \frac{530}{e^3} \qquad (10.14)$$

$$\beta = 0.643 - \frac{0.196}{e} - \frac{3.36}{e^2} + \frac{6.60}{e^3} \qquad (10.15)$$

where e is the eccentricity expressed in inches.

For two lines of A325 bolts spaced 3 in. apart, the values of α and β to be used in Equation 10.13 are

$$\alpha = 0.923 + \frac{71.9}{e} + \frac{425}{e^2} - \frac{636}{e^3} \tag{10.16}$$

$$\beta = 0.649 - \frac{0.217}{e} - \frac{2.81}{e^2} + \frac{5.69}{e^3} \tag{10.17}$$

Similar expressions are available for A490 bolts but will not be given here. The information given for one or two lines of A325 bolts will cover many practical cases.

Example 10.3

Given

Determine the ultimate resistance provided by the arrangement of 3/4 in. diameter A325 bolts shown in Figure 10.16. The bolts are in double shear.

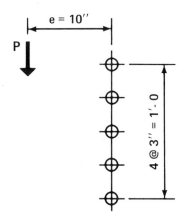

Figure 10.16
Design Example — Eccentric Bolted Connection

Solution

From Equation 10.13 and using the appropriate values of α and β from Equations 10.14 and 10.15,

$$K = 9.50 \ I^{0.60}$$

$$= 9.50(90)^{0.60} = 141$$

The double shear area of a 3/4 in. diameter bolt is 0.882 and therefore

$$P_{ult} = 141 \times 0.882 = 124 \text{ kips}$$

Using $\phi = 0.67$, the factored resistance is 83.1 kips

This problem can also be solved with the aid of the CISC Manual. For the data given, Tables 3-7 and 3-2 are used to obtain a factored resistance of 72 kips. Although the same method is used by the Manual as has been presented here, the Manual relates the strength to that tabulated for a single bolt in a relatively long line of fasteners (less than, but close to, 50 inches). Thus, the individual fastener strength is taken somewhat more conservatively than that used here.

The ultimate strength expression given by Equation 10.13 can also be used for welded connections of the type illustrated in Figure 10.15(c).[10.12] Equation 10.13 will give values of the ultimate load directly for each 1/16 in. of leg size for fillet welds made using E60 electrodes if the following values are used for the coefficients:

$$\alpha = -0.046 + \frac{6.75}{e} + \frac{6.05}{e^2} - \frac{45.75}{e^3} \tag{10.18}$$

$$\beta = 0.697 - \frac{1.45}{e} + \frac{5.96}{e^2} - \frac{17.4}{e^3} \tag{10.19}$$

If the C-shaped weld degenerates to a line weld, the coefficients should be taken as

$$\alpha = 0.0309 + \frac{3.70}{e} + \frac{11.80}{e^2} \tag{10.20}$$

$$\beta = 0.661 + \frac{0.106}{e} - \frac{3.58}{e^2} + \frac{5.32}{e^3} \tag{10.21}$$

The strengths calculated using these coefficients in Equation 10.13 should be multiplied by the number of sixteenths in the leg size of the weld being investigated. As will be illustrated in Example 10.4, the moment of inertia is that of the weld treated as a line. If the weld is made using E70 rather than E60 electrodes, the result given by Equation 10.13 should be increased in the ratio 70/60.

Example 10.4

Given

A pair of plates are to be welded to the flanges of a column to support an eccentric load (factored) as shown in Figure 10.17. Using E70 electrodes, determine the weld length required. Assume that the two plates will be properly stiffened such that the load is shared equally between them. The factored load per plate is therefore 90 kips.

Solution

Using Equation 10.13 and $I = \dfrac{L^3}{12}$, for a 1/16 in. weld size

$$P_{ult} = \alpha \left[\frac{L^3}{12} \right]^\beta = \frac{\alpha L^{3\beta}}{12^\beta}$$

Solving, $L = \left[\dfrac{P_{ult} \times 12^{\beta}}{\alpha}\right]^{1/3\beta}$ per 1/16 in. weld size.

Try 5/16 in. weld. Then the ultimate load per 1/16 in. is 90/5 = 18 kips

From Equations 10.20 and 10.21:

$\alpha = 0.4211, \beta = 0.648$

Substitution gives $L = \left[\dfrac{18 \times 5.004}{0.4211}\right]^{.5144} = 15.8$ in.

Since the parameters given do not include a performance factor, this length should be increased by dividing by $\phi = 0.67$. At the same time, the parameters relate to the use of E60 electrodes while E70 electrodes are being used here. Thus, the length can be decreased for this effect. Finally, then

$$L = 15.8 \times \dfrac{1}{0.67} \times \dfrac{60}{70} = 20.2 \text{ in., say 20 in.}$$

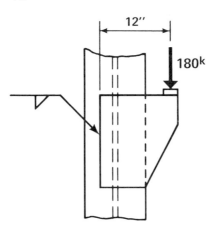

Figure 10.17
Design Example — Eccentric Welded Connection

The Manual provides tables covering eccentrically loaded welds, again based on the method described in Section 10.8. The results obtained using their tabulated values are, as was the case for eccentrically loaded bolts, more conservative than the values which would be obtained using the parameters just presented. Using the Manual, the connection just analyzed would be considered to carry a factored load of 149 kips.

10.9 Connections Carrying Shear, Thrust, and Moment

Connections occurring at the corners of rigid frames or at the intersections of beams and columns which are to be rigidly framed must be able to transfer all three possible components of force. It is obvious that the connection must be of adequate strength to accomplish this. It must also provide adequate rotation capacity, however, and both of these requirements must be met with economy in mind. Local elements of the connection must also be proportioned carefully so that their premature failure will not result in a lowering of overall connection strength.

Except in the case of prefabricated buildings, rigid frame connections are almost always welded. This gives a clean and compact connection in a region which tends to be otherwise crowded by the intersection of the main framing members as well as by the purlins and bracing. If splices are necessary, they should be made away from this region and at a location of lower shear and moment.

A straight corner connection formed by the intersection of two rolled shapes is shown in Figure 10.18(a). One arrangement is to run the beam through the connection, as shown, and provide extensions of the column flanges.

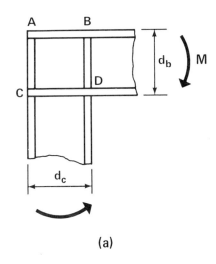

(a)

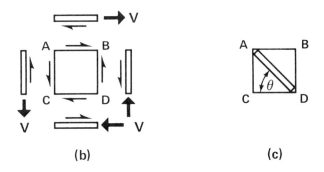

(b)   (c)

Figure 10.18
Connection Carrying Shear, Thrust, and Moment

In proportioning the connection, it is usual to assume that the bending moment and thrust are carried entirely by the flanges and that the shear is carried entirely by the web.[10.13] The force system resulting from application of these assumptions is shown in Figure 10.18(b). The value of the force in the flange, which is transferred into the web as a shear, is taken as

$$V \simeq \frac{M}{d_b} \qquad (10.22)$$

The moment to be used (M) would be that resulting from the application of the factored loads to the structure.

If the beam has been extended into the connection as shown, the portions AB and CD will be adequate in the connection if they were adequate in the beam. Nominally, the stress in the connection portion will be a little higher and the flange buckling strength a little lower because of the assumption that all the force is taken by the flanges but this can be disregarded. Portion AC is made either as a continuation of the column flange or as an equivalent plate groove welded to the column. Member BD can be made as a half or full-depth stiffener. It must transfer the compressive force from the column flange into the beam web.

Equating the shear resistance of the web (thickness w) to the applied shear force and assuming that the yield in shear $\tau_y = F_y/\sqrt{3}$,

$$d_c w \frac{F_y}{\sqrt{3}} = \frac{M}{d_b}$$

and solving, $w = \dfrac{\sqrt{3}\,M}{d_c d_b F_y}$

Applying the performance factor used for connections, this requirement becomes

$$w \geqslant \frac{\sqrt{3}\,M}{\phi d_c d_b F_y} = \frac{1.9M}{d_c d_b F_y} \qquad (10.23)$$

If the web of the beam supplied is not at least equal to the requirement given by Equation 10.23, doubler plates or a diagonal stiffener may be provided. The selection of a new beam size usually would not be economical. The diagonal stiffener, as shown in Figure 10.18(c), is the usual choice.

The stiffener is proportioned by first considering the equilibrium conditions at point A. The total force to be transmitted (V) is assumed to be shared by the stiffener and the web as

$$V = \frac{M}{d_b} = d_c w \frac{F_y}{\sqrt{3}} + F_y A_{st} \cos\theta \qquad (10.24)$$

where A_{st} is the total stiffener area required. Solving for this quantity, assuming that all parts have the same yield stress, and introducing the performance factor

$$A_{st} = \frac{1}{\phi \cos\theta} \left[\frac{M}{d_b F_y} - \frac{w\,d_c}{\sqrt{3}} \right] \tag{10.25}$$

Since this element is acting under a compressive load, the ratio of its width to thickness (b/t) should be established so as to avoid the possibility of premature local buckling. (This requirement is discussed in Chapter 4.)

For the corner arrangement that has been discussed, groove welds could be used at the junction of the column flanges and the lower flange of the beam. Fillet welds can be used at the other locations to transfer the necessary forces. The resulting fillet weld at the column web to beam flange may be rather large, however, and a groove weld is often used at this location as well. Details of the weld design are given in Example 10.5.

Example 10.5

Given

Design the corner connection between a column and a beam, both of which are W16 x 40 sections of A441 steel (F_y = 50 ksi). Use E70 electrodes. (The notation of Figure 10.18 will be followed.) The beam is to act as a Class 1 section.

Solution

The connection will be designed to carry the factored moment on the section which has been determined to be 273 ft. kips. The effects of the axial thrust and shear on the connection web can be neglected. These are small and are of the opposite sign to shears produced by the moment. The factored shear in the column, needed for the design of the weld between the column web and beam flange, is 153 kips. The web thickness required, using Equation 10.23 is

$$w = \frac{1.9 \times 273 \times 12}{16 \times 16 \times 50} = 0.49 \text{ in.}$$

The web thickness provided by a W16 x 40 is 0.307 in. Diagonal stiffeners (AD) will therefore be provided and, from Equation 10.25,

$$A_{st} = \frac{1}{0.90 \times .707} \left[\frac{273 \times 12}{16 \times 50} - \frac{0.307 \times 16}{\sqrt{3}} \right] = 1.98 \text{ sq. in.}$$

Provide 0.99 sq. in. in each of two stiffeners, one on each side of the beam web.

Try 3 x 7/16 plates, area = 1.31 sq. in. each.

Allowable b/t $\leqslant 54/\sqrt{F_y} = 54/\sqrt{50} = 7.6$

Actual b/t = 6.9 (Satisfactory)

Stiffeners at AC and BD—Provide 3-1/4 x 9/16 plates on each side of beam web. This provides the same area (approximately) as the column flanges. A full-depth stiffener will be used at AC. At BD, the depth will be based upon the weld length required.

Checking, $b/t = \dfrac{3\text{-}1/4}{9/16} = 5.8 < 7.6.$ (Satisfactory)

Welds:

1. Column flanges to beam flange—use full penetration groove welds to develop the full strength of the column flanges.

2. Column web to beam flange—transfer the factored shear force of 153 kips using fillet welds. For E70 electrodes, the strength of the weld metal for a 1/16 in. leg size

   $= 0.50 \, \phi \, A_w X_u$

   $= 0.50 \times 0.90 \times (1/16 \times .707) \times 70$

   $= 1.4$ kips/inch. (This value is tabulated in Table 3-17 of the Manual.)

   Weld length available = 2 x 14 in. = 28 in.

   Leg size required $= \dfrac{153}{28 \times 1.4}$

   $= 3.90$, say, 4 (sixteenths)

3. Stiffeners—use either groove welds or fillet welds at the ends of the stiffener to transfer the ultimate load of the stiffener. As shown in Figure 10.19, groove welds will be used here. Also shown are nominal size fillet welds running along the length of the stiffeners. These provide buckling resistance for both the connection web and the stiffeners.

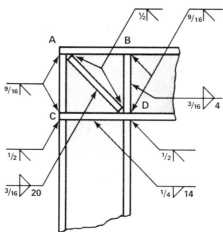

Figure 10.19
Design Example — Corner Connection

The only other type of connection required to carry all three force components that will be discussed is the interior type connection shown in Figure 10.20. An exaggerated view of the deformed connection (Figure 10.21) shows two of the possible failure modes; (a) buckling of the column web as the beam flange delivers its compressive load, (b) exhaustion of the ductility of the groove weld in the stiff region at the beam tension flange.

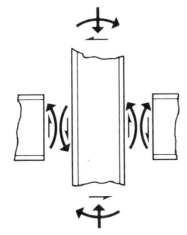

Figure 10.20
Interior Connection

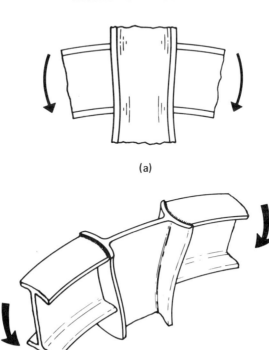

(a)

(b)

Figure 10.21
Interior Connection − Failure Modes

On the compression side, it may be assumed that the force from the beam flange is distributed out on a 2.5 to 1 slope, as shown in Figure 10.22, until the least cross section of the column web is reached (at the toe of the flange-to-web fillet). The total compressive force from the flange is assumed to be counteracted by the web resistance at this point. Equating the forces,

$$\frac{M_f}{d_b} = B_r$$

$$\text{or, } \frac{M_f}{d_b} = F_{yc} w_c \, (t_b + 5k) \qquad (10.26)$$

Writing this in the form of a requirement and introducing the performance factor,

$$B_r = \phi w_c \, (t_b + 5k) \, F_{yc} > \frac{M_f}{d_b} \qquad (10.27)$$

If Equation 10.27 is not satisfied, stiffeners are required opposite the beam compression flange. CSA S16.1 expresses this requirement in Clause 20.3.

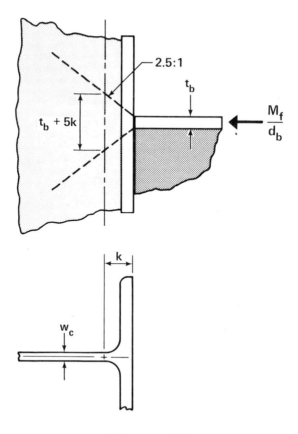

Figure 10.22
Delivery of Compressive Load

On a semi-empirical basis,[10.13] it has been established that a conservative requirement for stiffeners opposite the beam tension flange is given by

$$T_r = \phi 7t_c^2 F_{yc} > \frac{M_f}{d_b} \tag{10.28}$$

If Equation 10.28 is not satisfied, stiffeners are required at this location as well. From equilibrium considerations, the force that must be transmitted by the stiffener is

$$F_{st} = \frac{M_f}{d_b} - B_r \tag{10.29}$$

A check on the stability of the stiffener chosen should also be made. Horizontally placed stiffeners are usual and they should be used in pairs, one on each side of the column web.

As was the case in the corner connection, the web formed by the intersection of the beams and column must be checked here against excessive shear stress (see Clause 20.3 of S16.1). The situation is usually less critical than that occurring at a corner because only the unbalanced moment across any given direction of the connection must be carried into the web as a shear force. The direct column or beam shears will again be neglected since they act opposite to shears produced by the flange forces.

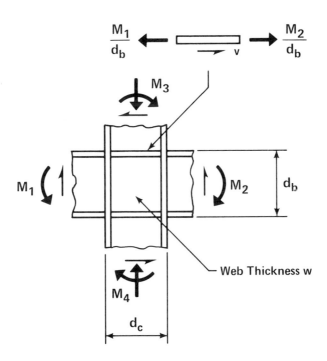

Figure 10.23
Interior Connection — Forces

Beams of equal depth are shown framing into a column in Figure 10.23. Considering the equilibrium requirements at the top of the panel formed by the intersection, it is seen that

$$V = \frac{M_1 - M_2}{d_b} \tag{10.30}$$

In terms of shear stress, and considering the algebraic difference of the factored moments, this can be written as

$$\tau = \frac{\Delta M_f}{d_b \, d_c \, w} \tag{10.31}$$

Setting this equal to the shear yield stress ($F_{yc}/\sqrt{3}$), introducing the performance factor, and solving for the web thickness w,

$$w = \frac{1.9 \, \Delta M_f}{d_b \, d_c \, F_y} \tag{10.32}$$

The same quantity must also be examined for shears resulting from the column moments. Since the change in moments on opposite sides of the connection will be the only variable in the analysis, this can be examined first in order to establish the governing case. If the actual web thickness is less than that described by Equation 10.32 a diagonal stiffener or double plates would be provided as was discussed for corner connections.

Further examples of connection design may be found in Part 3 of the CISC Manual.

10.10 Beam Bearing Plates, Column Base Plates

Compressive stresses in structural steel are substantially higher than the corresponding values in the masonry or reinforced concrete upon which a beam or column may rest. An intermediate component is usually required to "step-down" the relatively high compressive stresses in the steel to a value that is acceptable for the concrete or masonry. This intermediate stage is performed by a bearing plate in the case of beams (Figure 10.24) or by a base plate in the case of columns (Figure 10.25). The same function is carried out by a footing as it spreads out a load over a material of relatively low bearing capacity, the soil.

In the case of the beam bearing plate, it is assumed that the contact stress between the plate and the masonry is uniformly distributed and that the plate bends only about an axis which is parallel to the length of the beam. The face of bending is taken as the toe of the web-flange fillet and the plate is assumed to act as a cantilever between its free edge and this line. The designer must ensure that (a) sufficient plate area is provided such that the bearing stress on the masonry is within the permissible value for that material (b) the plate is thick enough to provide the necessary bending resistance. Since there is no possibility here of lateral buckling or a local failure, the resisting bending moment can be taken as the value prescribed for Class 1 and 2 sections (Clause 13.5.1 of S16.1).

270

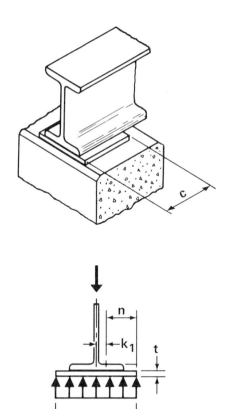

Figure 10.24
Beam Base Plate

Example 10.6

Given

A W18 x 55 beam is to be set on a 6 in. wide concrete wall. Choose a suitable bearing plate of A36 steel (F_y = 36 ksi) for a factored beam reaction of 80 kips and a permissible bearing stress in the concrete of 1.8 ksi.

Solution

Bearing area required = $\dfrac{80^k}{1.8 \text{ ksi}}$ = 44.4 sq. in.

Assuming a 5 in. usable width of wall,

B = $\dfrac{44.4 \text{ sq. in.}}{5 \text{ in.}}$ = 8.89, say 9 in.

The W18 x 55 has a flange width of 7-1/2 in. and a dimension k_1 = 5/8 in. The bending length is therefore

n = 9/2 − 5/8 = 3.88 in.

271

and considering a strip of plate 1 in. wide

$$M_{max} = (1.8)(3.88)(3.88)1/2 = 13.5 \text{ in.-kips}$$

The resistance of a section of plate 1 in. wide and of thickness t (i.e. ϕM_p) is

$$M_r = \frac{\phi F_y t^2}{4}$$

Using F_y = 36 ksi and ϕ = 0.90 and equating this to the applied factored moment,

$$t = \sqrt{\frac{4 \times 13.5}{0.90 \times 36}} = 1.29 \text{ in.}$$

In order to minimize deflections, it is also considered desirable that the thickness should be greater than about 1/5 of the amount by which the base plate extends beyond the beam flange. In this case, the projection is very small and the requirement will not be checked.

Use a 5 x 1-1/4 plate x 9 in.

A column base plate that is distributing the load due to an axially loaded column is treated in substantially the same way as the beam base plate just discussed. It is obvious from Figure 10.25 that the bending of the plate is not now restricted to one direction, however. It is probably not economically worthwhile to attempt any rigorous analysis and the usual procedure is to consider the bending as occurring independently about either of the principal axes of the column. The details of the design are illustrated in the example following.

Example 10.7

Given

An axially loaded column carries a factored load of 800 kips onto a concrete footing that is capable of a bearing pressure of 1.9 ksi. The column section used is a W12 x 85. Select a suitable base plate of A36 steel.

Solution

Bearing area required = $\frac{800 \text{ kips}}{1.9 \text{ ksi}}$ = 421 sq. in.

Try C = 22 in., B = 19-1/2 in. (Notation as in Figure 10.25).

Area provided = 22 in. x 19-1/2 in. = 429 sq. in. (Satisfactory)

Actual bearing stress: $f_p = \frac{800 \text{ kips}}{429 \text{ sq. in.}}$ = 1.86 ksi.

Other dimensions: 0.95d = 0.95 x 12.50 in. = 11.88 in.

$$m = \frac{22 - 11.88}{2} = 5.06 \text{ in.}$$

$$0.80b = 0.80 \times 12.10 \text{ in.} = 9.68 \text{ in.}$$

$$n = \frac{19.50 - 9.68}{2} = 4.91 \text{ in.}$$

(The dimensions m and n should be kept nearly equal.)

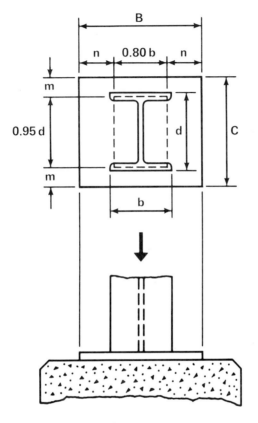

Figure 10.25
Column Base Plate — Axial Load

The factored moment on the plate will be that of a cantilever either m or n long acting under the 1.86 ksi loading. In this example, the dimension m is the larger and, considering a strip of plate 1 in. wide,

$$M_{max} = (1.86)(5.06)(5.06) \ 1/2 = 23.8 \text{ in.-kips}$$

The resistance of the plate, as for the beam bearing plate, can be taken as

$$M_r = \frac{\phi F_y t^2}{4}$$

Equating these two expressions and using the appropriate values of ϕ and F_y,

$$t = \sqrt{\frac{4 \times 23.8}{0.9 \times 36}} = 1.71 \text{ in.}$$

273

Use a 19-1/2 x 1-3/4 x 1'-10 plate.

Strictly speaking, a base plate for an axially loaded column would not require any anchor bolts since neither moment nor a horizontal force is present. However, in all practical situations, bolts would be provided to assist in locating the column, to provide a means of leveling the baseplate (using nuts on threaded rods), and to take care of small values of horizontal force and moment which may occur. The column would probably be shipped with the baseplate attached (using a minimum size fillet weld), although many different arrangements are possible.

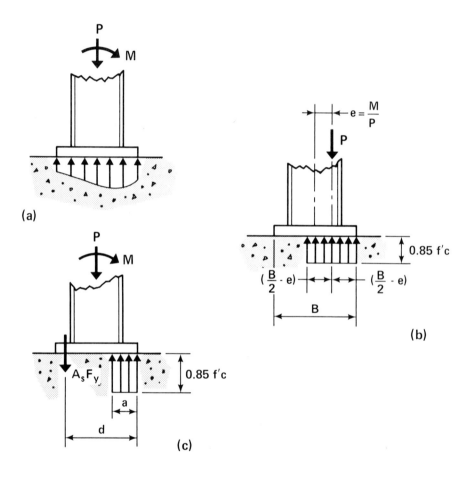

Figure 10.26
Base Plate — Axial Load and Moment

Column bases required to transfer both axial load and moment will only be discussed here. If the combination of axial load and moment produces a condition wherein compression is maintained over the entire base, it may be assumed that the anchor bolts are not effective in transmitting axial forces, either tensile or compressive. McGuire[10.14] suggests that the actual stress distribution in this case, Figure 10.26(a), be replaced by the idealization

274

shown in Figure 10.26(b) for values of e ⩽ B/6. The design can then be carried out on the basis of the procedures developed for base plates under axial load only.

If the combination of the factored axial load and moment does not produce compression over the entire base, then the anchor bolts must provide a tensile axial force as shown in Figure 10.26(c). Starting with trial values of the plate width B, the location of the anchor bolts d, and their area A, the values of the unknown width of the stress block a and the resisting moment provided by the tensile and compressive forces can be found using the equations of equilibrium.

References

10.1 Fisher, J. W. and Yoshida, N., "Large Bolted and Riveted Shingle Splices", Journal of the Structural Division, ASCE, Vol. 96, No. ST9, Sept, 1970.

10.2 Standard Specification for Carbon Steel Externally and Internally Threaded Standard Fasteners, ASTM A307-76b.

10.3 Standard Specification for High-Strength Bolts for Structural Steel Joints, Including Suitable Nuts and Plain Hardened Washers, ASTM A325-76c.

10.4 Standard Specification for Quenched and Tempered Alloy Steel Bolts for Structural Steel Joints, ASTM A490-76a.

10.5 Specification for Structural Joints Using ASTM A325 or A490 Bolts, Research Council on Riveted and Bolted Structural Joints, 1976.

10.6 Fisher, J. W., and Struik, J.A.H., "Guide to Design Criteria for Bolted and Riveted Joints", John Wiley and Sons, New York, 1974.

10.7 Christopher, R. J., Kulak, G. L., and Fisher, J. W., "Calibration of Alloy Steel Bolts", Journal of the Structural Division, ASCE, Vol. 92, ST2, April, 1966.

10.8 Canadian Standards Association, "Specification for Welded Steel Construction (Metal-Arc Welding)", CSA W59, 1977, Rexdale, Ontario.

10.9 Butler, L. J., and Kulak, G. L., "Strength of Fillet Welds as a Function of Direction of Load", Welding Journal, Welding Research Council, Vol. 36, No. 5, May, 1971.

10.10 Fisher, J. W., and Beedle, L. S., "Criteria for Designing Bearing-Type Bolted Joints", Journal of the Structural Division, ASCE, Vol. 94, ST10, October, 1968.

10.11 Crawford, S. F., and Kulak, G. L., "Eccentrically Loaded Bolted Connections", Journal of the Structural Division, ASCE, Vol. 97, ST3, March, 1971.

10.12 Butler, L. J., Pal, S., and Kulak, G. L., "Eccentrically Loaded Welded Connections", Journal of the Structural Division, ASCE, Vol. 98, ST5, May, 1972.

10.13 Plastic Design in Steel, ASCE Manuals and Reports on Engineering Practice No. 41, Second Edition, 1971.

10.14 McGuire, W., "Steel Structures", Prentice-Hall, 1968.

CHAPTER 11

BUILDING DESIGN

11.1 Introduction

The previous chapters have described the design process for individual members and connections. In the selection of the individual elements in a structure, the applied forces are known and the design procedure consists of selecting trial member sizes, then checking the trial members for compliance with the appropriate requirements of a design standard, in this case, CSA Standard S16.1-1974.

The overall design process is much less definite. In a very simple situation the floor area requirements and possibly the minimum height for the structure will be specified; the column arrangement may also be specified while the general framing scheme is left to the discretion of the designer. The designer must also interpret the requirements of the National Building Code[11.1] for the specific project, and thus determine the loads for which the structure will be designed, as well as the approximations to be made in the analysis of the structure. Only after these decisions have been taken and the various analyses performed, does the process of member selection take place.

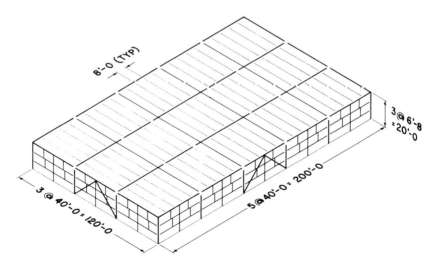

Figure 11.1
Example Building

In this chapter, the design procedure is illustrated using a single story rectangular building.[11.2] This simple building has been selected to illustrate the design process. Other building types would challenge the designer in different ways. For example, in a multi-story building the wind and stability effects become more important while in a heavy industrial structure loads due to cranes may govern the design of many structural elements. Figure 11.1 shows the framing scheme for a light industrial building, 200 feet by 120 feet in plan and 20 feet high. The bay sizes, 40 feet by 40 feet, have been established by functional requirements.

The roof is assumed to consist of a metal deck, supporting rigid insulation and built-up roofing. The cross-section is shown in Figure 11.2. The metal roof deck is supported by open web steel joists, spaced at 8 feet centre to centre. Special open web steel joists are used at each column line in the structure to stabilize the girders at these locations. The walls consist of metal cladding, supported by a girt system attached to the columns.

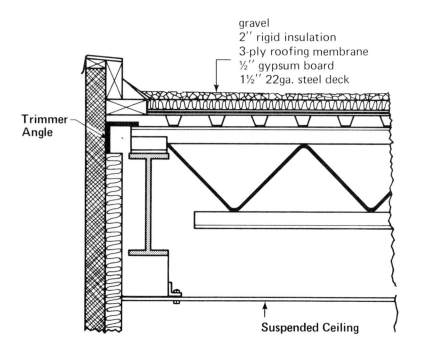

gravel
2″ rigid insulation
3-ply roofing membrane
½″ gypsum board
1½″ 22ga. steel deck

Trimmer Angle

Suspended Ceiling

Figure 11.2
Roof Construction

The roof girders are arranged in a cantilever system with the length of overhanging segments equal to approximately 12% of the span for the interior girder and 18% of the span for the exterior girders. The link beams are then simply supported from the cantilevered segments of the girders. The spandrel girders are simply supported at the ends and continuous over intermediate columns or posts. Although no specific attempt has been made to select the proportions so as to minimize the cost of the structure, the above arrangement is considered to represent good practice.[11.2]

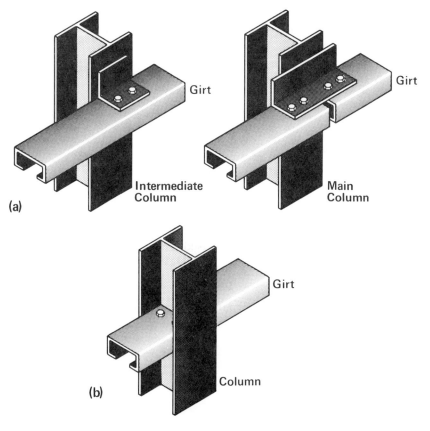

Figure 11.3
Girt Arrangement

The girt system is designed to transfer the lateral wind loads from the cladding to the exterior columns. The girts would normally be designed as simply supported at the main column lines and continuous over the intermediate columns or posts as shown in Figure 11.3(a). In this arrangement the girts contact an exterior column only on the outside flange. The column stability problems resulting from this type of support are outside the scope of this text[11.2] and for simplicity, the girts will be designed as simply supported members spanning 20 feet between columns. The girts will be framed into the webs of the columns as shown in Figure 11.3(b), thus, under normal conditions, providing complete lateral support to the columns at these points.[11.2]

Overall resistance to lateral load effects will be provided by bracing members in all four walls. Wind loads on the face of the building will be taken into the plane of the roof, or to the foundations, by the columns. The roof deck will be designed to act as a diaphragm and the loads taken out to the exterior walls and into the vertical bracing systems.[11.3]

Since the purpose of this chapter is primarily to illustrate the design process, only the major elements of the structure will be designed. In many cases simplifying assumptions will be made to ensure that the design is illustrative of the basic material contained in earlier portions of this text. Hopefully the resulting design will be reasonably efficient. However, alternate methods of treating various facets of design will undoubtedly be more economical for particular situations or particular fabricators.

11.2 Loads

Dead Load

The dead load supported by a roof girder in the example building includes the weights of the materials shown in Figure 11.2, in addition to the weight of any mechanical units on the roof, ductwork carried through the joists, lighting fixtures, fans, etc. as well as the weight of the steel girder itself. Typical weights of commonly used materials are given in the Handbook of Steel Construction,[11.4] as well as in various manufacturers catalogues.

For a 40 x 40 ft. bay size the specified dead load carried by a main girder in the example building can be estimated for preliminary design as:

roofing	5.5 psf
insulation	2.0
gypsum board	2.5
steel deck	1.9
ceiling	1.0
ductwork and fixtures	5.0
open web steel joists	1.8
total	19.7 psf

Snow Load

The live load that governs the design of roof systems for most locations in Canada is that caused by snow. Snow load on the roof of a building is determined by multiplying the ground snow load by a snow load coefficient to account for the influences of building exposure and roof shape[11.1]. The basic snow load coefficient, used to convert the ground snow load to a roof snow load, is 0.8 (for roofs exposed to wind this may be reduced to 0.6). Thus for normal conditions, for a building located in Halifax, Nova Scotia, the specified roof snow load would be:

0.80 x 45 = 36 psf

where 45 psf is the ground snow load for the Halifax area.[11.1]

Loads produced by the ponding of rainwater on the roof system will not be considered in this example. In most locations in Canada, ponding is not a problem. In a few areas, however, where the snow loading is relatively light, the design may be governed by ponding considerations.[11.2]

Wind Loads

Wind forces on low, flat roof buildings result in pressures on the windward wall, suctions on the leeward and side walls, and suctions over the roof. Using the simple procedure suggested in the National Building Code[11.1], the external pressures and suctions, at the specified load level, caused by wind acting at right angles to the building are given by:

$$p = C_e C_g C_p \, q$$

where p = the specified external pressure or suction acting normal to the surface, psf.

C_e = the exposure factor, equal to 1.0 for buildings less than 30 feet high,

C_g = the gust effect factor, equal to 2.0 when designing structural members and 2.5 when designing cladding or connections between the cladding and the frame,

C_p = the external pressure coefficient for the location being considered, and

q = the reference velocity pressure, psf.

Again using the data for Halifax as an example, the pressure on the windward wall or the suction on a side wall at the specified load level is:

$$p = 1.0 \times 2.0 \times 0.7 \times 11.0$$

$$= 15.4 \text{ psf}$$

and the suction on the end wall is

$$p = 1.0 \times 2.0 \times 0.5 \times 11.0$$

$$= 11.0 \text{ psf}$$

where 0.7 and 0.5 represent the pressure or suction coefficients for low rectangular buildings and 11.0 psf is the hourly wind pressure for Halifax, having a probability of 1 in 30 of being exceeded in any one year.

In addition to the pressures and suctions on the outside of the building, air leakage around doors and windows results in an internal pressure, p_i, (or suction, depending on the locations of the openings) given by:

$$p_i = C_e C_{pi} \, q$$

where C_{pi} is the internal pressure coefficient. The gust factor has been removed from the above equation, implying that internal gusts do not occur. In buildings that might be subjected to internal gusts, however, the internal pressure computed above would be multiplied by the appropriate gust factor, C_g.

For the example building the internal pressure is calculated as:

$p_i = 1.0 \times 0.7 \times 11.0 = 7.7$ psf

pressure or suction, where the coefficient of 0.7 implies that large openings exist along one wall of the structure only.

Earthquake Loads

In most areas of Canada it is necessary to design a building structure to resist wind and earthquake loads, combined separately with dead and live loads, as appropriate. For important structures, and for those particularly susceptible to dynamic effects, a dynamic analysis of the structure may be required.[11.1] For other structures an equivalent static approach is more usual. In either case the requirements of the National Building Code of Canada specify the design procedures. In most areas of Canada the design will be governed by either wind acting together with dead and live loads in the appropriate combinations, or earthquake loads acting together with dead and live loads. Loads due to wind and earthquake need not be considered together. The basic design approach is similar for both wind and earthquake, however, and thus only wind loads will be considered in this example.

11.3 Design of Roof System

A plan view of the roof framing scheme is shown in Figure 11.4. The metal deck is selected to span the 8'-0" distance between the open web steel joists. Joists, 24" in depth, are selected to span the 40'-0" distance between the main girder lines. Both these items are normally selected from manufacturers catalogues to satisfy both strength and deflection considerations. The typical joists are designed primarily to resist uniformly distributed loads, delivered to the joists through the metal deck. These joists are connected to the top flange of the supporting girders by field welds as shown in Figure 11.5(a) and are designed to resist the loading conditions specified in Clause 16.5.1 of CSA Standard S16.1-1974.[11.5] Bridging is used to stabilize the joists during construction.

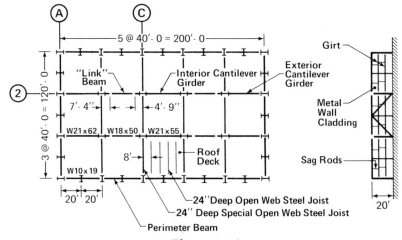

Figure 11.4
Example Building — Roof Framing

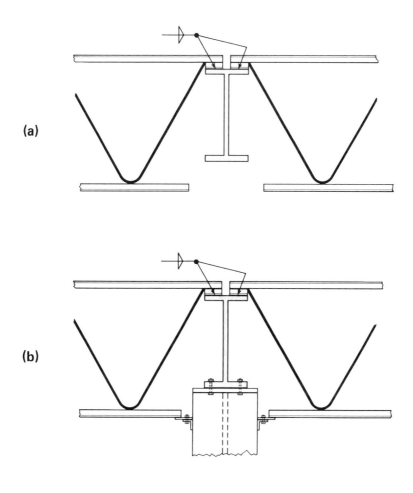

Figure 11.5
Joist Connections to Interior Girder

Along the column lines, special open web steel joists are provided. These joists are connected to the top flange of the girder and to the column as shown in Figure 11.5(b), in order to provide stability to the upper part of the column and to the compression (bottom) flange of the girder, at these locations. These special joists are designed as continuous members in accordance with the requirements of Clause 16.5.2 of CSA Standard S16.1-1974.

The interior segment of a typical girder system is shown schematically in Figure 11.6. Concentrated loads act on the girder segment at each joist location and at the point of attachment of the link beams, on the ends of the cantilevered portions of the girder. These loads are shown in Figure 11.6. The girder is supported vertically at each column. The top flange of the girder segment is supported laterally by the diaphragm action of the roof deck. At each column line, lateral support is also provided adjacent to the bottom flange of the girder by the attachment of the lower chord of the special joist, as illustrated in Figure 11.5(b).

283

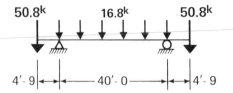

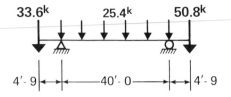

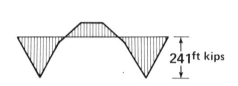

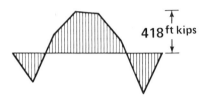

(a) Longest Negative Moment Region   (b) Largest Positive Moment

Figure 11.6
Design Conditions — Interior Girder

Under these conditions, and with the overhanging length less than approximately 12% of the span, it has been shown that the girder may be designed as a laterally supported member.[11.2] For other proportions, or for unusual loading conditions the strength of the girder system may be substantially reduced as failure may be triggered by lateral buckling.[11.2]

The National Building Code of Canada[11.1] requires that the girder system be designed to resist the factored dead and live loads acting over the complete system and also be designed to resist the factored loads with 50% of the live load removed from any one portion of the system. Under these conditions the maximum negative moment occurs at the column, when all portions of the link beams and (if joists are connected to the overhanging portions) the overhangs, are subjected to dead and live load. In addition, the longest negative moment region will be attained if 50% of the live load is removed from the interior portion of the girder. The latter consideration is significant in assessing the lateral stability of the system[11.2] and the bending moment diagram corresponding to this loading condition is shown in Figure 11.6(a).

The moment diagram corresponding to the maximum positive bending moment, is shown in Figure 11.6(b). This condition is achieved when 50% of the live load is removed from one of the link beams and (if joists are connected to the overhanging portions) the corresponding overhang region.

The factored loads are calculated using the right hand side of Equation 1.1. For this example, the loads applied to the girder system are equal to the joist reactions and are based on a tributary area of 8'-0 x 40'-0 = 320 square feet. The loads from the link beams are equal to the reactions from two joists. At the specified load level, recalling from Section 11.2 that the specified dead load is 19.7 psf and the specified live load due to snow is 36 psf, the loads at each joist location are:

DEAD LOAD = 320 x 19.7 = 6.3 kips, say 6.5 kips

LIVE LOAD = 320 x 36.0 = 11.5 kips

In the above calculation the dead load has been increased to compensate for the weight of the girder system itself.

The factored loads, corresponding to full dead and live load are then:

$$\text{FACTORED LOAD (100\%LL)} = \gamma \, (\alpha_D D + \alpha_L L)$$

$$= 1.00 \, (1.25 \times 6.5 + 1.50 \times 11.5)$$

$$= 25.4 \text{ kips}$$

In the above calculation $\gamma = 1.00$ is the importance factor, $\alpha_D = 1.25$ is the dead load factor and $\alpha_L = 1.50$ is the live load factor. The dead and live loads, 6.5 kips and 11.5 kips respectively, have been determined previously.

The factored loads, corresponding to full dead load and 50% live load is:

$$\text{FACTORED LOAD (50\%LL)} = 1.0 \, (1.25 \times 6.5 + 1.50 \times 11.5 \times 0.5)$$

$$= 16.8 \text{ kips}$$

The appropriate loads and the corresponding bending moment values are shown in Figure 11.6, where the maximum moment caused by the factored loads is 418 foot kips.

Using Equation 6.7, the required plastic modulus can be computed by assuming that the section selected will meet the requirements for a Class 2 section:

$$Z_x \text{ (required)} = \frac{Mmax}{\phi F_y}$$

$$= \frac{418 \times 12}{0.90 \times 44} = 127 \text{ in}^3$$

A W 21 x 55 section has a plastic modulus of 126 in³ and meets the requirements for a Class 2 section. It will be assumed that the small amount of underdesign in the above selection is acceptable. Additional calculations, not included, show that shear is not a significant problem.

The maximum live load deflection was calculated at the specified load level and found to be 1.5 inches. The allowable deflection for a girder supporting an asphaltic roof membrane is 1/240 times the span or 2.0 inches; again a W 21 x 55 section will be satisfactory.

Calculations similar to those outlined above were used to select the exterior cantilever girders, W 21 x 62 sections, and the link beams, W 18 x 50 sections. The final member sizes are shown on the roof plan in Figure 11.4.

The spandrel beams, along the edges of the structure, are designed as simply supported at their connections to the main columns and are continuous over intermediate columns, which are placed between the main column lines to reduce the span of the girts. The resulting continuity, as well as the significantly reduced loading results in a much lighter section. In this case W 10 x 19 sections were used.

The girder-to-column connections will be discussed below once the columns have been selected. One possibility for the link beam to cantilever girder connection is illustrated in Figure 11.7. The fasteners and plates in this connection must transfer a reaction of 50.8 kips through the eccentricity resulting from the detail of the joint.

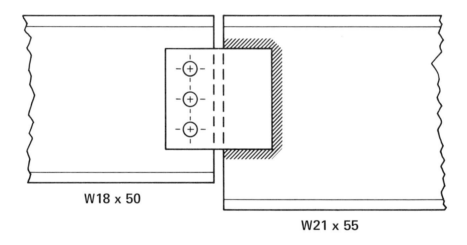

W18 x 50

W21 x 55

Figure 11.7
Link Beam Connection

11.4 Design of Interior Columns

The interior columns are designed as axially loaded members, restrained at the lower end by the base plate connection and at the upper end by the restraint provided by the special joist arrangement (see Figure 11.5b).[11.2] A detail of this connection is shown in Figure 11.8(a).

Many different approaches are in use for the design of this type of column arrangement. In accordance with Clause 9.3.1 of CSA Standard S16.1-1974, the length of the column will be assumed equal to the distance between the top of the base plate and the centroid of the lower chord of the joist, in this case assumed to be 18'-0".

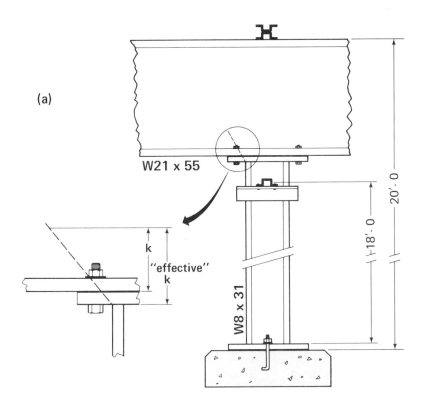

(a)

W21 x 55

"effective"
k

W8 x 31

(b)

50.8^k   25.4^k   50.8^k

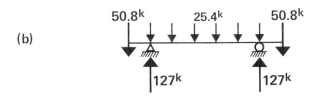

127^k   127^k

Figure 11.8
Interior Column

The maximum axial load will occur on an interior column when the tributary area is subjected to full snow load as well as dead load. This condition is shown in Figure 11.8(b) and the factored axial load on the column is 127 kips. As an initial trial, a W 8 x 31 section is selected. Assuming that failure is accompanied by weak axis bending (with $r_y = 2.01$ for the W 8 x 31 section) and further assuming that the column is pinned at the top and restrained by the action of the standard "pinned" base plate connection (G = 10.0) at the bottom, the effective length factor is 0.98 and the slenderness ratio is:

$$\frac{KL}{r} = \frac{0.98 \times 216}{2.01} = 105$$

The corresponding slenderness factor, given by Equation 4.15, is:

$$\lambda = \frac{KL}{r}\sqrt{\frac{F_y}{\pi^2 E}} = 105\sqrt{\frac{44}{\pi^2 \times 29000}} = 1.3$$

The factored compressive resistance of the column is calculated using Equation 4.16(b) as:

$$C_r = \phi A F_y \, (-0.111 + 0.636\lambda^{-1} + 0.087\lambda^{-2})$$

$$= 0.90 \times 9.12 \times 44 \, (-0.111 + 0.636 \times 1.3^{-1} + 0.087 \times 1.3^{-2})$$

$$= 155 \text{ kips}$$

Although the column has a capacity greater than that required, further calculations would show that lighter 10 inch and 8 inch sections are inadequate. Thus the W 8 x 31 sections will be selected for this example. In many cases hollow structural sections would provide a more economical choice, especially for the interior columns.

The detail at the base of the column is shown in Figure 11.8(a). The base plate was selected to resist the factored axial load of 127 kips according to the procedures illustrated in Section 10.10. Since the horizontal force to be resisted at the base is small (caused only by the possible out-of-plumb of the column) the welds connecting the base plate to the column are nominal and two 3/4 inch diameter anchor bolts are used to attach the base plate to the footing.

At the top of the column, the cap plate is provided simply as a convenience to assist in the connection between the girder and the column. The length of the cap plate is selected to provide sufficient space for bolting to the underside of the girder and the plate is of nominal thickness. As at the column base, the horizontal force to be resisted is small, thus the welds used to attach the cap plate to the column are nominal and the bolts are selected to be compatible with the size of the girder and column.

If the girder web had been slender, stiffeners would be used to "extend" the column flanges and thus eliminate the possibility of buckling or crippling of the girder web. In this example the factored compressive resistance at the girder flange-to-web fillet, B_r, is calculated using Equation 6.33:

$$B_r = 1.25 \, F_y \, \phi \, w \, (N + k)$$

$$= 1.25 \times 44 \times 0.90 \times 0.375 \, (8.00 + 0.375 + 1.125)$$

$$= 175 \text{ kips}$$

where the web thickness w = 0.375 for the W 21 x 55 girder and the length of the bearing plate is taken as the column depth, 8.00 inches. The "effective" k distance for the girder web includes the cap plate thickness as shown

288

in Figure 11.8(a), since the cap plate has not been designed to distribute the axial force over the overhanging portions.

Another important aspect of the detail at the top of the column, shown in Figure 11.8(a), is the positive lateral support provided along the top of the girder by the roof deck (and the attachment of the top chord of the joist) and the support provided adjacent to the cap plate by the attachment of the lower chord of the joist. The attachment at this point is consistent with the assumption that the design length of the column extends from the centroid of the lower chord of the joist to the top of the base plate, and the assumption that the girder is laterally supported at the compression (bottom) flange at each column line.

11.5 Design of Wall System

The general arrangement of the wall framing system is shown in Figure 11.4. Intermediate columns are used to provide reaction points for the girts mid-way between the main column lines and also serve as interior supports for the continuous spandrel beams. Thus the girts must span only a distance of 20'-0". In this example the girts will be designed as simply supported over the 20'-0" span although in many cases the continuous system shown in Figure 11.3(a) would be used.

The wall cladding must span between the girts and is usually attached to the girt system by means of self-tapping screws. The wall cladding is partially self-supporting but its weight is also taken through the girt system. It will be assumed, however, that the weight of the wall cladding does not induce bending moments in the girts. The girts are supported vertically at their points of attachment to the columns and also by sag rods at the mid-point of each girt, as shown in Figure 11.4.

Under these conditions the girts are designed solely to withstand the lateral loads caused by wind action. If the resultant force on the cladding is directed inward, the outside flange of the girt will be subject to compression. This situation is shown in Figure 11.9(a) where the outside flange of the girt is restrained from movement out of the plane of the applied load by its attachment to the wall cladding.

The loading condition giving rise to this situation might be that shown in Figure 11.10(a) where the wind is directed parallel to that wall containing openings, thus producing external pressure on the windward wall and internal suction throughout. The resultant uniformly distributed load produced by this condition is (15.4 + 7.7) x 6.67 = 154 pounds per foot (at the specified load level) for the girts on the windward wall.

If the resultant force on the girt is directed outward, as shown in Figure 11.9(b), the inner flange of the girt is subject to compression and is restrained from out of plane movement only at the points of attachment to the columns and at the sag rod locations. The loading condition that might give rise to this situation is shown in Figure 11.10(b) where wind directed perpendicular to the wall containing openings might produce an external suction on the sidewall and an internal pressure throughout. The net load would be the same as that in the previous case (154 pounds per foot) as will the maximum bending moment in the girt. However, this loading condition will govern selection of the girt since the moment must be resisted in the laterally unsupported condition. Figure 11.9(c) illustrates the detail at a sag rod location where a restraining couple can be developed by the action of the sag rod and the attachment of the girt to the cladding.[11.6] Thus the girt is laterally unsupported along the compression flange over the ten foot distance between the sag rod and the column, but is considered to be laterally supported at the columns and at sag rod locations.

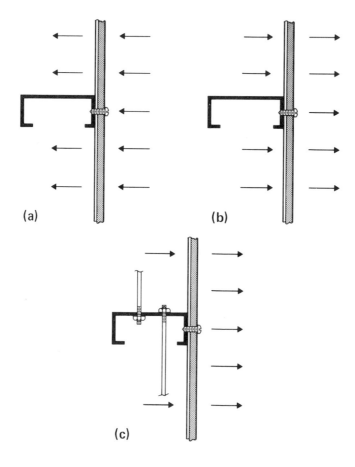

(a) (b) (c)

Figure 11.9
Girt Attachment

The sections normally used for girts are cold-rolled sections of steel having a yield stress of approximately 50 ksi. Although the standard for the design of cold-rolled sections does permit the use of the limit states approach, at the present time most manufacturers catalogues contain information relating to allowable stress design.[11.7] In this procedure, the maximum moment at the specified load level is matched against the allowable moment capacity specified by a manufacturer. The moment capacity is governed by lateral buckling of the section over a ten foot unsupported length. The resulting section for this example would be a 9" x 3 1/2" Cee section of 13 gauge material and weighs 5.36 pounds per foot of length.[11.8] A detail of the girt-to-column connection is shown in Figure 11.3(b).

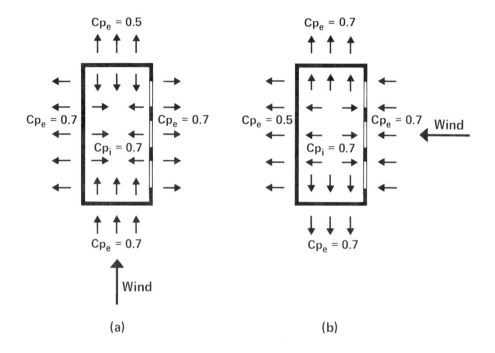

Figure 11.10
Internal and External Pressure Coefficients

11.6 Design of Exterior Columns

The arrangement of a typical exterior column is shown in Figure 11.11. The framing details are intended to be typical of column A2, located as shown on Figure 11.4. The loading on the column consists of an eccentric vertical load caused by the dead and live loads on the roof, as well as transverse loads produced by the effects of wind pressure or suction. The vertical load would be transferred to the inner flange of the column through the girder-to-column connection while the transverse loads are delivered through the girt connections, approximately at the third-point of the column.

The column is restrained at the base by the action of the base plate and at the upper end by the restraint offered by the connection to the girder. The latter effect will be assumed small in this example. The column is assumed to be braced laterally at the upper end by the spandrel girders and at the third points by the girts.[11.2]

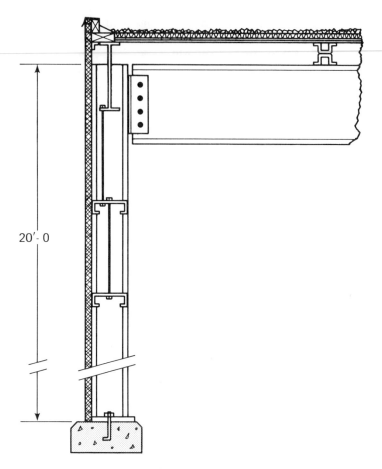

Figure 11.11
Exterior Column

Considering first the action of vertical dead and live loads only, the calculated girder reaction produced by the factored dead and live loads is 66 kips. Assuming that the column depth is nominally 8 inches, the end moment produced by the eccentricity is approximately 66 x (4 + 2 1/4) = 413 inch kips, where the eccentricity includes the half-depth of the column as well as an assumed distance from the face of the column to the gauge line of the bolts in the connection.

Assuming that a W 8 x 17 column section will be used in this location, the interaction equations developed in Chapter 7 will be used to check the adequacy of the section. The W 8 x 17 section meets the requirements for a Class 2 section and the pertinent cross-sectional properties are listed in Appendix A and page 5-153 of the CISC Manual.

$$A = 5.01 \text{ in}^2 \quad I_y = 7.44 \text{ in}^4 \quad Z_x = 15.9 \text{ in}^3$$

$$d = 8.00 \text{ in} \quad r_x = 3.36 \text{ in} \quad t = 0.308 \text{ in}$$

$$r_y = 1.22 \text{ in} \quad J = 0.147 \text{ in}^4$$

The factored axial load on the column Cf = 66 kips and the factored end moment Mf = 413 inch kips. The loading condition is shown in Figure 11.12(a).

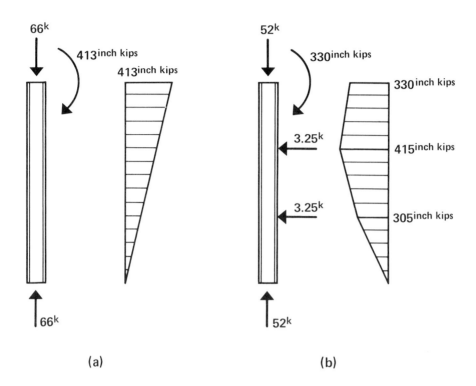

Figure 11.12
Design Conditions — Exterior Column

The factored compressive resistance of the section is:

$C_r = \phi\, AF_y = 0.90 \times 5.01 \times 44 = 200$ kips

and the factored moment resistance is given by Equation 6.7:

$M_r = \phi\, Z_x F_y = 0.90 \times 15.9 \times 44 = 630$ inch kips

The strength interaction equation, Equation 7.2, then becomes:

$$\frac{C_f}{C_r} + \frac{0.85 M_f}{M_r} \leqslant 1.0$$

$$\frac{66}{200} + \frac{0.85 \times 413}{630} \leqslant 1.0$$

$$0.89 \leqslant 1.0$$

293

For bending about the strong axis of the column the restraint offered by the base plate connection reduces the effective length factor from unity to 0.98. Thus the strong axis slenderness ratio is:

$$\frac{KL}{r_x} = \frac{0.98 \times (240\text{-}10.5)}{3.36} = 67$$

where the length of the column has been taken from the base plate to the mid-height of the girder. The non-dimensional slenderness factor is calculated from Equation 4.15 as:

$$\lambda_x = \frac{KL}{r_x}\sqrt{\frac{F_y}{\pi^2 E}} = 67\sqrt{\frac{44}{\pi^2 \times 29000}} = 0.8$$

For weak axis bending, the girts, together with the action of the cladding, effectively divide the column into three segments. Thus the weak axis slenderness ratio is:

$$\frac{KL}{r_y} = \frac{1.0 \times (240/3)}{1.22} = 66$$

Since $\dfrac{KL}{r_x}$ is greater than $\dfrac{KL}{r_y}$, the factored compressive resistance will be based on $\lambda_x = 0.8$ and is given by Equation 4.16(a):

$$C_r = \phi\, AF_y\, (1.035\text{-}0.202\lambda - 0.222\lambda^2)$$

$$= 0.90 \times 5.01 \times 44\, (1.035\text{-}0.202 \times 0.8 - 0.222 \times 0.8^2)$$

$$= 145 \text{ kips}$$

The elastic buckling strength of the member is:

$$C_e = \frac{286000}{\left(\dfrac{KL}{r_x}\right)^2} A = \frac{286000 \times 5.01}{(67)^2} = 320 \text{ kips}$$

and the equivalent moment factor $\omega = 0.6$ from Equation 7.12, with the smaller end moment equal to zero.

For the W 8 x 17 section with a laterally unbraced length of 6'-8", the factored moment resistance will be reduced slightly from that determined previously using Equation 6.7, because of lateral buckling. From Equations 6.26(a) and 6.28 the factored moment resistance is $M_r = 625$ inch kips. The quantities necessary to perform a check of the stability interaction equation have now been determined and Equation 7.11 is:

$$\frac{C_f}{C_r} + \frac{\omega M_f}{M_r\left(1 - \dfrac{C_f}{C_e}\right)} \leqslant 1.0$$

$$\frac{66}{145} + \frac{0.6 \times 413}{625\left(1 - \dfrac{66}{320}\right)} \leqslant 1.0$$

$$0.95 \leqslant 1.0$$

Satisfactory

Thus the W 8 x 17 section is adequate in this situation to resist the force and bending moments produced by dead and live loads acting on the roof.

When wind forces are added to those produced by dead and live loads, the reaction from each joist on the girder system will be reduced from 25.4 kips (dead and live loads only) to a value of:

FACTORED LOAD (with wind) = 1.00 (1.25 x 6.5 + 0.70 x 1.50 x 11.5)
= 20.2 kips

In the above calculation $\gamma = 1.00$ is the importance factor, $\alpha_D = 1.25$ is the dead load factor and $\alpha_L = 1.50$ is the live load factor. The dead and live loads, 6.5 kips and 11.5 kips respectively, have been determined previously. $\psi = 0.70$ is the load combination factor. This factor has been reduced from 1.00 to 0.70, to reflect the reduced probability of maximum snow and wind loads occurring simultaneously. Correspondingly, the axial force on the column is reduced to 52 kips and the end moment produced by the load eccentricity is 330 inch kips. In addition, however, the wind acting on the wall cladding delivers concentrated transverse loads to the columns at the third points, as shown in Figure 11.12(b). The factored wind loads would be based on a tributary wall area 20 feet long by 6'-8" high and on an external suction of 15.4 pounds per square foot combined with an internal pressure of 7.7 pounds per square foot (both at the specified load level). The reaction delivered by the girt to the column at the factored load level is then:

GIRT LOAD = 20 x 6.67 x 1.00[0.70 x 1.50 x (15.4 + 7.7)]
= 3.25 kips

The total bending moment diagram, caused by the transverse loads and the vertical load eccentricity, is shown in Figure 11.12(b) with the maximum bending moment having a value of 415 inch kips.

The strength interaction equation, Equation 7.2, is checked at the point of maximum moment:

$$\frac{C_f}{C_r} + \frac{0.85 M_f}{M_r} \leqslant 1.0$$

$$\frac{52}{200} + \frac{0.85 \times 415}{630} \leqslant 1.0$$

$0.82 \leqslant 1.0$ (satisfactory)

The stability interaction equation, Equation 7.11, is again checked but this time using $\omega = 1.0$ since transverse loads are involved.

$$\frac{C_f}{C_r} + \frac{\omega M_f}{M_r\left(1 - \dfrac{C_f}{C_e}\right)} \leqslant 1.0$$

$$\frac{52}{145} + \frac{1.0 \times 415}{625\left(1 - \dfrac{52}{320}\right)} \leqslant 1.0$$

$$1.15 \not< 1.0 \text{ (not satisfactory)}$$

Thus the W 8 x 17 does not meet the requirements under the combined loading condition and would not be used. Subsequent calculations show that either the W 8 x 24 section or the W 10 x 21 section would be adequate.

As in the case of the interior column, particular attention must be given to the design of the details and provision of bracing mechanisms to ensure the integrity of the member.

11.7 Roof Diaphragm Considerations

Although many of the individual members in the structure shown in Figure 11.1 have now been designed to resist the vertical dead and live loads and the horizontal loads caused by wind, the capacity of the structure to transfer the horizontal load to the foundations has not yet been ensured.

As an example, wind blowing perpendicular to the long face of the building shown in Figure 11.1 will produce pressure on the wall cladding on the windward face of the structure and suction on the leeward face (in addition to other effects). The cladding system, including the girts and exterior columns, has been designed to resist the equivalent forces on the areas tributary to the individual members. This same action, however produces a net lateral force on the building that must be transferred to the foundations.

In some buildings resistance to lateral load is provided within each line of columns in the structure. In these structures, wind forces are transferred from the wall cladding, through the girts to the exterior columns, then resisted directly by the stiffnesses of each line of columns (and the appropriate girders, etc.) parallel to the wind direction. In the example building, however, and in many light industrial structures, resistance to lateral load is not provided along the interior column lines and the entire lateral force on the structure must be resisted in the exterior walls. In this situation the wind loads, transferred through the wall cladding and girts to the exterior columns in the walls perpendicular to the wind direction, are further transferred (directly to the foundations for the exterior columns) into the plane of the roof. The entire roof must then act as a deep horizontal girder so that the loads brought into the plane of the roof by the exterior columns may be resisted by bending and shear in the roof deck. The reactions for the horizontal roof girder are provided by vertical trusses in the end walls of the structure parallel to the direction of the wind.

The loading pattern is illustrated in Figure 11.13 for wind blowing against the long face of the building. The loads delivered to the roof diaphragm at each exterior column location are based on a tributary wall area 20 feet long and 10 feet high (the wind load on the lower half of the panel is taken directly into the column footing through the anchor bolts). For dead load combined with wind load the factored load is:

FACTORED LOAD $= 20 \times 10 \times 1.00 \times 1.50 \times 15.4$

$= 4.62$ kips (pressure on windward face)

FACTORED LOAD $= 20 \times 10 \times 1.00 \times 1.50 \times 11.0$

$= 3.30$ kips (suction on leeward face)

In the above calculations the importance factor γ has been taken as 1.00 and the live load factor $\alpha_L = 1.50$. The wind pressure and suction at the specified load level, 15.4 psf and 11.0 psf respectively, have been calculated previously.

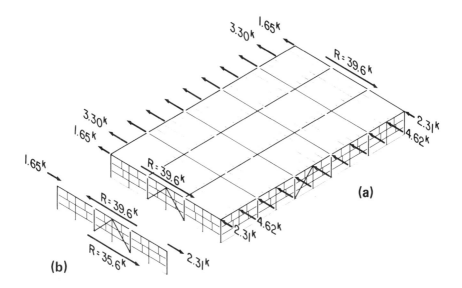

Figure 11.13
Loading Condition — Roof Diaphragm

The forces are shown in Figure 11.13(a) together with the reactions, which must be developed at each side wall, of 39.6 kips. The net shear, of 35.6 kips must be resisted by the action of the trussed bay in the side wall, as shown in the elevation view in Figure 11.13(b).

Figure 11.14(a) shows the loading condition for the roof diaphragm of the example building. The shear force diagram and bending moment diagram are shown in Figures 11.14(b) and (c) respectively. The web of the girder is formed by the metal roof deck. The top chords of the open web joist

297

system, the top flanges of the main roof girder system and the interconnection among the various elements also participate in diaphragm action. The flanges of the girder are assumed to be formed by the perimeter framing members such as the continuous trimmer angle, shown in section in Figure 11.2. The trimmer angles also serve as connecting elements between the roof deck and the wall cladding.

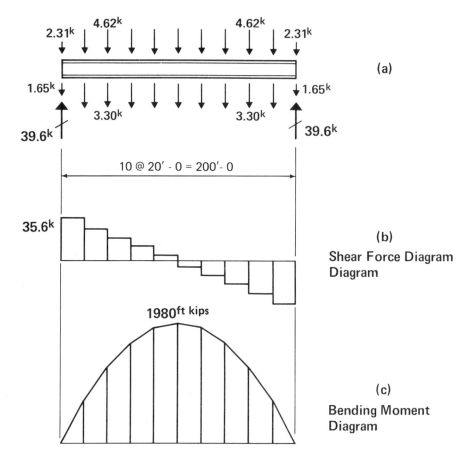

Figure 11.14
Shear and Moment Diagrams — Roof Diaphragm

The Canadian Sheet Steel Building Institute has published a design guide[11.3] that outlines the various provisions that must be met for the roof system to function properly as a girder or diaphragm. In the example structure, the flanges (continuous trimmer angles) along the long sides of the structure, must be capable of resisting a force of 1980/120 = 16.4 kips, where the maximum bending moment is 1980 foot kips and the depth of the "girder" is 120 feet.

The roof system must also be capable of resisting the shears appropriate to the particular location. The shear capacity of the roof will depend upon the thickness of the metal deck, the connections between the deck units, between the deck units and the top chord of the joists, and between the joists and the main girder system.[11.3] For example, along the short sides of the structure, the connection between the roof deck and the spandrel girders must be capable of resisting a total force of 35.6 kips.

The discussion above relates to the design of the roof diaphragm for wind blowing perpendicular to the long face of the building. Similar considerations apply for wind perpendicular to the short face. Load transfer may also be achieved by designing the primary roof system so that it forms a horizontal truss, rather than using the diaphragm action of the metal deck. Since the deck must be provided in any case, however, the additional costs of ensuring diaphragm action appear to be less than those involved in the use of a horizontal truss system.[11.2]

11.8 Frame Stability Considerations

It has been assumed in this example that all columns in the structure are effectively pinned in spite of the fact that some restraint is offered by the base plate details and the connections between the columns and girders. Thus the stability of the entire structure must be ensured by the proper design of the vertical trusses in the exterior walls. An elevation view of one such trussed bay is shown in Figure 11.13(b).

To examine the overall stability of the structure, three separate loading cases will be considered: wind load combined with dead load, wind load combined with dead and live load, and dead and live load acting alone but through the out-of-plumbs possibly produced by the erection procedures.

One common approach to the truss design is to assume that only the diagonal member in tension is effective. Thus in Figure 11.13(b) one diagonal member is effective in resisting wind loads in the direction shown, while the other diagonal member would act if the wind direction were reversed. Thus both members would be proportioned to resist a tension force of 35.6/0.707 = 50.3 kips. A single angle, for example, would adequately resist the load and provide room for easily making the connection. The use of this member might result in an excessive slenderness ratio, based on an unsupported horizontal length of 20 feet (see clause 10.2.2 of CSA Standard S16.1-1974). If excessive slenderness were a problem in this situation a larger member could be used or provisions made to attach the diagonal members to the girts.

Under the action of wind, the structure will deflect laterally. For example, at the factored load level, the net shear force of 35.6 kips would result in a lateral deflection of approximately 0.5 inches. Assuming that the roof deck is rigid in its own plane, this implies that each column in the structure would sway an amount equal to this deflection. The effect of this movement on the side wall columns is shown in Figure 11.15(a) by the dashed lines. If any one column in the structure is isolated as shown in Figure 11.15(b), it is apparent that a horizontal force, $H = C\Delta/h$, must be developed at the column base as a result of the deflection of the structure. An equal and opposite force must be transferred through the roof diaphragm to the side walls of the structure where it will be resisted by the vertical trusses in the same manner as the forces caused by wind.

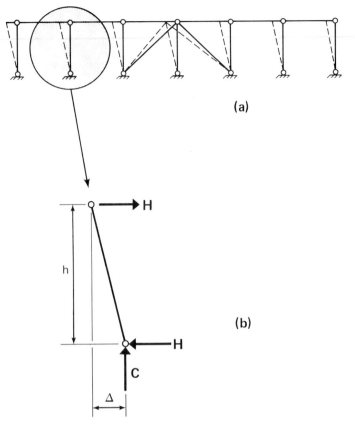

Figure 11.15
Frame Stability Considerations

Under the action of wind and dead load, since each column in the structure will undergo a similar sway movement, the effective lateral shear on the structure will be increased by an amount $\Sigma C\Delta/h$, where the summation includes all the vertical loads acting on the structure. Referring to Figure 11.13, the net horizontal shear to be resisted by the vertical truss in the undeformed position is 35.6 kips. This will be increased by:

$$120 \times 100 \times \frac{1.00}{1000} (1.25 \times 22) \times \frac{0.5}{240}$$

= 0.7 kips

where the area tributary to one side wall is 120 feet by 100 feet and the dead load (allowing for the girder weight) is 22 pounds per square foot at the specified load level. Again, in the above calculation, the importance factor has been taken as 1.00 and the dead load factor α_D = 1.25. The lateral deflection caused by the wind shear (35.6 kips) is 0.5 inches and 240 inches is the nominal column height.

Considering only dead load plus wind load, the vertical truss system would have to be designed to resist a shear of 35.6 kips plus 0.7 kips. The additional shear of 0.7 kips, caused by the sway of the structure, will not significantly affect the previously calculated deflection and the force in the truss diagonal will increase to a value of 51.3 kips, well within the capacity of the member selected originally.

If both dead loads and vertical live loads are combined with wind loads, the lateral shear due to wind is reduced to 35.6 x 0.7 = 24.9 kips. In this case a load combination factor of 0.70 is applied to the wind load to reflect the decreased likelihood of maximum values of both wind load and snow load occurring simultaneously. The lateral deflection is correspondingly reduced to 0.35 inches.

The additional shear caused by the sway of the structure is:

$$120 \times 100 \times \frac{1.00}{1000} \; [1.25 \times 22 + 0.70 \, (1.50 \times 36)] \; \times \frac{0.35}{240}$$

$$= 1.2 \text{ kips}$$

where the snow load is 36 pounds per square foot at the specified load level and a load combination factor of 0.70 has again been used.

Thus, under the action of vertical dead and live loads acting in combination with wind, each vertical truss system would have to be designed for a wind shear of 24.9 kips plus an additional shear of 1.2 kips for a total of 26.1 kips.

A third possibility should also be checked. This consists of the total vertical dead and live loads acting through the sway motion produced by possible out-of-plumbs in the columns. The maximum out-of-plumb for a column, permitted by CSA Standard S16.1-1974 in Clause 28.7.1, is 1/500 times the height; in the case of the example building, 240/500 or 0.48 inches. Using the total vertical dead and live load with a load combination factor of 1.00, the shear caused by the column out-of-plumbs on the side-wall truss would be:

$$120 \times 100 \times \frac{1.00}{1000} \, [1.25 \times 22 + 1.0 \, (1.50 \times 36)] \; \times \frac{0.48}{240}$$

$$= 2.0 \text{ kips}$$

For this loading case, however, the 2.0 kip shear is the total shear (increased slightly as a result of additional deflection caused by the 2.0 kip lateral shear) on the vertical truss and thus does not govern the design.

In summary, the governing design case for the vertical truss in each side wall would consist of vertical dead load combined with live load caused by wind. In this situation, each truss in the side wall (along the short side of the structure) would be designed to resist a total shear of 35.6 + 0.7 = 36.3 kips. The diagonal members selected for the first-order shear of 35.6/0.707 = 50.3 kips will be adequate to resist the increased (51.3 kips) force and the other members in the braced bays, as well as the connections, would be designed for the appropriate forces.

11.9 Summary

This chapter describes briefly the essential elements in the design of a small, rectangular building. The object was not to extend the material presented in previous chapters but rather to illustrate the procedures involved in applying member selection techniques in a design situation. The example used in this chapter was necessarily simplified for this purpose.

Single storey industrial buildings are found in all regions of Canada.

References

11.1 "National Building Code of Canada 1977", Issued by the Associate Committee on the National Building Code, National Research Council of Canada, Ottawa, 1977.

11.2 Nixon, C. D., "The Design of Light Industrial Buildings", Thesis to be presented in partial fulfillment of the requirements for the Ph.D. degree, Department of Civil Engineering, University of Alberta, Edmonton, Alberta, Canada, In preparation.

11.3 "Diaphragm Action of Rolled Steel Floor and Roof Deck Construction", Canadian Sheet Steel Building Institute, Willowdale, Ontario, 1972.

11.4 "Handbook of Steel Construction", 2nd Edition, Canadian Institute of Steel Construction, Toronto, Ontario, 1976.

11.5 Canadian Standards Association, CSA Standard S16.1-1974, "Steel Structures for Buildings — Limit States Design", Canadian Standards Association, Rexdale, Ontario, 1974.

11.6 Birkemoe, P. C., "Behaviour and Design of Girts and Purlins for Negative Pressure (Suctions)", Proceedings of 1976 Canadian Structural Engineering Conference, Canadian Steel Industries Construction Council, Toronto, Ontario.

11.7 Canadian Standards Association, CSA Standard S136-1974, "Cold Formed Steel Structural Members", Canadian Standards Association, Rexdale, Ontario, 1974.

11.8 Westland Metals Ltd., "Westland Light Gauge Structural Cee Sections", Edmonton, Alberta.

Table 7–1

CHEMICAL COMPOSITION — HEAT ANALYSIS[1]

Grade	C	Mn	P	S	Si	Grain Refining Elements	Cr	Ni	Cu[2]
33G	0.26	1.20	0.05	0.05	0.35	...	...	....	...
38W	0.20	0.50/1.50	0.04	0.05	0.35	...	...	....	...
44W	0.22	0.50/1.50	0.04	0.05	0.35	0.10	...	....	...
50W	0.23	0.50/1.50	0.04	0.05	0.35	0.10	...	....	...
44T	0.22	0.80/1.50	0.03	0.04	0.15/0.40	0.10	...	....	...
50T	0.22	0.80/1.50	0.03	0.04	0.15/0.40	0.10	...	....	...
50R	0.16	0.75	0.05/0.15	0.04	0.75	...	0.30/1.25	0.90	0.20/0.60
50A	0.20	0.75/1.35	0.03	0.04	0.15/0.40	0.10	0.70	0.90	0.20/0.60
100Q	0.20	1.50	0.03	0.04	0.15/0.35	...	(Boron 0.0005/0.005)		

(1) All percentages are maxima unless otherwise indicated.
(2) Copper content of 0.20% minimum may be specified.

Table 7–2

GRADES, TYPES, STRENGTH LEVELS

Type	Yield Strength, Ksi								
	33	38	42	44	50	55	60	70	100
G	33G	38W	42W *	44W	50G	55W *	60G	70W	
W	33W	38T		44T	50W	55T *	60W	70T	
T					50T		60T		
R					50R				
A					50A		60A		
Q									100Q

*These grades are available in hollow structural sections only.

Editor's Note: All Tables in this Appendix are reprinted from the CISC Handbook of Steel Construction, Second Edition, Seventh Printing, 1977. Tables designated 7-1 to 7-5 inclusive relate to steel materials covered by CSA Standards G40.20 and G40.21. These Standards should be consulted for more complete information.

Table 7–3

STRUCTURAL SHAPE SIZE GROUPINGS FOR TENSILE PROPERTY CLASSIFICATION

Structural Shape	Group 1	Group 2	Group 3
Wide Flange (Nominal depth by weight in lb./ft.) (W Shapes)	W24 x 55, 61 W21 x 44, 49 W18 x 35 to 60 incl. W16 x 26 to 50 incl. W14 x 22 to 53 incl. W12 x 14 to 58 incl. W10 x 11.5 to 45 incl. W8 x 10 to 48 incl. W6 x 8.5 to 25 incl. W5 x 16 to 18.5 incl. W4 x 13	W36 x 135 to 194 incl. W33 x 118 to 152 incl. W30 x 99 to 210 incl. W27 x 84 to 177 incl. W24 x 68 to 160 incl. W21 x 55 to 142 incl. W18 x 64 to 114 incl. W16 x 58 to 96 incl. W14 x 61 to 136 incl. W12 x 65 to 106 incl. W10 x 49 to 112 incl. W8 x 58 to 67 incl.	W36 x 230 to 300 incl. W33 x 200 to 240 incl. W14 x 142 to 211 incl. W12 x 120 to 190 incl.
Light Miscellaneous Beams and Columns (M Shapes)	to 35 lb./ft. incl.	Over 35 lb./ft.	
Standard I Beams (S Shapes)	to 35 lb./ft. incl.	Over 35 lb./ft.	
H Bearing Piles (HP Shapes)		to 102 lb./ft. incl.	Over 102 lb./ft.
Standard Channels (C Shapes)	to 21 lb./ft. incl.	Over 21 lb./ft.	
Miscellaneous Car and Shipbuilding Channels (MC Shapes)	to 28.5 lb./ft. incl.	Over 28.5 lb./ft.	
Angles, Bulb Angles, Zees and Rolled Tees	to ½ in. incl.	Over ½ to ¾ in. incl.	Over ¾ in.

Structural Shape	Group 4	Group 5	
Wide Flange (Nominal depth by weight in lb./ft.)	W14 x 219 to 550 incl.	W14 x 605 to 730 incl.	

Note : *Structural tees cut from W, M and S shapes fall in the same group as the structural shape from which they are cut.*

Table 7–4

MECHANICAL PROPERTIES — ROLLED STRUCTURAL SHAPES

Grade	Nominal Maximum Size Group	Tensile Strength Ksi	Yield Point—Ksi, Min.			Elongation %, Min.	
			Group 1 and 2	Group 3 and 4	Group 5	In 8"	In 2"
33G	5	55–75	33	33	33	21	24
38W	4	60–85	38	38	–	20	23
44W	3	65–85	44	42	–	20	23
50W	2	65–90	50	–	–	19	–
44T	5	65–85	44	42	40	20	23
50T	4	70–95	50	48	–	19	22
50R	1	70–95	50	–	–	19	–
50A	5	70–95	50	50	46	19	21
100Q	–	–	–	–	–	–	–

– *Indicates not available.*

Table 7–5

MECHANICAL PROPERTIES — PLATES, BARS AND WELDED SHAPES

Grade	Nominal Maximum Thickness Inches	Tensile Strength Ksi	Yield Point, Ksi, Min. (a) Size Range			Elongation %, Min.	
			≤1½"	>1½" and ≤2½"	>2½"	In 8"	In 2"
33G	12	55–72	33	33	33	21	24
38W	1½	60–85	38	–	–	20	23
44W	1½	65–85	44	–	–	20	23
50W	1½	65–90	50	–	–	19	22
44T	4	65–85	44	42	40	20	23
50T	4	70–95	50	48	46	19	22
50R	½	70–95	50	–	–	19	–
50A	8	70–95	50	50	50	19	21
100Q	2	115–135	100	100	–	–	18

(a) *For 100Q, the strength indicated is yield strength (0.2% offset).*
– *Indicates not available.*

Designation	Total Area	Area dw	h/w	d/A_f	Axis X-X				Axis Y-Y		
					I_x	S_x	r_x	Z_x	I_y	S_y	r_y
	In.²	In.²		In.⁻¹	In.⁴	In.³	In.	In.³	In.⁴	In.³	In.
W24											
X160*	47.1	16.2	34.2	1.55	5120	414	10.4	465	530	75.2	3.35
X145*	42.7	14.9	36.9	1.71	4570	373	10.3	417	471	67.1	3.32
X130*	38.3	13.7	39.7	1.92	4020	332	10.2	370	412	58.9	3.28
W24											
X120	35.4	13.5	40.4	2.16	3650	300	10.2	338	274	45.3	2.78
X110	32.5	12.3	44.0	2.35	3330	276	10.1	309	249	41.4	2.77
X100	29.5	11.2	48.0	2.58	3000	250	10.1	280	223	37.2	2.75
W24											
X94	27.7	12.5	43.7	3.07	2690	222	9.85	253	108	23.8	1.97
X84	24.7	11.3	48.0	3.46	2370	197	9.80	224	94.5	21.0	1.96
X76	22.4	10.5	51.2	3.90	2100	176	9.68	201	82.6	18.4	1.92
X68	20.0	9.86	54.2	4.55	1820	154	9.54	176	70.0	15.6	1.87
W24											
X61*	18.0	9.94	53.8	5.71	1540	130	9.25	152	34.3	9.77	1.38
X55*	16.2	9.33	56.9	6.69	1340	114	9.09	134	28.9	8.26	1.34
W21											
X142*	41.8	14.1	29.2	1.49	3410	318	9.03	357	414	63.1	3.15
X127*	37.4	12.5	32.8	1.65	3020	284	8.99	318	366	56.0	3.13
X112*	33.0	11.1	36.6	1.87	2620	250	8.91	278	317	48.8	3.10
W21											
X96*	28.3	12.2	33.5	2.50	2100	199	8.61	227	115	25.4	2.02
X82*	24.2	10.4	38.6	2.93	1760	169	8.53	192	95.6	21.3	1.99
W21											
X73	21.5	9.66	43.4	3.46	1600	151	8.63	172	70.6	17.0	1.81
X68	20.0	9.09	46.0	3.73	1480	140	8.60	160	64.7	15.6	1.80
X62	18.3	8.40	49.4	4.14	1330	127	8.53	144	57.5	14.0	1.77
X55	16.2	7.80	52.7	4.85	1140	110	8.39	126	48.3	11.8	1.73
W21											
X49*	14.4	7.66	53.7	6.00	971	93.3	8.21	108	24.7	7.58	1.31
X44*	13.0	7.19	56.8	7.05	843	81.6	8.05	95.3	20.7	6.37	1.26

*Not available from Canadian Mills.

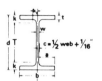

Wt. per Foot	Depth d	Flange Width b		Flange Mean Thickness t		Web Thickness w		a	T	k	k₁	c
Lb.	In.	In.		In.		In.		In.	In.	In.	In.	In.
160	24.72	24¾	14.09	14⅛	1.14	1⅛	.656	⅝	6¾	20⅞	1¹⁵⁄₁₆	1¹⁄₁₆	⅜
145	24.49	24½	14.04	14	1.02	1	.608	⅝	6¾	20⅞	1¹³⁄₁₆	1¹⁄₁₆	⅜
130	24.25	24¼	14.00	14	.900	⅞	.565	⁹⁄₁₆	6¾	20⅞	1¹¹⁄₁₆	1	⅜
120	24.31	24¼	12.09	12⅛	.930	¹⁵⁄₁₆	.556	⁹⁄₁₆	5¾	20⅞	1¹¹⁄₁₆	1	⁵⁄₁₆
110	24.16	24⅛	12.04	12	.855	⅞	.510	½	5¾	20⅞	1⅝	1	⁵⁄₁₆
100	24.00	24	12.00	12	.775	¾	.468	⁷⁄₁₆	5¾	20⅞	1⁹⁄₁₆	¹⁵⁄₁₆	⁵⁄₁₆
94	24.29	24¼	9.06	9	.872	⅞	.516	½	4¼	21	1⅝	1	⁵⁄₁₆
84	24.09	24⅛	9.02	9	.772	¾	.470	½	4¼	21	1⁹⁄₁₆	¹⁵⁄₁₆	⁵⁄₁₆
76	23.91	23⅞	8.99	9	.682	¹¹⁄₁₆	.440	⁷⁄₁₆	4¼	21	1⁷⁄₁₆	¹⁵⁄₁₆	⁵⁄₁₆
68	23.71	23¾	8.96	9	.582	⁹⁄₁₆	.416	⁷⁄₁₆	4¼	21	1⅜	¹⁵⁄₁₆	¼
61	23.72	23¾	7.02	7	.591	⁹⁄₁₆	.419	⁷⁄₁₆	3¼	21	1⅜	¹⁵⁄₁₆	¼
55	23.55	23½	7.00	7	.503	½	.396	⅜	3¼	21	1¼	¹⁵⁄₁₆	¼
142	21.46	21½	13.13	13⅛	1.10	1⅛	.659	¹¹⁄₁₆	6¼	17¾	1⅞	1	⅜
127	21.24	21¼	13.06	13	.985	1	.588	⁹⁄₁₆	6¼	17¾	1¾	1	⅜
112	21.00	21	13.00	13	.865	⅞	.527	½	6¼	17¾	1⅝	¹⁵⁄₁₆	⁵⁄₁₆
96	21.14	21⅛	9.04	9	.935	¹⁵⁄₁₆	.575	⁹⁄₁₆	4¼	17¾	1¹¹⁄₁₆	¹⁵⁄₁₆	⅜
82	20.86	20⅞	8.96	9	.795	¹³⁄₁₆	.499	½	4¼	17¾	1⁹⁄₁₆	¹⁵⁄₁₆	⁵⁄₁₆
73	21.24	21¼	8.30	8¼	.740	¾	.455	⁷⁄₁₆	3⅞	18½	1⅜	¹³⁄₁₆	⁵⁄₁₆
68	21.13	21⅛	8.27	8¼	.685	¹¹⁄₁₆	.430	⁷⁄₁₆	3⅞	18½	1⁵⁄₁₆	¹³⁄₁₆	¼
62	20.99	21	8.24	8¼	.615	⅝	.400	⅜	3⅞	18½	1¼	¾	¼
55	20.80	20¾	8.22	8¼	.522	½	.375	⅜	3⅞	18½	1⅛	¾	¼
49	20.82	20⅞	6.52	6½	.532	⁹⁄₁₆	.368	⅜	3⅛	18½	1³⁄₁₆	¾	¼
44	20.66	20⅝	6.50	6½	.451	⁷⁄₁₆	.348	⅜	3⅛	18½	1¹⁄₁₆	¾	¼

W SHAPES
W18 - W16
PROPERTIES

Designation	Total Area	Area dw	h/w	d/A_f	Axis X-X				Axis Y-Y		
					I_x	S_x	r_x	Z_x	I_y	S_y	r_y
	In.²	In.²		In.⁻¹	In.⁴	In.³	In.	In.³	In.⁴	In.³	In.
W18											
X114*	33.5	11.0	27.7	1.58	2040	221	7.80	248	274	46.3	2.86
X105*	30.9	10.2	29.8	1.71	1850	202	7.74	227	249	42.2	2.84
X96*	28.2	9.30	32.2	1.86	1680	185	7.72	206	225	38.3	2.82
W18											
X85*	25.0	9.64	31.4	2.28	1440	157	7.59	178	105	23.8	2.05
X77*	22.7	8.63	34.7	2.49	1290	142	7.54	161	94.1	21.4	2.04
X70*	20.6	7.88	37.7	2.74	1160	129	7.50	145	84.0	19.2	2.02
X64*	18.9	7.20	40.9	2.99	1050	118	7.45	132	75.8	17.4	2.00
W18											
X60	17.7	7.59	40.5	3.47	986	108	7.46	123	50.1	13.3	1.68
X55	16.2	7.07	43.2	3.82	891	98.3	7.42	112	45.0	12.0	1.67
X50	14.7	6.44	47.1	4.21	802	89.1	7.39	101	40.2	10.7	1.65
X45	13.2	5.98	50.3	4.79	706	79.1	7.31	89.7	34.8	9.31	1.62
X40	11.7	5.32	56.2	5.42	618	69.7	7.27	78.8	27.3	7.34	1.53
W18											
X35*	10.3	5.28	56.6	6.88	513	57.9	7.06	66.8	15.5	5.17	1.23
W16											
X96*	28.2	8.73	27.2	1.62	1360	167	6.94	186	224	38.9	2.82
X88*	25.9	8.14	28.9	1.77	1220	151	6.86	169	202	35.1	2.79
W16											
X78*	23.0	8.63	27.5	2.17	1050	129	6.76	146	92.5	21.5	2.01
X71*	20.9	7.85	30.0	2.38	941	116	6.71	132	82.8	19.4	1.99
X64*	18.8	7.09	32.9	2.63	836	105	6.67	118	73.3	17.2	1.97
X58*	17.1	6.46	35.8	2.91	748	94.3	6.61	106	65.3	15.4	1.95
W16											
X50	14.7	6.18	39.5	3.66	657	80.9	6.69	91.8	37.1	10.5	1.59
X45	13.3	5.58	43.3	4.07	584	72.5	6.63	82.1	32.8	9.32	1.57
X40	11.8	4.91	48.8	4.54	517	64.6	6.62	72.8	28.8	8.23	1.56
X36	10.6	4.74	50.1	5.30	447	56.4	6.49	64.0	24.4	6.98	1.52
W16											
X31	9.13	4.36	54.4	6.49	374	47.2	6.40	54.0	12.5	4.52	1.17
X26	7.67	3.91	59.8	8.25	300	38.3	6.25	44.0	9.59	3.49	1.12

*Not available from Canadian Mills.

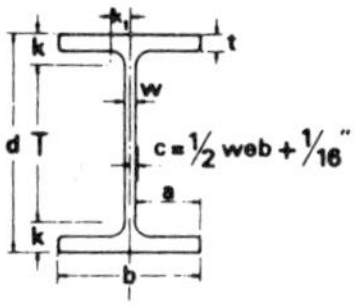

W SHAPES
W18 - W16
DIMENSIONS

Wt. per Foot	Depth d		Flange Width b		Flange Mean Thickness t		Web Thickness w		Distance a	Distance T	Distance k	Distance k₁	Distance c
Lb.	In.		In.		In.		In.		In.	In.	In.	In.	In.
114	18.48	18½	11.83	11⅞	.991	1	.595	⅝	5⅝	15⅛	1 11/16	15/16	⅜
105	18.32	18⅜	11.79	11¾	.911	15/16	.554	9/16	5⅝	15⅛	1⅝	15/16	5/16
96	18.16	18⅛	11.75	11¾	.831	13/16	.512	½	5⅝	15⅛	1½	⅞	5/16
85	18.32	18⅜	8.84	8⅞	.911	15/16	.526	½	4⅛	15⅛	1⅝	⅞	5/16
77	18.16	18⅛	8.79	8¾	.831	13/16	.475	½	4⅛	15⅛	1½	⅞	5/16
70	18.00	18	8.75	8¾	.751	¾	.438	7/16	4⅛	15⅛	1 7/16	⅞	5/16
64	17.87	17⅞	8.72	8¾	.686	11/16	.403	⅜	4⅛	15⅛	1⅜	13/16	¼
60	18.25	18¼	7.56	7½	.695	11/16	.416	7/16	3⅝	15⅞	1 3/16	11/16	¼
55	18.12	18⅛	7.53	7½	.630	⅝	.390	⅜	3⅝	15¾	1 3/16	⅝	¼
50	18.00	18	7.50	7½	.570	9/16	.358	⅜	3⅝	15⅞	1 1/16	⅝	¼
45	17.86	17⅞	7.48	7½	.499	½	.335	5/16	3⅝	15⅞	1	⅝	¼
40	17.74	17¾	7.44	7½	.440	7/16	.300	5/16	3⅝	15⅞	15/16	⅝	3/16
35	17.71	17¾	6.00	6	.429	7/16	.298	5/16	2⅞	15¾	1	⅝	3/16
96	16.32	16⅜	11.53	11½	.875	⅞	.535	9/16	5½	13⅛	1⅝	⅞	5/16
88	16.16	16⅛	11.50	11½	.795	13/16	.504	½	5½	13⅛	1½	⅞	5/16
78	16.32	16⅜	8.59	8⅝	.875	⅞	.529	½	4	13⅛	1⅝	⅞	5/16
71	16.16	16⅛	8.54	8½	.795	13/16	.486	½	4	13⅛	1½	⅞	5/16
64	16.00	16	8.50	8½	.715	11/16	.443	7/16	4	13⅛	1 7/16	⅞	5/16
58	15.86	15⅞	8.46	8½	.645	⅝	.407	7/16	4	13⅛	1⅜	13/16	¼
50	16.25	16¼	7.07	7⅛	.628	⅝	.380	⅜	3⅜	13¾	1¼	¾	¼
45	16.12	16⅛	7.04	7	.563	9/16	.346	⅜	3⅜	13¾	1 3/16	11/16	¼
40	16.00	16	7.00	7	.503	½	.307	5/16	3⅜	13¾	1⅛	11/16	3/16
36	15.85	15⅞	6.99	7	.428	7/16	.299	5/16	3⅜	13¾	1 1/16	11/16	3/16
31	15.84	15⅞	5.53	5½	.442	7/16	.275	¼	2⅝	13¾	1 1/16	11/16	3/16
26	15.65	15⅝	5.50	5½	.345	⅜	.250	¼	2⅝	13¾	15/16	⅝	3/16

W SHAPES
W14
PROPERTIES

Designation	Total Area	Area dw	h/w	d/A_f	Axis X-X				Axis Y-Y		
					I_x	S_x	r_x	Z_x	I_y	S_y	r_y
	In.²	In.²		In.⁻¹	In.⁴	In.³	In.	In.³	In.⁴	In.³	In.
W14											
X730*	215	68.9	4.11	.255	14400	1280	8.18	1660	4720	528	4.69
X665*	196	61.2	4.47	.272	12500	1150	7.99	1480	4170	473	4.61
X605*	178	54.4	4.86	.289	10900	1040	7.83	1320	3680	423	4.55
X550*	162	48.3	5.29	.308	9450	933	7.64	1180	3260	379	4.49
X500*	147	43.0	5.77	.330	8250	841	7.49	1050	2880	339	4.43
X455*	134	38.3	6.29	.352	7220	758	7.34	938	2560	304	4.37
W14											
X426*	125	35.0	6.73	.369	6610	707	7.27	869	2360	283	4.35
X398*	117	32.4	7.13	.388	6010	656	7.17	802	2170	262	4.31
X370*	109	29.7	7.63	.410	5450	608	7.07	737	1990	242	4.27
X342*	101	27.1	8.17	.435	4910	559	6.97	673	1810	221	4.23
X320*	94.1	31.8	6.68	.481	4140	493	6.63	592	1640	196	4.17
X314*	92.3	24.3	8.92	.464	4400	512	6.90	611	1630	201	4.20
X287*	84.4	22.0	9.64	.498	3910	465	6.81	551	1470	182	4.17
X264*	77.6	19.9	10.5	.531	3530	428	6.74	502	1330	166	4.14
X246*	72.3	18.3	11.2	.562	3230	398	6.68	464	1230	154	4.12
W14											
X237*	69.7	17.6	11.6	.580	3080	382	6.65	445	1170	147	4.10
X228*	67.1	16.7	12.1	.597	2940	368	6.62	427	1120	141	4.09
X219*	64.4	16.0	12.6	.618	2800	353	6.59	408	1070	135	4.08
X211*	62.1	15.4	12.9	.638	2670	339	6.56	391	1030	130	4.07
X202*	59.4	14.5	13.6	.660	2540	325	6.54	373	980	124	4.06
X193*	56.7	13.8	14.2	.686	2400	310	6.51	355	930	118	4.05
X184*	54.1	12.9	15.0	.713	2270	295	6.48	338	883	113	4.04
X176*	51.7	12.5	15.4	.743	2150	282	6.45	321	838	107	4.03
X167*	49.1	11.8	16.2	.777	2020	267	6.41	303	790	101	4.01
X158*	46.5	11.0	17.3	.812	1900	253	6.39	286	745	95.8	4.00
X150*	44.1	10.3	18.2	.850	1790	241	6.37	270	703	90.6	3.99
X142*	41.8	10.0	18.6	.895	1670	226	6.32	255	660	85.2	3.97
W14											
X136*	40.0	9.74	19.1	.941	1590	216	6.30	243	568	77.1	3.77
X127*	37.3	8.92	20.7	.997	1480	202	6.30	226	528	71.9	3.76
X119*	35.0	8.27	22.1	1.06	1370	189	6.26	211	492	67.2	3.75
X111*	32.7	7.76	23.4	1.13	1270	177	6.23	196	455	62.2	3.73
X103*	30.3	7.05	25.5	1.20	1170	164	6.21	181	420	57.6	3.72
X95*	27.9	6.57	27.1	1.30	1060	150	6.16	166	384	52.8	3.71
X87*	25.6	5.88	30.1	1.40	967	138	6.15	151	350	48.3	3.70
W14											
X84*	24.7	6.40	28.0	1.52	928	131	6.13	145	225	37.4	3.02
X78*	22.9	6.02	29.5	1.63	851	121	6.10	134	207	34.5	3.01

*Not available from Canadian Mills.

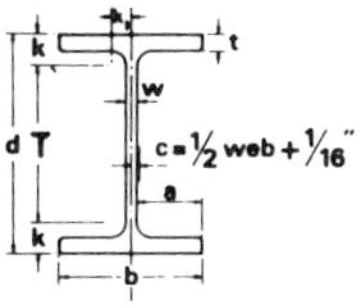

W SHAPES
W14
DIMENSIONS

Wt. per Foot	Depth d		Flange				Web Thickness w		Distance				
			Width b		Mean Thickness t				a	T	k	k1	c
Lb.	In.		In.		In.		In.		In.	In.	In.	In.	In.
730	22.44	22 1/2	17.89	17 7/8	4.91	4 15/16	3.07	3 1/16	7 3/8	11 1/4	5 5/8	2 3/16	1 5/8
665	21.67	21 5/8	17.65	17 5/8	4.52	4 1/2	2.83	2 13/16	7 3/8	11 1/4	5 3/16	2 1/16	1 1/2
605	20.94	21	17.42	17 3/8	4.16	4 3/16	2.60	2 5/8	7 3/8	11 1/4	4 7/8	1 15/16	1 3/8
550	20.26	20 1/4	17.21	17 1/4	3.82	3 13/16	2.39	2 3/8	7 3/8	11 1/4	4 1/2	1 13/16	1 1/4
500	19.63	19 5/8	17.01	17	3.50	3 1/2	2.19	2 3/16	7 3/8	11 1/4	4 3/16	1 3/4	1 3/16
455	19.05	19	16.83	16 7/8	3.21	3 3/16	2.01	2	7 3/8	11 1/4	3 7/8	1 5/8	1 1/16
426	18.69	18 3/4	16.70	16 3/4	3.03	3 1/16	1.88	1 7/8	7 3/8	11 1/4	3 3/4	1 9/16	1
398	18.31	18 1/4	16.59	16 5/8	2.84	2 13/16	1.77	1 3/4	7 3/8	11 1/4	3 1/2	1 1/2	15/16
370	17.94	18	16.48	16 1/2	2.66	2 11/16	1.66	1 5/8	7 3/8	11 1/4	3 3/8	1 7/16	7/8
342	17.56	17 1/2	16.37	16 3/8	2.47	2 7/16	1.55	1 9/16	7 3/8	11 1/4	3 1/8	1 3/8	13/16
320	16.81	16 3/4	16.71	16 3/4	2.09	2 1/16	1.89	1 7/8	7 3/8	11 1/4	2 3/4	1 9/16	1
314	17.19	17 1/4	16.24	16 1/4	2.28	2 5/16	1.42	1 7/16	7 3/8	11 1/4	3	1 5/16	3/4
287	16.81	16 3/4	16.13	16 1/8	2.09	2 1/16	1.31	1 5/16	7 3/8	11 1/4	2 3/4	1 5/16	11/16
264	16.50	16 1/2	16.03	16	1.94	1 15/16	1.21	1 3/16	7 3/8	11 1/4	2 5/8	1 1/4	11/16
246	16.25	16 1/4	15.95	16	1.81	1 13/16	1.13	1 1/8	7 3/8	11 1/4	2 1/2	1 3/16	5/8
237	16.12	16 1/8	15.91	15 7/8	1.75	1 3/4	1.09	1 1/16	7 3/8	11 1/4	2 7/16	1 3/16	5/8
228	16.00	16	15.87	15 7/8	1.69	1 11/16	1.05	1 1/16	7 3/8	11 1/4	2 3/8	1 1/8	9/16
219	15.87	15 7/8	15.83	15 7/8	1.62	1 5/8	1.01	1	7 3/8	11 1/4	2 5/16	1 1/8	9/16
211	15.75	15 3/4	15.80	15 3/4	1.56	1 9/16	.980	1	7 3/8	11 1/4	2 1/4	1 1/8	9/16
202	15.63	15 5/8	15.75	15 3/4	1.50	1 1/2	.930	15/16	7 3/8	11 1/4	2 3/16	1 1/8	1/2
193	15.50	15 1/2	15.71	15 3/4	1.44	1 7/16	.890	7/8	7 3/8	11 1/4	2 1/8	1 1/16	1/2
184	15.38	15 3/8	15.66	15 5/8	1.38	1 3/8	.840	13/16	7 3/8	11 1/4	2 1/16	1 1/16	1/2
176	15.25	15 1/4	15.64	15 5/8	1.31	1 5/16	.820	13/16	7 3/8	11 1/4	2	1 1/16	1/2
167	15.12	15 1/8	15.60	15 5/8	1.25	1 1/4	.780	3/4	7 3/8	11 1/4	1 15/16	1	7/16
158	15.00	15	15.55	15 1/2	1.19	1 3/16	.730	3/4	7 3/8	11 1/4	1 7/8	1	7/16
150	14.88	14 7/8	15.52	15 1/2	1.13	1 1/8	.695	11/16	7 3/8	11 1/4	1 13/16	1	7/16
142	14.75	14 3/4	15.50	15 1/2	1.06	1 1/16	.680	11/16	7 3/8	11 1/4	1 3/4	1	3/8
136	14.75	14 3/4	14.74	14 3/4	1.06	1 1/16	.660	11/16	7	11 1/4	1 3/4	15/16	3/8
127	14.62	14 5/8	14.69	14 3/4	.998	1	.610	5/8	7	11 1/4	1 11/16	15/16	3/8
119	14.50	14 1/2	14.65	14 5/8	.938	15/16	.570	9/16	7	11 1/4	1 5/8	15/16	3/8
111	14.37	14 3/8	14.62	14 5/8	.873	7/8	.540	9/16	7	11 1/4	1 9/16	7/8	5/16
103	14.25	14 1/4	14.58	14 5/8	.813	13/16	.495	1/2	7	11 1/4	1 1/2	7/8	5/16
95	14.12	14 1/8	14.55	14 1/2	.748	3/4	.465	7/16	7	11 1/4	1 7/16	7/8	5/16
87	14.00	14	14.50	14 1/2	.688	11/16	.420	7/16	7	11 1/4	1 3/8	13/16	1/4
84	14.18	14 1/8	12.02	12	.778	3/4	.451	7/16	5 3/4	11 1/4	1 7/16	7/8	5/16
78	14.06	14	12.00	12	.718	11/16	.428	7/16	5 3/4	11 1/4	1 3/8	7/8	1/4

W SHAPES
W14 - W12
PROPERTIES

Designation	Total Area	Area dw	h/w	d/A_f	Axis X-X				Axis Y-Y		
					I_x	S_x	r_x	Z_x	I_y	S_y	r_y
	In.²	In.²		In.⁻¹	In.⁴	In.³	In.	In.³	In.⁴	In.³	In.
W14											
X74*	21.8	6.39	28.1	1.80	797	112	6.05	126	133	26.4	2.47
X68*	20.0	5.88	30.2	1.95	724	103	6.02	115	121	24.1	2.46
X61*	17.9	5.26	33.4	2.16	641	92.2	5.98	102	107	21.4	2.44
W14											
X53	15.6	5.16	34.1	2.63	542	77.8	5.89	87.1	57.5	14.3	1.92
X48	14.1	4.68	37.2	2.90	485	70.2	5.87	78.4	51.3	12.8	1.91
X43	12.6	4.21	41.0	3.24	429	62.7	5.84	69.7	45.1	11.3	1,89
W14											
X38	11.2	4.42	41.8	4.06	386	54.7	5.87	61.6	26.6	7.85	1.54
X34	10.0	4.02	45.6	4.58	340	48.6	5.83	54.6	23.3	6.90	1.53
X30	8.83	3.74	48.5	5.37	290	41.8	5.73	47.2	19.5	5.79	1.49
W14											
X26	7.67	3.54	51.2	6.61	244	35.1	5.64	40.0	8.86	3.53	1.07
X22	6.49	3.16	56.7	8.19	198	28.9	5.52	33.1	7.00	2.80	1,04
W12											
X190	55.9	15.2	10.3	.654	1890	263	5.81	311	590	93.1	3.25
X161	47.4	12.6	12.1	.746	1540	222	5.70	259	486	77.7	3.20
X133	39.1	10.1	14.4	.875	1220	182	5.59	210	390	63.1	3.16
X120	35.3	9.32	15.4	.963	1070	163	5.51	186	345	56.0	3.13
X106	31.2	7.99	17.6	1.07	931	145	5.46	164	301	49.2	3.11
X99	29.1	7.42	18.7	1.14	859	135	5.43	152	278	45.6	3.09
X92	27.1	6.88	20.0	1.21	789	125	5.40	140	256	42.1	3.07
X85	25.0	6.19	22.0	1.30	723	116	5.38	129	235	38.8	3.07
X79	23.2	5.82	23.2	1.39	663	107	5.35	119	216	35.8	3.05
X72	21.2	5.27	25.4	1.52	597	97.5	5.31	108	195	32.4	3.03
X65	19.1	4.73	28.0	1.67	533	88.0	5.28	97.0	175	29.2	3.03
W12											
X58	17.1	4.38	30.4	1.90	476	78.1	5.28	86.5	107	21.4	2.50
X53	15.6	4.16	31.6	2.09	426	70.6	5.23	78.1	96.1	19.2	2.48
W12.											
X50	14.7	4.52	29.4	2.35	395	64.8	5.18	72.5	56.4	14.0	1.96
X45	13.2	4.05	32.5	2.60	351	58.2	5.16	64.8	50.0	12.4	1.95
X40	11.8	3.51	37.1	2.89	310	51.9	5.13	57.5	44.1	11.0	1.93
W12											
X36	10.6	3.73	36.6	3.45	281	45.9	5.15	51.6	25.5	7.77	1.55
X31	9.13	3.20	42.1	3.98	239	39.5	5.12	44.1	21.6	6.62	1.54
X27	7.95	2.83	47.1	4.60	204	34.1	5.07	38.0	18.3	5.63	1.52
W12											
X22*	6.47	3.20	44.1	7.20	156	25.3	4.91	29.3	4.64	2.30	.85
X19*	5.59	2.88	48.4	8.69	130	21.4	4.82	24.7	3.76	1.88	.82
X16.5*	4.87	2.76	49.8	11.2	105	17.5	4.64	20.6	2.88	1.44	.77
X14*	4.12	2.36	57.9	13.4	88.0	14.8	4.62	17.3	2.34	1.18	.75

314

*Not available from Canadian Mills.

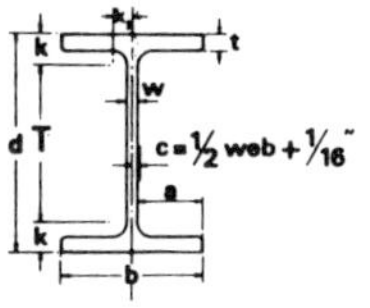

W SHAPES
W14 - W12
DIMENSIONS

Wt. per Foot	Depth d		Flange				Web Thickness w		Distance				
			Width b		Mean Thickness t				a	T	k	k₁	c
Lb.	In.		In.		In.		In.		In.	In.	In.	In.	In.
74	14.19	14¼	10.07	10⅛	.783	13/16	.450	7/16	4¾	11¼	1½	⅞	5/16
68	14.06	14	10.04	10	.718	11/16	.418	7/16	4¾	11¼	1⅜	13/16	¼
61	13.91	13⅞	10.00	10	.643	⅝	.378	⅜	4¾	11¼	1 5/16	13/16	¼
53	13.94	14	8.06	8	.658	11/16	.370	⅜	3⅞	11¼	1⅜	13/16	¼
48	13.81	13¾	8.03	8	.593	9/16	.339	5/16	3⅞	11¼	1¼	13/16	¼
43	13.68	13⅝	8.00	8	.528	½	.308	5/16	3⅞	11¼	1 3/16	13/16	3/16
38	14.12	14⅛	6.78	6¾	.513	½	.313	5/16	3¼	11⅞	1⅛	11/16	¼
34	14.00	14	6.75	6¾	.453	7/16	.287	5/16	3¼	11⅞	1 1/16	11/16	3/16
30	13.86	13⅞	6.73	6¾	.383	⅜	.270	¼	3¼	11⅞	1	11/16	3/16
26	13.89	13⅞	5.03	5	.418	7/16	.255	¼	2⅜	11⅞	1	11/16	3/16
22	13.72	13¾	5.00	5	.335	5/16	.230	¼	2⅜	11⅞	15/16	⅝	3/16
190	14.38	14⅜	12.67	12⅝	1.74	1¾	1.06	1 1/16	5¾	9½	2 7/16	1 3/16	9/16
161	13.88	13⅞	12.52	12½	1.49	1½	.905	⅞	5¾	9½	2 3/16	1 1/16	½
133	13.38	13⅜	12.37	12⅜	1.24	1¼	.755	¾	5¾	9½	1 15/16	1	7/16
120	13.12	13⅛	12.32	12⅜	1.11	1⅛	.710	11/16	5¾	9½	1 13/16	1	7/16
106	12.88	12⅞	12.23	12¼	.986	1	.620	⅝	5¾	9½	1 11/16	15/16	⅜
99	12.75	12¾	12.19	12¼	.921	15/16	.582	9/16	5¾	9½	1⅝	15/16	⅜
92	12.62	12⅝	12.16	12⅛	.856	⅞	.545	9/16	5¾	9½	1 9/16	⅞	5/16
85	12.50	12½	12.11	12⅛	.796	13/16	.495	½	5¾	9½	1½	⅞	5/16
79	12.38	12⅜	12.08	12⅛	.736	¾	.470	½	5¾	9½	1 7/16	⅞	5/16
72	12.25	12¼	12.04	12	.671	11/16	.430	7/16	5¾	9½	1⅜	⅞	¼
65	12.12	12⅛	12.00	12	.606	⅝	.390	⅜	5¾	9½	1 5/16	13/16	¼
58	12.19	12¼	10.01	10	.641	⅝	.359	⅜	4⅞	9½	1⅜	13/16	¼
53	12.06	12	10.00	10	.576	9/16	.345	⅜	4⅞	9½	1¼	13/16	¼
50	12.19	12¼	8.08	8⅛	.641	⅝	.371	⅜	3⅞	9½	1⅜	13/16	¼
45	12.06	12	8.04	8	.576	9/16	.336	5/16	3⅞	9½	1¼	13/16	¼
40	11.94	12	8.00	8	.516	½	.294	5/16	3⅞	9½	1¼	13/16	3/16
36	12.24	12¼	6.57	6⅝	.540	9/16	.305	5/16	3⅛	10⅛	1 1/16	⅝	3/16
31	12.09	12⅛	6.53	6½	.465	7/16	.265	¼	3⅛	10⅛	1	⅝	3/16
27	11.96	12	6.50	6½	.400	⅜	.237	¼	3⅛	10⅛	15/16	9/16	3/16
22	12.31	12¼	4.03	4	.424	7/16	.260	¼	1⅞	10⅜	15/16	⅝	3/16
19	12.16	12⅛	4.01	4	.349	⅜	.237	¼	1⅞	10⅜	⅞	9/16	3/16
16.5	12.00	12	4.00	4	.269	¼	.230	¼	1⅞	10⅜	13/16	9/16	3/16
14	11.91	11⅞	3.97	4	.224	¼	.198	3/16	1⅞	10⅜	¾	9/16	3/16

W SHAPES
W10 - W8
PROPERTIES

Designation	Total Area	Area dw	h/w	d/Af	I_x	S_x	r_x	Z_x	I_y	S_y	r_y
	In.²	In.²		In.⁻¹	In.⁴	In.³	In.	In.³	In.⁴	In.³	In.
W10											
X112	32.9	8.59	11.8	.875	719	126	4.67	148	235	45.1	2.67
X100	29.4	7.62	13.0	.961	625	112	4.61	130	207	40.0	2.65
X89	26.2	6.69	14.4	1.06	542	99.6	4.55	114	181	35.2	2.63
X77	22.7	5.68	16.6	1.20	457	86.1	4.49	97.8	153	30.0	2.60
X72	21.2	5.36	17.4	1.28	421	80.2	4.46	90.6	142	27.9	2.59
X66	19.4	4.74	19.4	1.37	382	73.6	4.44	82.8	129	25.5	2.58
X60	17.7	4.25	21.4	1.49	344	67.1	4.41	75.0	116	23.0	2.56
X54	15.9	3.72	24.1	1.63	306	60.5	4.39	67.1	104	20.7	2.56
X49	14.4	3.40	26.1	1.79	273	54.6	4.35	60.3	93.0	18.6	2.54
W10											
X45	13.2	3.54	25.4	2.04	249	49.2	4.34	54.9	53.2	13.3	2.01
X39	11.5	3.16	27.9	2.36	210	42.3	4.27	46.9	44.9	11.2	1.98
X33	9.71	2.85	30.4	2.83	171	35.1	4.20	38.8	36.5	9.17	1.94
W10											
X29	8.54	2.95	31.9	3.52	158	30.9	4.30	34.7	16.3	5.62	1.38
X25	7.36	2.54	36.6	4.07	133	26.4	4.25	29.6	13.7	4.76	1.36
X21	6.20	2.38	38.4	5.06	107	21.6	4.15	24.1	10.8	3.76	1.32
W10											
X19*	5.61	2.56	37.8	6.47	96.3	18.8	4.14	21.6	4.28	2.13	.87
X17*	4.99	2.43	39.4	7.67	81.9	16.2	4.05	18.6	3.55	1.77	.84
X15*	4.41	2.30	41.1	9.29	68.9	13.8	3.95	16.0	2.88	1.44	.81
X11.5*	3.39	1.78	52.6	12.2	52.0	10.5	3.92	12.2	2.10	1.06	.79
W8											
X67	19.7	5.18	12.4	1.16	272	60.4	3.72	70.2	88.6	21.4	2.12
X58	17.1	4.46	14.0	1.32	227	51.9	3.64	59.7	74.9	18.2	2.09
X48	14.1	3.44	17.6	1.53	184	43.3	3.61	49.0	60.9	15.0	2.08
X40	11.8	3.01	19.5	1.83	146	35.4	3.52	39.8	49.0	12.1	2.04
X35	10.3	2.56	22.6	2.05	126	31.0	3.50	34.7	42.5	10.6	2.03
X31	9.12	2.30	24.8	2.31	110	27.5	3.47	30.4	37.0	9.25	2.01
W8											
X28	8.23	2.30	25.0	2.66	97.8	24.3	3.45	27.1	21.6	6.61	1.62
X24	7.06	1.94	29.1	3.07	82.5	20.8	3.42	23.1	18.2	5.60	1.61
W8											
X20	5.89	2.02	29.8	4.09	69.4	17.1	3.43	19.1	9.22	3.50	1.25
X17	5.01	1.84	32.1	4.95	56.6	14.2	3.36	15.9	7.44	2.83	1.22
W8											
X15*	4.43	1.99	30.6	6.44	48.1	11.8	3.30	13.6	3.40	1.69	.88
X13*	3.83	1.84	32.6	7.87	39.6	9.90	3.22	11.4	2.72	1.36	.84
X10*	2.96	1.34	44.1	9.83	30.8	7.80	3.23	8.86	2.08	1.06	.84

*Not available from Canadian Mills.

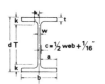

Wt. per Foot	Depth d		Flange Width b		Flange Mean Thickness t		Web Thickness w		a	T	k	k_1	c
Lb.	In.		In.		In.		In.		In.	In.	In.	In.	In.
112	11.38	$11\frac{3}{8}$	10.42	$10\frac{3}{8}$	1.25	$1\frac{1}{4}$	.755	$\frac{3}{4}$	$4\frac{7}{8}$	$7\frac{3}{4}$	$1\frac{13}{16}$	$\frac{15}{16}$	$\frac{7}{16}$
100	11.12	$11\frac{1}{8}$	10.35	$10\frac{3}{8}$	1.12	$1\frac{1}{8}$	.685	$\frac{11}{16}$	$4\frac{7}{8}$	$7\frac{3}{4}$	$1\frac{11}{16}$	$\frac{7}{8}$	$\frac{3}{8}$
89	10 88	$10\frac{7}{8}$	10.28	$10\frac{1}{4}$	.998	1	.615	$\frac{5}{8}$	$4\frac{7}{8}$	$7\frac{3}{4}$	$1\frac{9}{16}$	$\frac{13}{16}$	$\frac{3}{8}$
77	10.62	$10\frac{5}{8}$	10.20	$10\frac{1}{4}$	.868	$\frac{7}{8}$	.535	$\frac{9}{16}$	$4\frac{7}{8}$	$7\frac{3}{4}$	$1\frac{7}{16}$	$\frac{13}{16}$	$\frac{5}{16}$
72	10.50	$10\frac{1}{2}$	10.17	$10\frac{1}{8}$	.808	$\frac{13}{16}$	.510	$\frac{1}{2}$	$4\frac{7}{8}$	$7\frac{3}{4}$	$1\frac{3}{8}$	$\frac{13}{16}$	$\frac{5}{16}$
66	10.38	$10\frac{3}{8}$	10.12	$10\frac{1}{8}$	.748	$\frac{3}{4}$	.457	$\frac{7}{16}$	$4\frac{7}{8}$	$7\frac{3}{4}$	$1\frac{5}{16}$	$\frac{3}{4}$	$\frac{5}{16}$
60	10.25	$10\frac{1}{4}$	10.08	$10\frac{1}{8}$	.683	$\frac{11}{16}$	.415	$\frac{7}{16}$	$4\frac{7}{8}$	$7\frac{3}{4}$	$1\frac{1}{4}$	$\frac{3}{4}$	$\frac{1}{4}$
54	10.12	$10\frac{1}{8}$	10.03	10	.618	$\frac{5}{8}$	.368	$\frac{3}{8}$	$4\frac{7}{8}$	$7\frac{3}{4}$	$1\frac{3}{16}$	$\frac{11}{16}$	$\frac{1}{4}$
49	10.00	10	10.00	10	.558	$\frac{9}{16}$	.340	$\frac{5}{16}$	$4\frac{7}{8}$	$7\frac{3}{4}$	$1\frac{1}{8}$	$\frac{11}{16}$	$\frac{1}{4}$
45	10.12	$10\frac{1}{8}$	8.02	8	.618	$\frac{5}{8}$	.350	$\frac{3}{8}$	$3\frac{7}{8}$	$7\frac{3}{4}$	$1\frac{3}{16}$	$\frac{11}{16}$	$\frac{1}{4}$
39	9.94	10	7.99	8	.528	$\frac{1}{2}$	.318	$\frac{5}{16}$	$3\frac{7}{8}$	$7\frac{3}{4}$	$1\frac{1}{8}$	$\frac{11}{16}$	$\frac{1}{4}$
33	9.75	$9\frac{3}{4}$	7.96	8	.433	$\frac{7}{16}$	.292	$\frac{5}{16}$	$3\frac{7}{8}$	$7\frac{3}{4}$	1	$\frac{11}{16}$	$\frac{3}{16}$
29	10.22	$10\frac{1}{4}$	5.80	$5\frac{3}{4}$	.500	$\frac{1}{2}$	.289	$\frac{5}{16}$	$2\frac{3}{4}$	$8\frac{1}{8}$	$1\frac{1}{16}$	$\frac{5}{8}$	$\frac{3}{16}$
25	10.08	$10\frac{1}{8}$	5.76	$5\frac{3}{4}$	.430	$\frac{7}{16}$	.252	$\frac{1}{4}$	$2\frac{3}{4}$	$8\frac{1}{8}$	1	$\frac{5}{8}$	$\frac{3}{16}$
21	9.90	$9\frac{7}{8}$	5.75	$5\frac{3}{4}$	.340	$\frac{5}{16}$	.240	$\frac{1}{4}$	$2\frac{3}{4}$	$8\frac{1}{8}$	$\frac{7}{8}$	$\frac{9}{16}$	$\frac{3}{16}$
19	10.25	$10\frac{1}{4}$	4.02	4	.394	$\frac{3}{8}$	.250	$\frac{1}{4}$	$1\frac{7}{8}$	$8\frac{3}{8}$	$\frac{15}{16}$	$\frac{5}{8}$	$\frac{3}{16}$
17	10.12	$10\frac{1}{8}$	4.01	4	.329	$\frac{5}{16}$	.240	$\frac{1}{4}$	$1\frac{7}{8}$	$8\frac{3}{8}$	$\frac{7}{8}$	$\frac{9}{16}$	$\frac{3}{16}$
15	10.00	10	4.00	4	.269	$\frac{1}{4}$	.230	$\frac{1}{4}$	$1\frac{7}{8}$	$8\frac{3}{8}$	$\frac{13}{16}$	$\frac{9}{16}$	$\frac{3}{16}$
11.5	9.87	$9\frac{7}{8}$	3.95	4	.204	$\frac{3}{16}$	.180	$\frac{3}{16}$	$1\frac{7}{8}$	$8\frac{3}{8}$	$\frac{3}{4}$	$\frac{9}{16}$	$\frac{1}{8}$
67	9.00	9	8.29	$8\frac{1}{4}$	.933	$\frac{15}{16}$	.575	$\frac{9}{16}$	$3\frac{7}{8}$	$6\frac{1}{8}$	$1\frac{7}{16}$	$\frac{3}{4}$	$\frac{3}{8}$
58	8.75	$8\frac{3}{4}$	8.22	$8\frac{1}{4}$	.808	$\frac{13}{16}$	.510	$\frac{1}{2}$	$3\frac{7}{8}$	$6\frac{1}{8}$	$1\frac{5}{16}$	$\frac{11}{16}$	$\frac{5}{16}$
48	8.50	$8\frac{1}{2}$	8.12	$8\frac{1}{8}$	.683	$\frac{11}{16}$	.405	$\frac{3}{8}$	$3\frac{7}{8}$	$6\frac{1}{8}$	$1\frac{3}{16}$	$\frac{5}{8}$	$\frac{1}{4}$
40	8.25	$8\frac{1}{4}$	8.08	$8\frac{1}{8}$	.558	$\frac{9}{16}$	.365	$\frac{3}{8}$	$3\frac{7}{8}$	$6\frac{1}{8}$	$1\frac{1}{16}$	$\frac{5}{8}$	$\frac{1}{4}$
35	8.12	$8\frac{1}{8}$	8.03	8	.493	$\frac{1}{2}$	.315	$\frac{5}{16}$	$3\frac{7}{8}$	$6\frac{1}{8}$	1	$\frac{5}{8}$	$\frac{1}{4}$
31	8.00	8	8.00	8	.433	$\frac{7}{16}$	.288	$\frac{5}{16}$	$3\frac{7}{8}$	$6\frac{1}{8}$	$\frac{15}{16}$	$\frac{5}{8}$	$\frac{3}{16}$
28	8.06	8	6.54	$6\frac{1}{2}$	.463	$\frac{7}{16}$	.285	$\frac{5}{16}$	$3\frac{1}{8}$	$6\frac{1}{8}$	$\frac{15}{16}$	$\frac{5}{8}$	$\frac{3}{16}$
24	7.93	$7\frac{7}{8}$	6.50	$6\frac{1}{2}$	.398	$\frac{3}{8}$	.245	$\frac{1}{4}$	$3\frac{1}{8}$	$6\frac{1}{8}$	$\frac{7}{8}$	$\frac{9}{16}$	$\frac{3}{16}$
20	8.14	$8\frac{1}{8}$	5.27	$5\frac{1}{4}$	.378	$\frac{3}{8}$	.248	$\frac{1}{4}$	$2\frac{1}{2}$	$6\frac{3}{8}$	$\frac{7}{8}$	$\frac{9}{16}$	$\frac{3}{16}$
17	8.00	8	5.25	$5\frac{1}{4}$	.308	$\frac{5}{16}$	.230	$\frac{1}{4}$	$2\frac{1}{2}$	$6\frac{3}{8}$	$\frac{13}{16}$	$\frac{1}{2}$	$\frac{3}{16}$
15	8.12	$8\frac{1}{8}$	4.02	4	.314	$\frac{5}{16}$	.245	$\frac{1}{4}$	$1\frac{7}{8}$	$6\frac{1}{2}$	$\frac{13}{16}$	$\frac{9}{16}$	$\frac{3}{16}$
13	8.00	8	4.00	4	.254	$\frac{1}{4}$	.230	$\frac{1}{4}$	$1\frac{7}{8}$	$6\frac{1}{2}$	$\frac{3}{4}$	$\frac{1}{2}$	$\frac{3}{16}$
10	7.90	$7\frac{7}{8}$	3.94	4	.204	$\frac{3}{16}$	.170	$\frac{3}{16}$	$1\frac{7}{8}$	$6\frac{1}{2}$	$\frac{11}{16}$	$\frac{1}{2}$	$\frac{1}{8}$

STANDARD CHANNELS

PROPERTIES

Designation	Total Area	Area dw	h/w	Axis X-X			Axis Y-Y			
				I_x	S_x	r_x	I_y	S_y	r_y	x
	In.²	In.²		In.⁴	In.³	In.	In.⁴	In.³	In.	In.
C15										
X50	14.7	10.7	19.1	404	53.9	5.24	11.0	3.77	.87	.80
X40	11.8	7.80	26.3	349	46.5	5.44	9.23	3.37	.88	.78
X33.9	9.96	6.00	34.3	315	42.0	5.62	8.13	3.11	.90	.79
C12										
X30	8.82	6.12	21.6	162	27.0	4.29	5.14	2.06	.76	.67
X25	7.35	4.64	28.4	144	24.0	4.43	4.47	1.88	.78	.67
X20.7	6.09	3.38	39.0	129	21.5	4.60	3.88	1.73	.80	.70
C10										
X30*	8.82	6.73	13.6	103	20.6	3.42	3.94	1.65	.67	.65
X25	7.35	5.26	17.4	91.2	18.2	3.52	3.36	1.48	.68	.62
X20	5.88	3.79	24.1	78.9	15.8	3.66	2.81	1.32	.69	.61
X15.3	4.49	2.40	38.0	67.4	13.5	3.87	2.28	1.16	.71	.63
C9										
X20	5.88	4.03	18.2	60.9	13.5	3.22	2.42	1.17	.64	.58
X15	4.41	2.57	28.7	51.0	11.3	3.40	1.93'	1.02	.66	.59
X13.4	3.94	2.10	35.1	47.9	10.6	3.49	1.76	.96	.67	.60
C8										
X18.75	5.51	3.90	14.8	44.0	11.0	2.83	1.98	1.01	.60	.56
X13.75	4.04	2.42	23.8	36.1	9.03	2.99	1.53	.86	.62	.55
X11.5	3.38	1.76	32.8	32.6	8.15	3.11	1.32	'.78	.62	.57
C7										
X14.75*	4.33	2.93	15.0	27.2	7.77	2.51	1.38	.78	.56	.53
X12.25	3.60	2.20	20.0	24.2	6.91	2.59	1.17	.70	.57	.52
X9.8	2.87	1.47	29.8	21.3	6.09	2.72	.97	.63	.58	.54
C6										
X13	3.83	2.62	12.2	17.4	5.80	2.13	1.05	.64	.52	.51
X10.5	3.09	1.88	16.9	15.2	5.07	2.22	.87	.56	.53	.50
X8.2	2.40	1.20	26.6	13.1	4.37	2.34	.69	.49	.54	.51
C5										
X11.5	3.36	2.36	9.23	10.4	4.16	1.76	.82	.54	.49	.51
X9	2.64	1.63	13.4	8.90	3.56	1.84	.63	.45	.49	.48
X6.7	1.97	.95	22.9	7.49	3.00	1.95	.48	.38	.49	.48
C4										
X7.25	2.13	1.28	10.6	4.59	2.30	1.47	.43	.34	.45	.46
X6.25	1.82	.99	13.8	4.10	2.05	1.50	.38	.32	.46	.46
X5.4	1.59	.74	18.5	3.85	1.93	1.56	.32	.28	.45	.46
C3										
X6	1.76	1.07	6.88	2.07	1.38	1.08	.31	.27	.42	.45
X5	1.47	.77	9.49	1.85	1.23	1.12	.25	.23	.41	.44
X4.1	1.21	.51	14.4	1.66	1.11	1.17	.20	.20	.40	.44

*Not available from Canadian Mills.

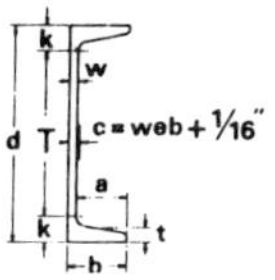

STANDARD CHANNELS

DIMENSIONS

Weight per Foot	Depth d		Flange Width b		Flange Mean Thickness t		Web Thickness w		Distance a	Distance T	Distance k	Distance c
Lb.	In.		In.		In.		In.		In.	In.	In.	In.
50	15.00	15	3.72	3¾	.650	⅝	.716	11/16	3	12⅛	1 7/16	¾
40	15.00	15	3.52	3½	.650	⅝	.520	½	3	12⅛	1 7/16	9/16
33.9	15.00	15	3.40	3⅜	.650	⅝	.400	⅜	3	12⅛	1 7/16	7/16
30	12.00	12	3.17	3⅛	.501	½	.510	½	2⅝	9¾	1⅛	9/16
25	12.00	12	3.05	3	.501	½	.387	⅜	2⅝	9¾	1⅛	7/16
20.7	12.00	12	2.94	3	.501	½	.282	5/16	2⅝	9¾	1⅛	⅜
30	10.00	10	3.03	3	.436	7/16	.673	11/16	2⅜	8	1	¾
25	10.00	10	2.89	2⅞	.436	7/16	.526	½	2⅜	8	1	9/16
20	10.00	10	2.74	2¾	.436	7/16	.379	⅜	2⅜	8	1	7/16
15.3	10.00	10	2.60	2⅝	.436	7/16	.240	¼	2⅜	8	1	5/16
20	9.00	9	2.65	2⅝	.413	7/16	.448	7/16	2¼	7⅛	15/16	½
15	9.00	9	2.48	2½	.413	7/16	.285	5/16	2¼	7⅛	15/16	⅜
13.4	9.00	9	2.43	2⅜	.413	7/16	.233	¼	2¼	7⅛	15/16	5/16
18.75	8.00	8	2.53	2½	.390	⅜	.487	½	2	6⅛	15/16	9/16
13.75	8.00	8	2.34	2⅜	.390	⅜	.303	5/16	2	6⅛	15/16	⅜
11.5	8.00	8	2.26	2¼	.390	⅜	.220	¼	2	6⅛	15/16	5/16
14.75	7.00	7	2.30	2¼	.366	⅜	.419	7/16	1⅞	5¼	⅞	½
12.25	7.00	7	2.19	2¼	.366	⅜	.314	5/16	1⅞	5¼	⅞	⅜
9.8	7.00	7	2.09	2⅛	.366	⅜	.210	3/16	1⅞	5¼	⅞	¼
13	6.00	6	2.16	2⅛	.343	5/16	.437	7/16	1¾	4⅜	13/16	½
10.5	0.00	6	2.03	2	.343	5/16	.314	5/16	1¾	4⅜	13/16	⅜
8.2	6.00	6	1.92	1⅞	.343	5/16	.200	3/16	1¾	4⅜	13/16	¼
11.5	5.00	5	2.03	2	.320	5/16	.472	½	1½	3½	¾	9/16
9	5.00	5	1.88	1⅞	.320	5/16	.325	5/16	1½	3½	¾	⅜
6.7	5.00	5	1.75	1¾	.320	5/16	.190	3/16	1½	3½	¾	¼
7.25	4.00	4	1.72	1¾	.296	5/16	.321	5/16	1⅜	2⅝	11/16	⅜
6.25	4.00	4	1.65	1⅝	.296	5/16	.247	¼	1⅜	2⅝	11/16	5/16
5.4	4.00	4	1.58	1⅝	.296	5/16	.184	3/16	1⅜	2⅝	11/16	¼
6	3.00	3	1.60	1⅝	.273	¼	.356	⅜	1¼	1⅝	11/16	7/16
5	3.00	3	1.50	1½	.273	¼	.258	¼	1¼	1⅝	11/16	5/16
4.1	3.00	3	1.41	1⅜	.273	¼	.170	3/16	1¼	1⅝	11/16	¼

TWO ANGLES — UNEQUAL LEGS
Long Legs Back to Back
PROPERTIES OF SECTIONS

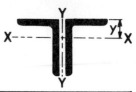

Size	Thick-ness	Wt. per Ft. 2 Angles	Area of 2 Angles	Axis X-X				Radii of Gyration about Axis Y-Y					
				I	S	r	y	Back to Back of Angles, Inches					
In.	In.	Lb.	In.²	In.⁴	In.³	In.	In.	0	¼	⅜	½	⅝	¾
4 x 3½													
	⅝	29.4	8.60	12.7	4.7	1.22	1.29	1.46	1.55	1.60	1.65	1.70	1.75
	½	23.8	7.00	10.6	3.9	1.23	1.25	1.44	1.53	1.58	1.63	1.67	1.72
	⁷⁄₁₆	21.2	6.18	9.5	3.4	1.24	1.23	1.44	1.52	1.57	1.62	1.66	1.71
	⅜	18.2	5.34	8.4	3.0	1.25	1.21	1.43	1.52	1.56	1.61	1.66	1.70
	⁵⁄₁₆	15.4	4.50	7.1	2.5	1.26	1.18	1.42	1.50	1.55	1.59	1.64	1.69
	¼	12.4	3.62	5.8	2.1	1.27	1.16	1.41	1.49	1.54	1.58	1.63	1.67
4 x 3													
	⅝	27.2	7.96	12.1	4.6	1.23	1.37	1.22	1.31	1.36	1.41	1.46	1.51
	½	22.2	6.50	10.1	3.8	1.25	1.33	1.20	1.29	1.33	1.38	1.43	1.48
	⁷⁄₁₆	19.6	5.74	9.0	3.4	1.25	1.30	1.18	1.27	1.32	1.36	1.41	1.46
	⅜	17.0	4.96	7.9	2.9	1.26	1.28	1.18	1.26	1.31	1.35	1.40	1.45
	⁵⁄₁₆	14.4	4.18	6.8	2.5	1.27	1.26	1.17	1.25	1.30	1.35	1.39	1.44
	¼	11.6	3.38	5.5	2.0	1.28	1.24	1.16	1.25	1.29	1.34	1.38	1.43
3½ x 3													
	½	20.4	6.00	6.9	2.9	1.07	1.13	1.25	1.34	1.38	1.43	1.48	1.53
	⁷⁄₁₆	18.2	5.30	6.2	2.6	1.08	1.10	1.23	1.32	1.37	1.41	1.46	1.51
	⅜	15.8	4.60	5.4	2.3	1.09	1.08	1.22	1.31	1.36	1.40	1.45	1.50
	⁵⁄₁₆	13.2	3.86	4.7	1.9	1.10	1.06	1.22	1.30	1.35	1.39	1.44	1.49
	¼	10.8	3.12	3.8	1.6	1.11	1.04	1.21	1.29	1.34	1.38	1.43	1.48
3½ x 2½													
	½	18.8	5.50	6.5	2.8	1.09	1.20	.99	1.08	1.13	1.18	1.23	1.29
	⁷⁄₁₆	16.6	4.86	5.8	2.5	1.09	1.18	.98	1.07	1.12	1.17	1.22	1.27
	⅜	14.4	4.22	5.1	2.2	1.10	1.16	.97	1.07	1.11	1.16	1.21	1.26
	⁵⁄₁₆	12.2	3.56	4.4	1.9	1.11	1.14	.96	1.05	1.10	1.15	1.20	1.24
	¼	9.8	2.88	3.6	1.5	1.12	1.11	.95	1.04	1.09	1.13	1.18	1.23

TWO ANGLES — UNEQUAL LEGS
Long Legs Back to Back
PROPERTIES OF SECTIONS

Size	Thick-ness	Wt. per Ft. 2 Angles	Area of 2 Angles	Axis X-X				Radii of Gyration about Axis Y-Y					
				I	S	r	y	Back to Back of Angles, Inches					
In.	In.	Lb.	In.²	In.⁴	In.³	In.	In.	0	¼	⅜	½	⅝	¾
3 x 2½													
	½	17.0	5.00	4.2	2.1	.91	1.00	1.04	1.14	1.18	1.23	1.28	1.34
	⁷⁄₁₆	15.2	4.42	3.8	1.9	.92	.98	1.03	1.12	1.17	1.22	1.27	1.33
	⅜	13.2	3.84	3.3	1.6	.93	.96	1.02	1.11	1.16	1.21	1.26	1.31
	⁵⁄₁₆	11.2	3.24	2.8	1.4	.94	.93	1.01	1.10	1.14	1.19	1.24	1.29
	¼	9.0	2.62	2.3	1.1	.95	.91	1.00	1.09	1.13	1.18	1.23	1.28
	³⁄₁₆	6.8	2.00	1.8	.86	.95	.89	.99	1.08	1.13	1.17	1.22	1.27
3 x 2													
	½	15.4	4.50	3.8	2.0	.92	1.08	.80	.89	.94	1.00	1.04	1.10
	⁷⁄₁₆	13.6	4.00	3.5	1.8	.93	1.06	.79	.88	.93	.98	1.03	1.09
	⅜	11.8	3.46	3.1	1.6	.94	1.04	.78	.87	.92	.97	1.02	1.07
	⁵⁄₁₆	10.0	2.94	2.6	1.3	.95	1.02	.77	.86	.90	.95	1.00	1.06
	¼	8.2	2.38	2.2	1.1	.96	.99	.75	.84	.89	.93	.99	1.04
	³⁄₁₆	6.14	1.80	1.7	.83	.97	.97	.75	.83	.88	.93	.98	1.03
2½ x 2													
	⅜	10.6	3.10	1.8	1.1	.77	.83	.82	.91	.96	1.01	1.06	1.11
	⁵⁄₁₆	9.0	2.62	1.6	.93	.78	.81	.81	.91	.95	1.00	1.05	1.10
	¼	7.24	2.12	1.3	.76	.78	.79	.80	.89	.94	.99	1.04	1.09
	³⁄₁₆	5.50	1.62	1.0	.59	.79	.76	.79	.88	.92	.96	1.02	1.07
	⅛	3.7	1.10	.70	.40	.80	.74	.77	.86	.90	.95	1.00	1.05
2½ x 1½													
	⁵⁄₁₆	7.84	2.30	1.4	.89	.79	.90	.57	.66	.71	.77	.82	.88
	¼	6.38	1.88	1.2	.73	.79	.88	.56	.65	.70	.75	.81	.86
	³⁄₁₆	4.88	1.44	.92	.56	.80	.85	.55	.64	.69	.74	.78	.84
2 x 1½													
	⁵⁄₁₆	6.78	2.00	.76	.58	.62	.69	.61	.71	.75	.81	.86	.92
	¼	5.54	1.62	.63	.47	.62	.66	.59	.69	.74	.79	.84	.90
	³⁄₁₆	4.24	1.24	.50	.36	.63	.64	.59	.68	.72	.78	.83	.88
	⅛	2.88	0.84	.35	.25	.64	.62	.59	.68	.72	.77	.82	.88
1¾ x 1¼													
	¼	4.68	1.38	.40	.35	.54	.60	.50	.60	.65	.70	.75	.81
	³⁄₁₆	3.60	1.06	.32	.27	.55	.58	.49	.58	.63	.68	.74	.79
	⅛	2.46	0.72	.23	.19	.56	.56	.48	.57	.62	.67	.72	.78

DETAILING PRACTICE

Listed below are usual gauges for angles, W and M Shapes and Standard Channels. Certain fabricators may utilize gauges other than those indicated below.

Consideration should be given to the duplication of details as much as possible. Gauges on an individual member preferably should not be varied throughout the length of that member.

USUAL GAUGES FOR ANGLES, INCHES

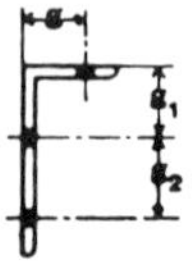

Leg	8	7	6	5	4	3½	3	2½	2	1¾	1½	1⅜	1¼	1
g	4½	4	3½	3	2½	2¼	1¾	1⅜	1⅛	1	⅞	⅞	¾	⅝
g_1	3	2½	2¼	1¾										
g_2	3	3	2½	2										

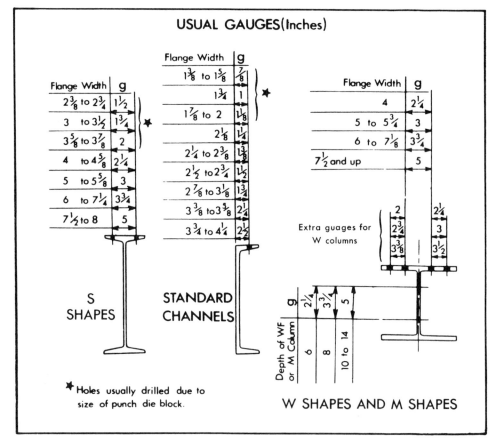

USUAL GAUGES (Inches)

S SHAPES

Flange Width	g
2⅜ to 2¾	1½ *
3 to 3½	1¾ *
3⅝ to 3⅞	2 *
4 to 4⅝	2¼
5 to 5⅝	3
6 to 7¼	3¾
7½ to 8	5

STANDARD CHANNELS

Flange Width	g
1⅜ to 1⅝	⅞ *
1¾	1 *
1⅞ to 2	1⅛ *
2⅛	1¼
2¼ to 2⅜	1⅜
2½ to 2¾	1½
2⅞ to 3⅛	1¾
3⅜ to 3⅝	2¼
3¾ to 4¼	2½

W SHAPES AND M SHAPES

Flange Width	g
4	2¼
5 to 5¾	3
6 to 7⅛	3¾
7½ and up	5

Extra guages for W columns: 2, 2¾, 3⅜ and 2¼, 3, 3½

Depth of WF or M Column	g
6	2¼
8	3¾
10 to 14	5

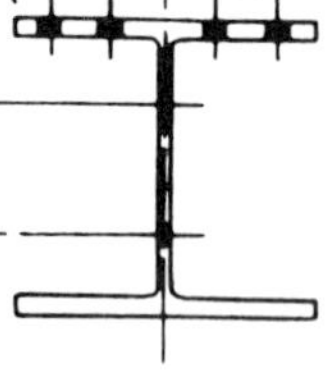

* Holes usually drilled due to size of punch die block.

NOTE: The maximum size of hole is governed by minimum edge distance requirements.

INDEX